UNDERSTANDING OLD AGE

By

JEANNE G. GILBERT, Ph.D.

DIPLOMATE IN CLINICAL PSYCHOLOGY,
AMERICAN BOARD OF EXAMINERS IN PROFESSIONAL PSYCHOLOGY;
LECTURER IN PSYCHOLOGY, FORDHAM UNIVERSITY
GRADUATE SCHOOL AND LONG ISLAND
UNIVERSITY GRADUATE SCHOOL

THE RONALD PRESS COMPANY · NEW YORK

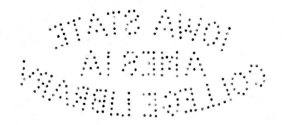

Library of Congress Catalog Card Number: 52-11292

PRINTED IN THE UNITED STATES OF AMERICA

To the memory of
my father—
one of the best examples of
successful aging I have ever known

PREFACE

This book is intended as a guide to better professional understanding of elderly people. The book is addressed particularly to psychologists, general physicians, social workers, hospital employees, nurses, and institutional personnel. The textbook and reference needs of college instructors in preprofessional courses have also been borne in mind throughout.

The study of gerontology or the psychology of aging was once confined to a relatively small number of specialists. It has steadily grown in importance as the age level of our population has risen. The need of accurate and understandable information in this field is today felt by a host of readers whose personal, occupational, or professional interests require them to reach a better understanding of elderly persons. Among the groups who must deal more and more with the personal problems of aging individuals are clergymen, educational and personnel administrators, lawyers, probation officers, and judges.

The book discusses life changes in aging under two general headings. Under normal changes are included the unavoidable alterations that sooner or later come into the lives of all of us. These normal changes are treated in considerable detail, with stress upon the attitudes of both the aging individual and his associates.

The less usual but not uncommon disabilities that result in abnormal aging are discussed specifically and with emphasis on therapy. These abnormal changes include psychoneuroses and psychoses as well as physical disorders.

Throughout the discussion of life changes in aging, the book takes a psychosomatic approach to problems of behavior. Many of these problems are primarily medical ones, and the author has drawn upon the medical literature in discussing these geriatric

problems. An acquaintance with the medical problems of aging
provides a necessary basis for understanding intellectual, emotional, and psychosexual changes and the resulting changes in
the social relations of the older age group.

The number of older persons is increasing in such proportions that work with the aging is rapidly becoming an integral
part of many professions. The book treats of practical ways
of dealing with the problems of older persons and of various
types of professional work with the aging in the community and
in institutions.

Many colleagues and friends of the author have provided
valuable suggestions and criticisms. Special acknowledgment
is made to Dr. Robert A. Wilson, Dr. Frank A. Cassino, Elli
Shouby, Richard Johnson, Rev. Joseph G. Keegan, S. J., and
Ann S. McHugh.

JEANNE G. GILBERT

Brooklyn, New York
    July, 1952

CONTENTS

PART I

Normal Life Changes in Aging

PART II

Abnormal Life Changes in Aging

PART III

Professional Work with the Aging

PART I
NORMAL LIFE CHANGES IN AGING

Chapter 1

GENERAL PHYSICAL CHANGES

Gerontology is the scientific study of the phenomena of aging. Geriatrics refers more specifically to that branch of medicine which deals with the study and treatment of the diseases of the aged. Although rightfully the term "gerontology" refers to the aging of all living matter—plants, lower animals, and man—we shall in this book confine ourselves entirely to the study of the process of aging in the human being.

Why study old age and the diseases of the aged? Why this sudden and growing interest in this area? A few decades ago the terms "gerontology" and "geriatrics" were seldom heard, yet today the literature abounds with research and popular articles and books on growing old. One reason, discussed below, is that each year more and more individuals are reaching the older years.

When is one old and when does old age begin? This, of course, depends upon the point of view. To the small child the adolescent of fifteen is old; to the youth of twenty-five the man of forty-five is old; to the man of seventy-five only the nonagenarian is really old. Then too, there are individual differences in the rate of growing old, so that one person may be "old," physically, mentally, and emotionally, at fifty and another "young" at seventy. In this text we shall deal primarily with the aging processes of man during the middle and later years of life.

There are many practical reasons for this growing interest in the years of later life. In the first place, the population of the aged is growing very rapidly (Figure 1, page 4). In 1900, for example, there were only a little over three million persons

3

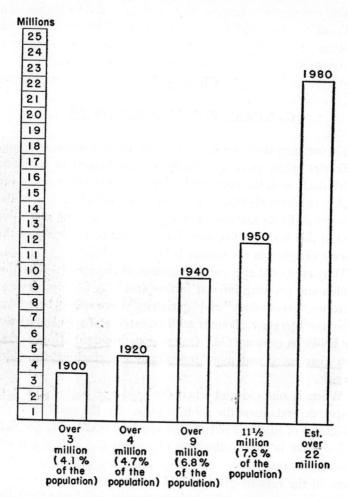

Fig. 1. Number of persons in the United States over 65 years of age.

Source for 1900 and 1920: United States Bureau of the Census. Prepared by the Bureau of Labor Statistics, United States Department of Labor, Washington, D.C.
    Source for 1940: *Current Population Reports* (Washington, D.C., United States Bureau of the Census, 1951).
    Source for 1950 and estimate for 1980: *Employment Problems for Older Workers* (Washington, D.C.: United States Bureau of Labor Statistics, 1950). Report prepared for Conference on Aging, held in Washington, August, 1950.

in this country over sixty-five years of age. By 1920 this number had risen to over four million, and by 1940 to over nine million. Today there are more than thirteen million persons, representing almost 9 per cent of our population, over sixty-five years of age in this country. This represents a life expectancy increase of approximately twenty years over a fifty-year period. The life expectancy in 1900 was forty-seven years, whereas it is

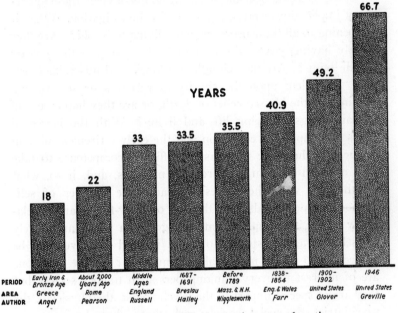

PERIOD	Early Iron & Bronze Age	About 2,000 Years Ago	Middle Ages	1687-1691	Before 1789	1838-1854	1900-1902	1946
AREA	Greece	Rome	England	Breslau	Mass. & N.H.	Eng. & Wales	United States	United States
AUTHOR	Angel	Pearson	Russell	Halley	Wigglesworth	Farr	Glover	Greville

Fig. 2. Average length of life from ancient to modern times.

From L. I. Dublin, A. J. Lotka, and M. Spiegelman, *Length of life* (rev. ed.), p. 42. Copyright, 1949, by The Ronald Press Co.

now more than sixty-seven years and constantly rising. Figure 2 shows the almost spectacular rise of life expectancy from early Greek and Roman times to the present. Of course, it must be remembered that much of this rise has been due primarily to the decrease of infant mortality (24).

The median age of the population, i.e., the age at which one half the population falls above and one half below, likewise has advanced considerably, so that although the median age in 1900 was 22.9 years, the median age in 1946 was 29.9 years (29.6 years for the males and 30.1 for the females), and the rising trend is becoming more marked each year. It has been estimated that, by 1980, 27 per cent of the voters will be sixty years of age and over and approximately 14 per cent of the total population will be sixty-five or more years of age (23, 24).

From both practical and scientific points of view, these figures carry implications and suggestions for investigation. What is happening to all these people who are living to be old? Are they merely having years added to their lives, or are these years worth living? Are they eking out a lonely and miserable existence, dependent upon the charity of relatives or society and waiting for the blessed relief of death, or are they happy, useful human beings enjoying life and living? With the increased years of compulsory education and the early retirement now in vogue, are they able to amass a sufficient competence to take care of themselves in their retirement years, and, if so, what do they do with themselves? Because the number of self-supporting individuals over the age of sixty-five years is relatively small, is it implied that the aged as a whole are largely a useless drag on society, or is it implied that we may be neglecting to utilize much valuable material? These questions are of interest to every thinking person in today's society but they are of special import to the psychologist, the physician, the psychiatrist, the social worker, and others whose business concerns people and their adjustment to life.

Also, with the reports of the astounding ages some individuals have reached, one cannot but speculate upon the possibility that man was really meant to live many more years than he usually does at present and that with the rapid advances of science, it may soon be commonplace to live to be one hundred ten or one hundred twenty years of age. Basylewicz (3) is one of the investigators who believes the normal span of life to be one hundred to one hundred twenty years in spite of the fact that senility and death customarily occur much earlier than this.

In studying an apparently unusual group of seventy-two nonagenarians and centenarians, he found most of the individuals lacking in symptoms of infirmity. The only definite changes were a lowered basal metabolic rate, probably due to a weakening of the thyroid, pituitary, and ovarian glands, and a decreased consumption of food and water. In general, the hereditary factors for longevity were good. The implications of this would be that we must take measures to prevent premature aging and death.

Instances in history, too, of individuals who have lived in good health far beyond the years we have come to expect as the upper limit of old age are too numerous to be dismissed lightly as figments of the imagination. For example, Henry Jenkins, of York, England, is said to have lived to be one hundred sixty-nine years of age. Thomas Parr of Shropshire, England, lived to be one hundred fifty-two years of age. Although this figure has been disputed by many, it apparently was accepted by William Harvey, the great physician, who did the post-mortem examination on him. His son, who died in 1761, lived to be one hundred twenty-seven years old. Drakenberg, a Norwegian, known in the eighteenth century as the "old man of the North," lived to be one hundred forty-six years of age and spent ninety-one years of his life as a sailor (46). Louis Enriquez of San Antonio, Texas, claims to be one hundred twenty-eight years old and is said to have perfect blood pressure and all but three of his teeth. Ripley reports that Sze Tsien of Shantung, China, started life as a sickly quintuplet, the only one of five to survive, and lived to be one hundred thirty years of age. Ripley also reports that Señora Felipa Grijalba Aldana of Tunja, Colombia, married at the age of one hundred, bore a son at one hundred one, and died when she was one hundred twenty years old. True, these cases are most unusual, and the authenticity of the reports may be open to question, but the fact remains that some individuals do live to an extreme old age, and in time many more may do so. If this is the case, it behooves us to learn more of the normal aging process, the early and abnormal decline into senility, ways of retarding decline, and methods of making the increasing years worth living.

Factors in Longevity

Why does one person live to an advanced age and another die in what should be the prime of life? Why does one maintain his essential physical and mental alertness all his life, while another shows rapid physical and mental deterioration in relatively early years? These questions are difficult to answer. For centuries men have sought the "fountain of youth" and tried numerous methods of rejuvenation. On the one hand, we hear it said that the only way to ensure a long life is to choose long-lived ancestors, whereas on the other hand we hear very aged people attribute their longevity to "never taking a smoke or a drink of liquor," "smoking and drinking all my life," "being very careful of my diet and never eating meat," and "eating all I want and lots of meat." These statements leave us rather confused as to the roles of heredity and environment and the efficacy of dietary considerations.

It has long been noted that persons who attain a ripe old age usually had parents who also lived longer than the average number of years, and it has been said by someone that to determine your own probable life span you should add the age, at death, of your parents and four grandparents and divide by six. Some interpret this familial longevity as proof that heredity is the determining factor in the length of our lives, whereas others insist that this means merely that these families had a better understanding of hygiene and provided better environmental conditions and health habits for their offspring. The answer probably is somewhere between the two extremes. Certainly the genetic factors in longevity cannot be minimized, nor can man's own capacity for change and improvement be overlooked.

The work of Kallman and his associates (33, 34) on senescent monozygotic and dizygotic twin pairs brings out clearly the importance of genetic factors both in the matter of longevity itself and in the ability to maintain physical and mental health throughout senescence. In all the studies reported by these researchers, the monozygotic twins showed striking physical and psychological similarities despite sometimes marked dissimilarity of environment, and at all times these similarities were more marked in the monozygotic than in the dizygotic twins. For example, the intrapair differences in life span of the monozygotic twins were one half those of the dizygotic twins, considering twins of the same sex only. Likewise, in matters of health, marital and reproductive histories, physical signs of aging, mental changes, intellectual performances, and emotional adjustment, the monozygotic twins were found to be very similar and decidedly more alike than the dizygotic pairs. Kallman points out further that, although heredity and constitution play the basic roles in determining the differential ability to maintain relative physical and mental health through old age, within these genetically controlled limits life can be lengthened or shortened by environmental factors and the efficiency with which constitutional potentialities are utilized. Nevertheless, in the final analysis, it is vital capacity which controls human life's ultimate length.

However, although these studies show unmistakably the importance of genetic constitution in longevity and the maintenance of one's capacities, we must not overlook the importance of certain environmental factors, especially in the matter of health, disease, diet, and accident. Kennedy and French (35) state that "Aging is, in essence, defective nutrition and oxygenation, and the supply of oxygen to the cells of the nervous system determine this energy content, longevity, and health." Stieglitz (63) points out that, although there is still much to be learned about nutrition, we do know that good nutrition is essential to good health and vigor. In a good diet he would include raw fruits and vegetables, calories balanced to energy needs, adequate protein intake, liberal vitamins, and adequate minerals, bulk, and water. Some stress has been laid lately upon the importance of a high protein diet for longevity. Research (55) too shows that in rats an increase of four times the normal requirement of vitamin A will result in an increase in length of reproductive life and a life-span increase of about 10 per cent in males and about 12 per cent in females. Thiamine requirements also seem to increase with advancing age.

Research similarly shows the importance of other environmental factors in longevity (23, 24). For example, there is a relationship between socioeconomic status and longevity, those of higher socioeconomic status tending to live longer than those of lower socioeconomic status. Likewise, married people tend to live longer and to be healthier than those who are unmarried. Location apparently is another factor in longevity, the Midwest and Northwest sections of this country tending to be favorable to longevity, whereas the Atlantic seaboard seems to be inferior in this respect. Illnesses, industrial and other accidents, excessive overweight or underweight, emotional maladjustment, and hazardous occupations and pursuits are detrimental to a long life.

From these findings, then, it would seem that we inherit the limitations of our constitutions but that within these limitations we can do considerable either to lengthen or to shorten the life span. Good mental and physical hygiene, residence in a desirable location, and employment in a healthful and interesting occupation will serve as aids to longevity.

Psychosomatic Character of Aging

Aging of the organism implies, of course, aging in all areas—aging physically, mentally, emotionally, socially, etc. Being the psychosomatic individual he is, man cannot rightfully be said to age in one area alone, for a change in any one part or aspect of the whole results in an alteration of the total pattern. It is for the sake of convenience and clarity alone that we must separate the aging process into its various aspects and treat them individually, and we must always remember that the interrelationship of body and mind is so close that any changes which occur are actually changes in the whole organism.

Changes in General Appearance

Generally speaking, the signs of advancing age are unmistakable, although, of course, there are marked individual differences in this respect. There tends to be a general increase in bulk with increasing age and changes in body build. The abdomen, hips, and thighs usually become heavier and more prominent. This tendency remains evident until extreme old age, when the body generally becomes thin and undernourished. The slouching posture and the "dowager's hump," which so frequently appear in the elderly, accentuate the changes in bulk and body build. Hair either falls out, resulting in partial or complete baldness, or turns gray and then white. The skin changes in texture, becomes wrinkled, and tends to alter its color in keeping with the color changes of the hair. Gait usually becomes slower, more lumbering, and less steady. Agility is markedly decreased.

These changes are the normal accompaniment of old age, but they can occur prematurely or become accentuated by poor physical and mental hygiene. Conversely, the development and maintenance of correct posture (a feat in itself not easy to attain and one requiring much practice), the habit of keeping a good gait and being interested in one's surroundings, regular exercise, good grooming, and the practice of eating food which is adequate and interesting but not too high in caloric value, can do much to retard the outward signs of advancing age.

General Changes in Cells and Tissues

Nevertheless, the outward signs of aging will become evident sometime if one lives long enough. This is because these outward signs are the manifestations of the normal physiological changes which are constantly occurring throughout the body, and to them are added the insults offered to the body in the process of living. These physiological changes are the processes of aging, which begin at the moment of conception and continue until death. Each cell has its own life span, this span varying with the type of cell, and at its death is replaced by a new cell. Thus, the process of necrocytosis (cellular death) and regeneration is inherent in the basic makeup of the organism and takes place in all cells of the body with the exception of the functioning nerve cells (57). However, when necrocytosis proceeds at a more rapid pace than regeneration, we get, instead of growth or maintenance of the status quo in the tissues, a condition of atrophy or shrinkage of the tissues. This is essentially what occurs throughout most of the body in senescence: the rate of cellular regeneration declines, whereas the rate of necrocytosis becomes more rapid, with the result that the tissues involved gradually atrophy. The physiological and biochemical causes of these changes in the rate of cellular growth and death are as yet unknown, although there is much speculation on the subject. Some believe that growth and aging processes with resultant death are inherent in the germ plasm, while others point to the fact that tissue cells, transplanted on suitable nutrient media, can be kept alive and vigorous indefinitely and will avert senescence by mitosis (cell division) as proof of the essential immortality of the cells, and insist that necrocytosis is due solely to the deleterious effects of an unfavorable environment. There is probably much of truth in both these viewpoints, and it is possible that they are not entirely irreconcilable. It is recognized that transplanted tissue can be kept alive only by the use of special media and the most careful and sterile procedures, and we know that no such optimal environment exists within the organism. It may be therefore that, although the individual cells are potentially immortal, other environmental factors, inherent in the germ plasm, prevent the attainment of this immortality. It has already been mentioned that each cell has its own life span, and it is likely that the differences in longevity of these cells are related to differences in exposure of the cells to oxygen, nutrition, or noxious stimuli (56). This affects not only the rate of necrocytosis but also the relationships between cells themselves and between cells and their environment, resulting in a disturbance of the organs of the body and eventually of the body itself, ending finally in death, since maintenance of intercellular organization is essential to life. It will be seen as we proceed that aging in the organs of the body is characterized not only by atrophy of body cells but by an increase of intercellular tissue and an accumulation of fat and other inert materials.

Sensory Changes

The Eye.—The eye is not only a very complex organ but also a remarkably efficient one, with a potential life span exceeding that of the organism as a whole. Nevertheless, both structural and functional changes occur in the eye with increasing age (4, 27, 56).

To begin with, there is a diminution of orbital fat with increasing age, so that the eyes often appear sunken in their cavities. The eyelids gradually become thinner and tend to lose their elasticity. A loss of tone in the eyelid is usually noticeable beginning in the sixth decade and tends to increase as age advances. In extreme cases the loss of elasticity is noticeable in a turning inside out of the lower lid. The lining of the eyelid likewise becomes thinner in old age, shows a loss of lymphoid tissue, and sometimes shows an obvious dilatation of veins.

The color of the iris (colored part of the eye) fades in senescence, possibly in part at least because the anterior layers of fibers tend to increase in density and thus overshadow the deeper-lying pigment. The posterior cells also frequently show some loss of pigment, although aside from this they seem to be normal.

The pupil or opening (6) shows a significant reduction in size with increasing age, and this is noticeable under both light and dark conditions. This reduction of size seems to bear no relationship either to the color of the iris or that of the skin. The pupillary reactions become feeble.

The cornea (external coat of the eye) loses some of its transparency with age and tends also to lose its luster. The corneal fibers thicken, and the water content of the tissues is reduced.

The lens shows constant changes throughout life, new fibers continuously being laid down on top of old ones, so that the whole structure at any age is partly old and partly new. Aging of the lens, however, involves an increase in the relative proportion of old to new tissue. Increasing amounts of inert, desiccated tissue become concentrated in its center, and its rate of growth gradually declines. Growth never stops entirely, however, unless the tissue dies when cataracts are formed. These changes in the lens result in decreased accommodation. It is interesting to emphasize at this point that it is the lens which is primarily responsible for decreased accommodation, since the ciliary muscle shows no appreciable decline in power. There is, however, a relationship between accommodation and willingness to exert muscular effort to accommodate. There is also an increase in the incidence of lens opacity.

The retina likewise shows changes. It tends in general to become thinner and denser, and this apparently is due to a loss of water. There is also a tendency toward atrophy in the periphery. Since the zone of atrophy is generally farthest from the main arterial supply of the retina, it seems likely that this atrophy is due to local arteriosclerosis. The greater the arteriosclerosis, the more extensive the atrophy.

The optic nerve frequently also atrophies in the aged, and it seems likely that this too is the result of local arteriosclerosis.

The sclera (rear coat of the eyeball) tends to become desiccated, thinner, and denser and shows a loss of elasticity, resulting in increased ocular rigidity, this condition normally becoming first noticeable in the sixth decade.

Thickening of the arteries and increased interstitial tissue are common in varying parts of aging eyes.

In general, calcification and thickening of the blood vessels of the eye tend to cause far-sightedness and cataract formation.

Far-sightedness is almost universal in old age, and cataracts are not unusual (1).

In spite of the aforementioned efficiency of the eye as a functioning organ and its potentially long life span, investigations show a steady decline of all measurable visual functions with increasing age.

Visual acuity (5) becomes poorer with age and is correlated with the degree of retinal degeneration. This decline is evident in both bright and dim illumination (7). Degenerative changes in the eye increase with age. In a study by Birren and Bick (5), only one of forty-nine persons over seventy years of age was found to be free of one of the degenerative conditions. These investigators also found a marked correlation between the visual acuity of the right and left eyes, and this correlation was greater than the correlation between the degenerative condition of the two eyes.

The extent of the visual field is less in the aged than in young people; there is a gradual narrowing of the visual field as one grows older.

It is claimed by some that the speed of adaptation to the dark decreases and the minimal threshold of light perception increases with advancing age (62). Birren and Shock (2), however, report that the rate of visual dark adaptation shows no change with age and the observed elevated light thresholds are not primarily the result of alteration in the rates of visual dark adaptation.

The ability to match colors diminishes and there is some indication that there may be more color-blind individuals among the aged than among younger individuals (11). Critical foveal flicker (minimum number of intermittent visual stimuli necessary for the perception of the whole as one visual impression) decreases in old age. It is thought by some that this is probably due to the degeneration of the optic nerve and cerebrum (47). Also, the decrease seems to be greater with greater intensities of light (48).

To summarize the visual changes normally occurring with advancing years, we might say that the eye is an efficient organ with a long life expectancy, but that, in spite of its potentialities, there is a steady decrease of average efficiency of all measurable visual functions, and this decrease is evident even in otherwise healthy eyes. Some believe, however, that many of the visual disturbances attributed to age may, in reality, be due to faulty circulation and degeneration resulting from vascular changes. The characteristic senile morphological and chemical changes of ocular tissues include increased density, desiccation, increased fibrillar tissue, accumulation in some portions of the organ of an increased amount of inert material, loss of fat, and loss of elasticity.

The almost universal use of glasses in the middle-aged and old attests to the decline of visual functioning with increasing age, and far-sightedness has long been popularly recognized as one of the signs of growing old. Of course, glasses, for some reason, seem to be more acceptable than hearing aids to most persons, but even so, the increasing difficulty in seeing and the need of a visual aid are to many persons very disturbing emotionally.

The most prevalent eye diseases of the aged are cataracts and glaucoma. As noted previously, cataracts are not at all unusual among the aged, and while glaucoma is probably not found quite as frequently as cataract, its occurrence is more common than that of other eye conditions. The causes of cataract and glaucoma are not yet fully known, but it is generally agreed that local arteriosclerosis is probably an important factor. There are also indications which would lead one to believe that vitamin deficiencies and faulty metabolism of the lens play a part, but these have not been definitely proved.

The Ear.—A decline in acuity of hearing in senescence has long been recognized and considered by most as a normal accompaniment of old age. However, scientific studies (26, 30, 57) show that it is very difficult to differentiate between impaired hearing which is due to aging alone and impaired hearing which is due to a combination of aging and other factors, such as the effect of toxins or inexplicable degenerations which sometimes occur early in life. As the clinical picture of the impaired hearing is the same, it is possible that some of the "nerve deafness" in elderly people so frequently dismissed as "due to old age" may in reality be the result of disease processes in no way, or only partially, connected with age.

Actually, there are few structural changes found in the ears of elderly persons which can definitely be attributed to the age factor. Except for the coarsening of hairs in the outer ear, no observable organic changes have been consistently found either in the vestibular apparatus, the inner, the middle, or the external ear, although admittedly much research needs yet to be done in this area. However, it is clear that there is now no proof that aging as such causes organic lesions in the ear. Nevertheless, it has been observed that the bony tissue becomes more brittle with advancing age, possibly because of an increase of inorganic content, and circulatory changes are frequently found here as elsewhere in the body. Possibly this accounts for the fact so frequently noted that bone conduction of sound shows marked impairment in the aged and that the loss is significantly greater than hearing loss by air conduction.

Simple atrophy is the lesion most commonly found in the inner ear of the elderly, and the cause of this atrophy is not known. The atrophy is responsible for the often severe impairment of hearing for high tones and is an atrophy of the nerve, or of the nerve and end organ in the basal turn of the cochlea (spirally-wound tube forming part of the inner ear). Some attribute this atrophy to arteriosclerosis or other circulatory disturbance, but as yet there is no conclusive evidence on this point.

The decline of acuity of hearing for high tones, that is, for tones above high C of the musical scale, increases with each decade of life, and the higher the tone in the scale the greater is the average impairment. Usually hearing for extremely high tones is entirely lost. This impairment of hearing for tones of high frequencies is more pronounced in males than in females, whereas the decline in the auditory acuity for tones of low frequencies tends to be greater in females than in males.

Although, as mentioned above, there is marked impairment of bone conduction of sound, whether the tones be of low or high frequencies, most old people have nearly as good hearing as young people for tones below high C on the musical scale when the tone is received by air conduction. Therefore, more than a slight impairment of hearing for low tones (that is, by air conduction) in senescence can be considered abnormal.

Because there is a differential loss in auditory acuity for high and low sound frequencies and because this loss comes on gradually, it often passes unnoticed for many years and causes no special difficulty to the individual. As it has little or no effect upon the hearing of ordinary conversation, it generally results in no disturbance of social relationships. It does impair the hearing of certain overtones in symphonic and other complex musical compositions, but as the average old person either is uninterested in this type of music or unaware of his inability to hear it completely, the defect usually remains unnoticed.

Olfactory and Gustatory Changes.—The senses of smell and taste decline gradually, probably largely because of atrophy of the olfactory and gustatory nerves (56). Decrease in the number of taste buds likewise is probably partially responsible for the decline of the sense of taste. Arey *et al.* (2), working on cadavers in a study of taste buds throughout the life span, reported that during maturity the average number of taste buds was 208, whereas in individuals of ages seventy-five to eighty-five, the average number was only 88. While this decline in the senses of taste and smell has some advantage to the older person in that it makes unpleasant medicines, when these are required, less unpalatable, it has the disadvantage of making ordinary eating less appetizing. The delicacy of taste found in so many foods relished by the gourmet gradually becomes blunted, so that interest in this area lessens. Much of this, however, can be offset by pleasant surroundings at meals, attractive arrangement and serving of food, and agreeable companionship.

Skin Changes.—Changes in the human skin are probably among the most obvious, often the most distressing personally, and the most easily studied changes which occur in the senescent individual. Those most popularly noted include baldness, graying of the hair, wrinkling of the skin, increased susceptibility to excessive heat and cold, itchiness, and sometimes dystrophy of the toenails. It has been said by some physicians who minister to the aged that, if one lives long enough, the itchiness in some parts of the body may become intolerable. Fortunately, much of this can be relieved by the use of estrogens (female sex hormones). These changes in general are the result of atrophy, loss of subcutaneous fat, and degeneration of tissue, especially of elastic tissue (56, 67).

In a comparative and quantitative study of individuals aged between eighteen and twenty-five years and between sixty and eighty-six years, Kirk and Kvorning (39) found marked differences in the elastic qualities of the skin and the subcutaneous tissue over the tibia (shin bone), greater elasticity being found, as might be expected, in the younger group. They also noted that the old showed no differences in skin elasticity in the morning and in the afternoon after a day of activity.

Ma and Cowdry (44), in a later study of the elasticity of the human skin, found a decrease in the amount of elastic tissue in the aged, and this decrease was more evident in the subepidermal elastic plexus than in the deep fiber layers. This subepidermal plexus lies next to the epidermis and consists of fine fibers which interlace to form a fine network underneath it. In aging, these fibers become thinner, split up, and diminish in amount, and it is thought that this may be due to a loosening of the material which binds them. Also, in the tissue fluid between the deep and superficial layers, a cloudiness is noticeable which may be correlated with a decrease in permeability.

The causes of cutaneous aging are not entirely known, although considerable research is being done in this field, but they are thought to be connected with the condition of the organism as a whole. Certainly, heredity seems to play a part, but other factors, which may or may not be connected with heredity, are also important. The endocrines, for example, are known to be very significant in the process of aging of the human skin, although their exact role is as yet unknown. Likewise, cholesterol (constituent of animal fats), vitamins (especially the fat-soluble vitamins), and certain chemicals (particularly water, sulphur, chlorides, and arsenic) are known to be important.

Experiments have been made to determine the possibility of retarding the aging of the human skin and regenerating aging skin. Max Goldzieher (29) demonstrated regenerative changes in the atrophic epidermis and the elastic fibrils of the cutis by the application of estrogenic ointments. Later, Joseph W. Goldzieher (28) showed that both estrogen and testosterone (male testicular hormone) were directly capable of and equally effective in causing regeneration in senile epidermis of both sexes. Chieffi (17), following this line of investigation, found that local application of estrogen in oil to the skin of females resulted in improvement in the elasticity of the skin, although administration of estrogen by injection produced no such effect. Others disagree, however, and find marked changes in the skin with hormonal injection. No change in the elasticity of the skin of males was produced either by local application or injection of androgens (male hormones). Injections of testosterone propionate, however, resulted in an increased growth of beard in elderly men (16).

Changes in the Skeletal System and Teeth

As with other changes found in senescence, it is difficult to differentiate the changes in the skeletal system and teeth due to advancing age from those which result from disease or defect. Indeed, it seems at times that the two are inextricably interrelated. Tissues, for example, are constantly suffering injury from the environment and undergoing repair of this injury. In the aging organism, the process of repair is slower and less efficient, with the result that there is a cumulative effect of body insult and a consequent decline of function.

In discussing the skeletal system, we are including a discussion of the tissues which comprise the bones, smooth and striped muscles, tendons, ligaments, synovial membrane (lining of the joints), connective tissue, and teeth. In general, the changes of senescence which occur in these tissues consist mostly of dehydration with a lessening of intracellular fluid and an increase of intercellular fluid. There are also some alterations in the patterns and relationships between tissues, and it is thought by some that biochemical changes in the blood and body fluids may be at least partially responsible for these changes (56, 66).

Bony Structure.—The study of changes in bony structure shows us that growth in the hard, bony parts of the skeleton does not occur after adult physiological age has been reached, although growth does seem to continue in certain soft parts, such as the nose and ears. In advanced age, however, there does appear to be what looks like a settling or shrinkage of the skeleton, so that the whole frame seems to become smaller. This is due not to changes in the bones themselves, though, but rather to changes in other tissues of the body.

Tendons and Ligaments.—No clearly defined age changes are noted in tendons and ligaments. Synovial membrane, bursae, and connective tissue likewise demonstrate no changes that can be directly attributed to the age factor alone.

Muscles.—Smooth muscle seems to maintain its normal characteristics without change even in late senescence. Striped muscle, on the other hand, does show some changes with advancing age, and these changes are evident both in structure and in function. There is an increase in connective tissue and in the number of elastic fibers. In comparative autopsy studies of muscle tissue in small groups of young and old persons, Simms and Stolman (59) found chemical changes also in the muscle of the older group. In general, we find that in both men and women the skeletal muscle increases in bulk and density up to the age of about fifty. Functionally, however, there is a gradual waning of muscular strength and staying power after a peak at about the thirtieth year (25), and usually this decline is felt more keenly by men than by women because of the greater emphasis on physical efficiency among males. Studies of the skeletal muscle and of the cerebellum lead one to the belief that this decline in function may be due to changes in the controlling centers rather than in the muscle itself.

Teeth.—Changes in dental makeup which are due to age alone are extremely difficult to determine because of the influences of diet, dental hygiene, dentures, and repair. Nevertheless, the condition of the teeth often plays an important part in the health and happiness of old persons. Ill-fitting dentures, for example, may effect voice changes or make an old person socially less acceptable if they prevent efficient use of saliva and cause sloppy eating and speech. The frequent click of some dentures during eating and talking is also irritating to many persons, as is the peculiar odor of improperly cleansed plates.

With advancing age there is a decrease in permeability of the enamel and an increase of calcium content, and these facts may be partially responsible for the apparently slower formation of caries in older persons than in children. Because of the thickening of the secondary dentine, the teeth also tend to change color, generally growing more yellow with advancing age. There is as well some rebuilding of fibrillar tissue.

When we find changes in skeletal system or teeth other than those discussed above, or an intensification of the normally expected declines, we may assume these to be due to a defective or diseased organism or to an organism whose elasticity and resilience have been weakened by factors other than age alone.

Changes in the Nervous System

Scientifically accurate information concerning the normal aging of the nervous system is rather scanty, although there has been interest in this area for at least a couple of hundred years. Examination of a senile brain is reported as early as 1635, when William Harvey examined the brain of Thomas Parr, who reputedly died at the age of one hundred fifty-two. In the centuries following, others have examined the brains of persons who supposedly died at an extremely old age or who had senile dementia prior to death. Some of the data obtained in this way are sketchy and open to question in so far as scientific accuracy is concerned, so that much more research needs to be done in the field. Nevertheless, some facts are available (21, 56).

We know, for example, that the brain is very sensitive to a diminished flow of cerebral blood. This causes anoxia and sometimes temporary, brief loss of consciousness (36), resulting in otherwise unexplained accidents.

Meninges.—The meninges (membranes enveloping the brain and spinal cord) are, according to Critchley (21), almost always thickened and often adherent. Patches of calcification and sometimes ossification may appear in certain portions.

Cerebrum and Cerebellum.—The cerebrum shows marked changes, often a general atrophy which is visible even to the naked eye. The atrophy is apparent both in the white and in the gray matter of the cerebrum, but is more pronounced in the white matter. The lateral ventricles are widened, and their walls deformed. Sometimes the structural changes are so marked that the surface of the cerebral cortex presents a worm-eaten appearance. Nerve cells tend to disappear, and the remaining neurones are smaller than normal. In some areas, the nerve fibers may collect into coarse bundles and the nerve cells disappear altogether, leaving only a tangled mass behind. Frequently also there are deposits of various kinds throughout the senile brain. "Senile plaques," which are formations of this sort and consist of certain chemical substances and altered nerve cells and fibers, are commonly found throughout the cerebral cortex of the senile brain, especially when the individual has suffered from senile dementia prior to death. Cerebroarteriosclerosis is frequently present, although this should be considered pathological and distinct from the normal involutional changes found in the blood vessels. The cerebellum shows atrophic changes similar to those found in the cerebrum, except that in the cerebellum no senile plaques are found.

The Spinal Cord.—The spinal cord likewise shows atrophy of some cells, and in the gray matter these changes are most marked in the upper cervical segments. There is also an increase of neuroglial fibers (supporting structures) in some areas and sometimes a patchy degeneration of myelin sheaths (of nerve axes) will be found.

It is often very difficult to differentiate between normal and pathological aging of the nervous system because of the complication of other physical or psychological defects or disorders. Sensory defects and emotional disturbances offer particular difficulty in this respect. In general, the pathological changes of senility are diffuse and usually involve the whole of the peripheral and central nervous systems. This results in widespread clinical manifestations, although there does not always seem to be a direct relationship between the severity of a senile dementia and the extent of neurological damage found in the brain on post-mortem examination. Cerebrospinal arteriosclerosis, as mentioned above, often occurs together with changes in the nervous system, and while there is no direct causal relationship between the aging of the nervous system and the degenerative changes of the cerebrospinal blood vessels, its presence does complicate the picture.

Changes in the Cardiovascular System

The Heart.—The most efficient as well as most important organ of the body, the heart, shows changes with advancing age

(18, 19, 31, 56). Initially it occupies a somewhat upright position near the center of the chest cavity, but as the years go by, it tends to assume a more horizontal position and to become not so centrally located. It also increases in bulk, and there is a tendency for the pericardium (sac containing the heart) to become opaque. Increases of subpericardial fat can be observed along the grooves of the coronary vessels.

The valves of the heart lose their softness and pliability, probably because of an increase in fibrous tissue, changes in the quality of the elastic tissue, deposits of fat and the formation of calcium deposits. These changes are more pronounced in the valves of the left side of the heart than in those on the right side. The result is that the structure of the valves tends to become rigid, so that the valves do not function as neatly as they once did. The endocardium (lining of the heart) shows increasing thickness and a fibrous quality.

The striated muscles of the heart also show changes in character, among which is the tendency to become fragmented and desiccated.

The coronary arteries likewise undergo changes, although not all in a uniform manner. There is no increase in the number of arteries during life, but there is an increased demand for blood, and this is met by an increase in the diameter of the arteries. In some areas of the arteries there is a tendency for accelerated calcification, with ultimate development of constriction and thrombosis (formation of a clot). The causes of these changes in the arteries with advancing age are not entirely known, but the importance of heredity and diet has been pointed out. Boas (8, 9) considers that cholesterol metabolism is of special importance and a factor requiring further research.

The heart rhythm tends to become irregular with advancing age.

The heart rate shows changes throughout life. From one hundred thirty to one hundred forty at birth, it shows a slow decline to about seventy by the middle of the third decade. It remains on a plateau then until after the fifth decade, when it may show a slight further decline. Then in very advanced age it may show a slight rise, so that it may be nearly eighty by the age of ninety-five.

Arteries.—Throughout the body changes in the arteries are noted with advancing years, and these changes are more marked in the arteries of the heart and brain than in the arteries of the kidneys and liver. The reasons for this are uncertain, but the differential changes can be noted from artery to artery. The aorta, for example, shows no change in silica content with age but does calcify rapidly. The calcium content of the elastin (constituent of yellow elastic tissue) of the pulmonary artery, on the other hand, increases only slowly, and Boas (cited above) considers that this may be responsible for the infrequency of pulmonary atheramata (diseases of arteries in the lungs). Parts of the arteries become progressively thickened and disorganized or reorganized through an increase of connective tissue and depositions of calcium. There is also a decrease in glucose tolerance. Lansing, Alex, and Rosenthal (42) report that the production of plaques on the innermost coat of the artery in arteriosclerosis is conditioned by the degeneration and calcification of elastic fibers in the middle coat.

The causes of artery changes in general are not fully known, but it is thought that heredity, diet, structure, hormones, and the stresses of living are influential in this respect (41, 42, 43). The metabolic processes of the arteries are also important and may be causative factors in the development of coronary arteriosclerosis and aortic atherosclerosis (forms of arterial disease) in human subjects (49). Kirk *et al.* (38), in a study of 118 persons between the ages of forty-three and ninety-six reported that the low metabolic rate with calcification of some arteries suggests that the thyroid is important in the development of medial arteriosclerosis.

Blood pressures tend to rise with age, and this is especially true of systolic blood pressure (31, 54). A too great increase in blood pressure is common among older people and is often associated with renal disturbance.

That cardiovascular disorders in later life are too frequent is well known, and one cardiovascular survey of seventy-one persons, mostly over seventy years of age, in an institution for the aged (22) found 77.5 per cent with heart disease, the condition being more prevalent among the males than the females. Left ventricular enlargement was the most common fluoroscopic abnormality found. Arteriosclerosis alone or with hypertension was the most common causative factor. However, less than one half had diminished cardiac reserve. The data suggest that individuals in the eighth and ninth decades of life have a relatively benign form of cardiac disease which ordinarily requires little or no therapy. Boas (9) reports that in his patients most cardiovascular disturbances are the result of arteriosclerosis and hypertension.

Changes in the Digestive System

The Stomach.—Although the incidence of complaint of digestive disturbances is probably greater than the complaint of any other disturbance, actually there are relatively few deaths from digestive disorders or a general breakdown of the digestive system resulting from old age. As age advances, there is an increase of dyspepsia and gastric complaints, but as the digestive system is so influenced by emotional disturbances and other diseases, it is likely that these complaints are not due solely to the age factor (32, 56). There is good evidence for the belief that, when it is not directly affected by cancer or by an infectious or toxic process, the digestive system, like the eye, is capable of functioning beyond the ordinary life span of the organism as a whole.

Some atrophy of the tissues, however, is observable throughout the digestive system. The salivary glands tend to involute and to diminish their output of saliva and ptyalin, the starch-converting enzyme they contain. There is also a decrease in the output of gastric juice and pepsin. These result in a decrease in the amount of starch digested in the mouth and stomach.

As age advances, there is also an increasing number of persons whose stomachs do not secrete hydrochloric acid, and this increase is observable after the age of forty years. This condition apparently is largely the result of a physiological involution, although the importance of the diet, general health, and disease history of the individual must not be overlooked. The condition need not, of itself, be incompatible with good health, but it may prove a predisposing factor in other more serious conditions such as anemia, enteritis, and diarrhea. Also, impaired digestion may result in the presence of undesirable intestinal flora (52).

The Pancreas.—Not too much is yet known concerning the aging of the pancreas, although it is believed that pancreatic secretion declines with age (15). However, there is evidence that the pancreas secretes sufficient amylase, an enzyme, to digest at least cooked starch completely, thus offsetting to a large degree the decrease in the amount of starch digested by the mouth and stomach resulting from the above-mentioned diminished output of ptyalin.

Intestines.—Information concerning the absorptive processes of the intestines is likewise meager. It is known that intestinal absorption of galactose, a sugar, is diminished in the old, but it is not known just how efficient the intestines normally are in the absorption of various types of food, minerals, vitamins, etc. It is also undetermined to what extent the impaired efficiency of the gastrointestinal tract found in the old is due to the aging process itself or how much is the result of environmental insult and injury.

The Liver.—The liver is one of the organs of the digestive system which seems to have potentially a long life span, although it does show some impairment and becomes more vulnerable to disease as age advances. Rafsky and Newman (53), for example, report laboratory evidence of a subclinical state of liver impairment in forty-one out of forty-two cases of normal persons between the ages of sixty-five and eighty-six. Even in senescence, however, the liver shows marked regenerative powers, and there is reason to believe that, if protected from pathological processes, it may serve the body much longer than the usual life span. Hepatic function, though, is frequently interfered with by disease. Cirrhosis of the liver is one of the more commonly encountered diseases of this sort, although in examination of over thirty-one hundred patients, Bock (10) found only 4.3 per cent suffering from cirrhosis of the liver. This is higher than the incidence found in young persons, however, and with the general atrophy of tissues, decline of body function, and slower regenerative powers found in older persons, the disease is likely to have more serious consequences for them. The relationship of diet to the decreased vitamin content of both the pancreas and the liver is not known, but it is possible that this has an indirect effect on the aging process, since if vitamin B is low, the liver fails in its control of the estrogenic hormone.

The Gall Bladder.—The gall bladder retains its powers of evacuation well into old age provided it escapes disease. Women seem to suffer a higher incidence of gall-bladder disease, including cancer, and mortality from this cause than men, and in both the incidence of the disease increases with age. The greater prevalence of gall-bladder disease in women is thought to have some connection with pregnancy, as more women who have borne children are affected than those who have not.

The Colon.—The colon has been said by some to atrophy and show thinning of the musculature with age, but there is no scientific research to prove that this is the case. In fact, there is no evidence that there is a decrease in the capacity of the colon for absorption and for the secretion of mucus. Orla-Jensen *et al.* (52) contend that the increase of putrefactive processes often found in the colon of the aged is due to a decrease of hydrochloric acid in the stomach, which results in poorer digestion of proteins and the fact that the food leaving the stomach is so filled with bacteria, instead of being almost sterile, that the sugar from which acid is normally produced in the colon is already fermented.

Kidneys.—Little accurate information is available concerning the normal aging of the kidneys, but there is some indication that there is a progressive reduction after the fourth decade and that the excretory function diminishes and the amount of renal tissue declines after about the age of sixty years (64). It is known that the excretion of creatinine and uric acid diminishes with advancing age, and the evidence indicates that there is a close relationship between this diminution and the functioning of the adrenal cortex and possibly also that of other glands. Solomon and Shock (61), for example, point out that although the ability of the adrenal cortex to secrete the "S" hormone is not grossly impaired with advancing age, the kidney shows a diminished responsiveness to adrenocortical stimulation, resulting in a lessened secretion of uric acid. Also, the progressive diminution of 17-ketosteroids (urinary androgens) in the urine with age is considered by some to be due to the altered functioning of the gonads and adrenal cortex in males and of the adrenal cortex alone in females. There is also a high incidence of disease and death from kidney trouble and from kidney disorder in combination with other disorders, cardiovascular-renal disease probably being the most common of these. It is thought by many that aging of the kidney is in essence aging of the vascular system (37, 40, 51).

The Appendix.—The appendix shows a gradual obliteration of the lumen (clear space within), starting at the tip and extending toward the base, and this is thought by some to be a true involutional process not associated with disease. The mortality from appendicitis increases with age and is greater in men than in women. The relatively high death rate from this disorder is probably due to the atrophy of the lymphoid tissue, which normally serves as a protective agent against gangrene and spreading infection, and to the generally lower resistance and slower recuperative powers of old persons.

In general, then, it would seem that the digestive system is a healthy, potentially long-lived system, not readily affected by the process of aging per se but susceptible to the influences of emotional and organic disorder of the organism. During the normal course of life, gastrointestinal symptoms are probably more in evidence than symptoms referring to any other part or system of the body. Constipation, for example, is one of the better-known complaints and one played up by the advertisements as being inevitable for all persons over a certain age. However, there actually is little reason to believe that constipation is more common in the aged than in the young. Usually it is a lifelong or long-standing condition or complaint, and often a complaint without an actual condition, and it is thought that much of it may be of emotional origin. If, however, constipation in the aged is of recent origin, it may indicate neoplasm of the colon. In connection with this question of constipation in the aged, it is interesting to note that of a group of 1,082 college students and 824 persons over eighty, 31 per cent of both groups complained of constipation. Nevertheless, the gastrointestinal tract is so easily affected by other adverse conditions of the body that we may be tempted to agree with Josh Billings when he wrote, "I have finally kum tu the konklusion that a good reliable sett of bowels is worth more tu a man than enny quantity of brains."

Changes in the Respiratory System

The aging of the respiratory system is closely connected with the aging of the other systems of the body. As with the other systems, it is difficult to differentiate normal aging from deterioration resulting from the accumulated insults and injuries of the environment. However, scientific investigations (57) show that there is cellular decline in the epithelium (covering of the mucous membrane) along the entire respiratory tract, and there are changes also in the supportive and connective tissue. Aging of the blood vessels and the muscles, as well as of the tissues and special cells, are reflected in the aging of the respiratory system as a whole. Accompanying the structural changes occurring with advancing years, there is a reduction in vital capacity, so that the older one gets the greater is his limitation in the ability to expand and contract his thorax. There is also a reduction in the respiratory volume after exercise, and this too is more marked as age increases. Pulmonary disorders of the aged most frequently occur in combination with or as a complication of other diseases, particularly those connected with the malfunctioning of the heart and blood vessels. Senile pneumonia, however, is one of the common causes of death in the aged.

Changes in the Homeostatic Mechanisms

"Homeostasis" refers to the maintenance of equilibrium in the internal environment of the body—that is, the maintenance of relative constancy of the chemical and physical properties of the fluid matrix. We have already investigated the aging of tissue cells, organs, and systems of the body and found that, in an optimal environment and in the absence of injury or disease, the changes which can be directly attributed to the aging factor alone are relatively slight. Yet we know that the organism does age, and there is evidence for the belief that this aging may be due to alterations in the fluids of the body which ordinarily operate to provide the cells of the organism with a fairly constant environment in the face of external and internal changes (14, 20, 45). Among other things, homeostasis includes the maintenance of relatively steady states of body temperature, blood sugar, and acid-base balance (57, 58). It must maintain these states under the most widely diverse conditions, such as, for example, when the individual is subjected to either extreme heat or extreme cold, when he climbs a high mountain or descends into the bowels of the earth or under the water, when he lies at complete rest or when he engages in violent exercise or work.

It must also keep a balance of the internal environment when the organs are subjected to disease or injury. If the homeostatic mechanisms do not maintain a state of balance or equilibrium within the body, the cells will not function normally. Contrariwise, and this is of great importance in the consideration of aging, changes in the cells, organs, or systems of the body caused by disease, injury, or aging will make more difficult the regulation of homeostasis. Impairment of the homeostatic mechanisms will result in decreased adaptability of the organism to changing environmental conditions. Continual interaction is characteristic of the organism.

In many instances, a number of mechanisms may be used to maintain homeostatic balance (56), so that it is sometimes difficult to determine at what cost to the body equilibrium is preserved. Most organs have such reserve capacity that they can stand considerable physiological stress and strain, but it is probable that this reserve capacity is reduced under conditions of prolonged stress and in the normal process of aging (12). Thus, the effectiveness of the physiological factors which maintain balance are impaired, with the result that, although homeostasis is maintained, it is narrowed in range. The body then cannot stand as much stress and is slower to recover from strain.

Regulation of Body Temperature.—Uniformity of body temperature is maintained by a regulation of heat production and heat loss (14). Heat production depends upon the metabolic activities of the body, basic to which is the secretion of the thyroid gland. If thyroid secretion fails, the metabolic rate and the consequent output of heat may be reduced as much as 40 per cent. The body attempts to compensate for heat loss by such physiological adjustments as the secretion of adrenine, a hormone produced by the adrenal medulla, to accelerate the rate of internal combustion, the contraction of surface blood vessels to protect the inner warm blood from cooling, and shivering to liberate more heat. On the other hand, the body compensates for heat production by diminished muscular activity, the secretion of sweat to cool the body by evaporation, and the dilation of surface blood vessels in order to cool the warm blood from inside. Save in the extremes of heat and cold, these regulatory devices result in the maintenance of an even body temperature in spite of the temperature of the environment.

Studies of old persons show that the internal temperature is usually maintained within normal limits but that they feel extremes of heat and cold more than young persons do and that such extremes result in greater variations of body temperature. The increased susceptibility to cold may be due to the lowered basal metabolic rate which, in turn, results from partial involution of the thyroid gland with consequent diminished function, and to the lessened muscular vigor which ordinarily would offer a compensatory increase of heat.

The increased susceptibility to heat, on the other hand, may be due to skin changes and partial degeneration of the sweat glands and blood vessels. These things prevent a ready discharge of heat from the body, and the relief normally attained by perspiring cannot be achieved.

The limits of adaptation to extremes of heat and cold gradually grow narrower as age advances, but the normal old person tries to compensate for this decreased adaptability by avoiding temperature extremes or by regulating his dress in accordance with his individual needs.

Regulation of Blood Sugar.—The maintenance of a constant state of blood sugar involves a storage of glucose when there is an abundance of this substance supplied by the food, excretion through the kidneys as waste when there is an overabundance, and release when there is a special need of it as, for example, in those cases where extra energy is suddenly required (50, 60).

Most of the sugar is stored in the liver as glycogen, and this storage is dependent upon the functioning of the islet tissues of the pancreas. When there is a rise in blood sugar, either through release of these glycogen stores or through absorption of glucose ingested, the islets of the pancreas secrete insulin to check this rise. When the rise in blood sugar is greater than the insulin can check, the excess is excreted through the kidney. Thus, under normal conditions the body offers ample protection against a too great rise in blood sugar.

When there is a reduction of blood sugar, nervous centers in the brain stimulate the secretion of adrenaline by the adrenal gland, and the thyroid and posterior pituitary glands increase their hormonal secretions, all of which results in accelerating the release of glucose from the liver into the blood. Secretions from the adrenal cortex also help to guard against a too greatly lowered blood sugar by hastening the change of protein to carbohydrates in the liver and by retarding the rate of oxidation of glucose in the tissues. The anterior pituitary may also play a part in retarding the rate of oxidation of glucose in the tissues. These multiple precautions of the body against a too great fall in blood sugar are necessary because the higher nervous centers in the brain are especially susceptible to lowered blood sugar levels, the result being impaired functional activities over a widespread area (56).

There is increased glycosuria (abnormal excretion of sugar in the urine) in the aged. However, the fact that there seems to be impairment of the homeostatic mechanisms for blood sugar in the aged does not imply that there is a relationship between diabetes and aging of the organism, for actually although the initial incidence of diabetes increases up to the age of forty or fifty, it shows a sharp decline after the age of sixty. There is also some indication that older persons do not respond so readily with hypoglycemic reactions to injections of insulin.

Regulation of the Acid-Base Balance of the Blood.—The maintenance of uniform chemical reaction, particularly the acid-alkaline reaction, in the blood is a function primarily of the lungs, although the heart, blood vessels, and kidney likewise play an important part. Normally the blood has a slightly alkaline reaction, and this reaction is maintained through respiration (and concomitant activity of the heart and blood vessels) and through excretion by the kidney. Even though, as mentioned earlier, there is reduced vital capacity in the old, the lungs are able under normal resting conditions to maintain this balance even when there is a reduction of kidney function such as may occur in old age (58). However, when the older person is subjected to stress, limitations can be observed. In strenuous exertion, for example, the alkaline reserve is diminished and recovery tends to be slow. Likewise, the rate of recovery is much slower in the old than in the young when the acid-base equilibrium is disturbed by the administration of either acidifying or alkalinizing substances.

In regard to this general problem of the homeostasis of the fluid matrix of the aging organism, it might be said that it is fairly well preserved in that normally there is no marked change in body temperature, blood sugar, or the acid-base balance of the blood (14). When subjected to stress, however, the organism shows progressively less ability to maintain states of internal environment and to return to normal once the balance has been disturbed.

Summary

Gerontology is the scientific study of the phenomena of aging.

Each year increasing numbers of persons are surviving to old age. In order to make the later years worth living more knowledge is needed concerning the normal and pathological processes of aging, ways of preventing premature senility and death, and means of preserving good physical and mental health.

Both heredity and environment are factors in longevity.

Because psychosomatic unity is inherent in the human organism, a change in any part of this organism will result in an alteration of the total pattern.

Changes in general appearance include differential increases in bulk and changes in the skin and hair. These normal changes accompanying old age are often accentuated by disease, injury, or poor mental or physical hygiene.

Physiological aging goes back to the growth and death of the body cells, each of which has its own life span. In senescence the rate of cellular regeneration declines, whereas the rate of necrocytosis becomes more rapid, with the result that the tissues involved gradually atrophy. Aging of the organs involves not only cellular atrophy but also an increase of intercellular tissue and accumulation of fat and other inert materials.

The eye as a functioning organ has a life span potentially exceeding that of the organism as a whole, but nevertheless there is a steady decrease of average efficiency of all measurable visual functions—visual acuity, extent of visual field, ability to match colors, etc.

The most prevalent ocular diseases of the aged are cataract and glaucoma.

Decline of acuity of hearing for tones above high C of the musical scale increases with each decade of life, and the higher the tone the greater the impairment. Impairment of hearing for tones of high frequencies is more pronounced in males, of low frequencies in females.

The senses of smell and taste gradually decline with the years, probably largely because of atrophy of the olfactory and gustatory nerves and, in the case of taste, to a decrease in the number of taste buds.

Skin changes include baldness, graying of the hair, wrinkling of the skin, increased susceptibility to excessive heat and cold, itchiness, and sometimes dystrophy of the toenails. These, in general, are the result of atrophy, loss of subcutaneous fat, and degeneration of tissue, especially of elastic tissue.

Bones, tendons, ligaments, synovial membrane, bursae, connective tissue, and smooth muscle show few characteristic senile changes.

Striped muscle shows an increase in connective tissue and in the number of elastic fibers, some chemical changes, and up to the age of fifty an increase in bulk and density. Functionally there is a decrease of strength and staying power after the thirtieth year.

Teeth show a decrease in permeability of the enamel, an increase of calcium content, some rebuilding of fibrillar texture, and a thickening of the secondary dentine, which results in a tendency toward yellowing.

The brain, in general, shows some atrophy of tissue. The meninges become thickened and adherent and sometimes show patches of calcification and ossification. The cerebrum shows general atrophy and the formation of deposits of various kinds, some of which are known as "senile plaques." The cerebellum shows general atrophic changes. The spinal cord shows atrophy of some cells, an increase of neuroglial fibers in some areas, and sometimes a patchy degeneration of myelin sheaths.

With advancing age the heart tends to assume a more horizontal position and to become less centrally located; it also shows an increase in bulk and subpericardial fat. The valves tend to become rigid, the coronary arteries to become calcified in some areas, and the heart rhythm to become irregular.

The arteries show differential changes particularly with reference to chemical content, and some parts become progressively thickened and disorganized. There is also a decrease of glucose tolerance. Heredity, diet, structure, hormones, metabolic processes (particularly cholesterol metabolism), and the stresses of living are important factors in arterial aging.

Blood pressures, especially systolic blood pressure, tend to increase with age.

The digestive system, when not affected by disease, is capable of functioning beyond the ordinary life span of the organism as a whole. However, there is some atrophy of tissue, a tendency of the salivary glands to involute and diminish their output of saliva and ptyalin, a decrease in the output of gastric juice and pepsin, and sometimes a complete cessation of the secretion of hydrochloric acid by the stomach. The amount of starch digested in the mouth and stomach is diminished.

Pancreatic secretion is believed to decline with age.

In the absence of disease, the liver and gall bladder function well into advanced old age.

The kidney shows a decline in amount of renal tissue and a diminution of excretory function after the age of sixty.

The colon and appendix show some atrophy in late life, and there is an increased mortality from appendicitis because of lowered resistance and recuperative powers of the aged.

The respiratory system shows cellular decline and a reduction of vital capacity.

There is a decline with advancing years in the efficiency of the homeostatic mechanisms, but the change is not so much in the capacity of the organism to perform under normal demands as in its reserve capacity to meet unusual demands. The older organism becomes less resistant to certain disease processes, slower to heal itself, and slower to recover. As one grows older, the rate of aging becomes slower. There is a reduction of gross physical strength and speed, a slower rate of change, and slower repair and rehabilitation.

The practical implications of these changes are obvious in so far as the individual's adjustment to a normal society is concerned. Their relationship to other aspects of decline will also be seen more clearly as we proceed.

REFERENCES

1. AGARWAL, R. S. Presbyopia or old age sight. *Indiana med. J.,* 1946, **40**, 191-94.
2. AREY, L. B., TREMAINE, M. J., and MONZINGO, F. L. The numerical and topographical relation of taste buds to human circumvallate papillae throughout the life span. *Anat. Rec.,* 1935, **64**, 9-25.
3. BASYLEWICZ, I. Centenarians: the syndrome of normal senility. *R.I. med. J.,* 1949, **32**, 315.
4. BERENS, C. The aging eye. *N.Y. Med.,* 1946, **2**, 13-16.
5. BIRREN, J. E., and BICK, M. W. Visual acuity as a function of age and retinal and macular degeneration. Paper delivered before Gerontological Society, June, 1949.
6. BIRREN, J. E., CASPERSON, R. C., and BOTWINICK, J. Age changes in pupil size. *J. Geron.,* **5**, 216-21.
7. BIRREN, J. E., and SHOCK, N. W. Age changes in rate and level of visual dark adaptation. Paper delivered before Gerontological Society, Nov., 1949.
8. BOAS, E. P. Cardiovascular problems after age 70. *Geriatrics,* 1950, **5**, 85-89.
9. ——. Distinctive features of coronory disease in the aged. *J. Geron.,* 1949, **4**, 136-40.

10. Bock, J. Liver cirrhosis in the aged. *J. Geron.*, 1948, **3**, 111-18.
11. Boice, M. L., Tinker, M. A., and Paterson, D. G. Color vision and age. *Amer. J. Psychol.*, 1948, **61**, 520-26.
12. Bourlière, F. Quelques characteristiques physiologiques de la senescence chez la rat. *Rev. Canad. Biol.*, 1947, **6**, 245-54.
13. Burnstein, N. Supplementary treatment of diabetes mellitus with steroid hormones. *Geriatrics*, 1950, **5**, 93-98.
14. Cannon, W. B. Ageing of homeostatic mechanisms. In Cowdry, E. V. (ed.), *Problems of ageing*. Baltimore: The Williams & Wilkins Co., 1939.
15. Carlson, A. J. The thyroid, pancreatic islets, parathyroids, adrenals, thymus, and pituitary. In Cowdry, E. V. (ed.), *Problems of ageing*. Baltimore: The Williams & Wilkins Co., 1939.
16. Chieffi, M. Effect of testosterone administration on the beard growth of elderly males. *J. Geron.*, 1949, **4**, 200-4.
17. ——. An investigation of the effects of parenteral and topical administration of steroids on the elastic properties of senile skin. *J. Geron.*, 1950, **5**, 17-22.
18. Cohn, A. E. Cardiovascular system and blood. In Cowdry, E. V. (ed.), *Problems of ageing*. Baltimore: The Williams & Wilkins Co., 1939.
19. ——. Old age: the cardiovascular system. *J. Orthopsychiat.*, 1940, **10**, 43-53.
20. Cowdry, E. V. Ageing of tissue fluids. In Cowdry, E. V. (ed.), *Problems of ageing*. Baltimore: The Williams & Wilkins Co., 1939.
21. Critchley, M. Ageing of the nervous system. In Cowdry, E. V. (ed.), *Problems of ageing*. Baltimore: The Williams & Wilkins Co., 1939.
22. Dolgin, M., Grossman, M., Simon, A. J., Sorter, H., and Katz, L. N. Cardiovascular survey of residents in a custodial institution for the aged. *J. Geron.*, 1949, **4**, 39-47.
23. Dublin, L. I. Longevity in retrospect and prospect. In Cowdry, E. V. (ed.), *Problems of ageing*. Baltimore: The Williams & Wilkins Co., 1939.
24. Dublin, L. I., Lotka, A. J., and Spiegelman, M. *Length of life* (rev. ed.). New York: The Ronald Press Co., 1949.
25. Fisher, M. B., and Birren, J. E. Age and strength. *J. appl. Psychol.*, 1947, **31**, 490-97.
26. Fowler, E. P. The aging ear. *Arch. Otolaryng.*, Chicago, 1944, **40**, 475-80.
27. Friedenwals, J. S. The eye. In Cowdry, E. V. (ed.), *Problems of ageing*. Baltimore: The Williams & Wilkins Co., 1939.
28. Goldzieher, J. W. Direct effect of steroids on the senile human skin. *J. Geron.*, 1949, **4**, 104-12.
29. Goldzieher, M. A. The effects of estrogen on senile skin. *J. Geron.*, 1946, **1**, 196-201.
30. Guild, S. R. The ear. In Cowdry, E. V. (ed.), *Problems of ageing*. Baltimore: The Williams & Wilkins Co., 1939.
31. Howell, T. H.. *Old age*. London: H. K. Lewis & Co., Ltd., 1950.
32. Ivy, A. C. Digestive system. In Cowdry, E V. (ed.), *Problems of ageing*. Baltimore: The Williams & Wilkins Co., 1939.
33. Kallman, E. J., and Sanders, G. Twin studies on aging and longevity. *J. Hered.*, 1948, **38**, 349-58.
34. ——. Twin studies on senescence. *Amer. J. Psychiat.*, 1949, **106**, 29-36.

35. KENNEDY, F. Borderline mental problems in later maturity. Discussion by T. French. In *Mental health in later maturity*. Publ. Hlth. Rep., Wash., 1942, No. 168, 64-72.

36. KILOH, G. A. Syncope and similar states. *Med. Proc.*, 1948, **219**, 39-42.

37. KIRK, E. The urinary secretion of neutral 17-ketosteroids in middle-aged and old men. *J. Geron.*, 1949, **4**, 34-37.

38. KIRK, E., CHIEFFI, M., and KOUNTZ, W. B. The correlation between thyroid function and the incidence of arteriosclerosis. *J. Geron.*, 1949, **4**, 212-17.

39. KIRK, E., and KVORNING, S. A. Quantitative measurements of the elastic properties of the skin and subcutaneous tissue in young and old individuals. *J. Geron.*, 1949, **4**, 273-84.

40. KOWELESSKI, K. 17-ketosteroids in age. *J. Geron.*, 1950, **5**, 222-26.

41. KVORNING, S. A. The silica content of the aortic wall in various age groups. *J. Geron.*, 1950, **5**, 23-25.

42. LANSING, A. I., ALEX, M., and ROSENTHAL, T. B. Calcium and elastin in human arteriosclerosis. *J. Geron.*, 1950, **5**, 112-19.

43. LANSING, A. I., ROSENTHAL, T. B., and ALEX, M. Age changes in the pulmonary artery. *J. Geron.*, 1950, **5**, 211-15.

44. MA, C. K., and COWDRY, E. V. Aging of elastic tissue in human skin. *J. Geron.*, 1950, **5**, 203-10.

45. McCAY, C. M. Chemical aspects of ageing. In COWDRY, E. V. (ed.), *Problems of ageing*. Baltimore: The Williams & Wilkins Co., 1939.

46. MECHNIKOV, E. *The prolongation of life*. Translated by P. C. Mitchell. New York: G. P. Putnam's Sons, 1908.

47. MISIAK, H. Age and sex differences in critical flicker frequency. *J. exp. Psychol.*, 1947, **37**, 318-32.

48. ——. The decrease of critical flicker frequency with age. *Science*, 1951, **113**, 551-52.

49. MORRISON, L. M., and GONZALES, W. F. The effect of blood cholesterol disorders on the coronary arteries and aorta. *Geriatrics*, 1950, **5**, 188-95.

50. NEWBURGER, R. A. Glucose tolerance in the aged. Paper delivered before Gerontological Society, Nov., 1949.

51. OLIVER, J. R. Urinary system. In COWDRY, E. V. (ed.), *Problems of ageing*. Baltimore: The Williams & Wilkins Co., 1939.

52. ORLA-JENSEN, S., OLSEN, E., and GEILL, T. Senility and intestinal flora. *J. Geron.*, 1949, **4**, 5-15.

53. RAFSKY, H., and NEWMAN, B. Further studies on liver function tests in the aged. *Rev. Gastroenterol.*, 1949, **16**, 783-85.

54. RUSSEK, H. I., and ZOHMAN, B. L. Normal blood pressure in senescence: a study of 3,091 white male subjects between the ages of 50 and 95 years. *Geriatrics*, 1946, **1**, 113-20.

55. SHERMAN, H. D., and TRUPP, H. Y. Further experiments with vitamin A in relation to aging and length of life. *Proc. nat. Acad. Sci.*, Wash., 1949, **35**, 90-92.

56. SHOCK, N. W. Physiological aspects of mental disorders in later life. In KAPLAN, O. (ed.), *Mental disorders in later life*. Stanford, Calif.: Stanford University Press, 1945.

57. ——. Metabolism in old age. *Bull. N.Y. Acad. Med.*, 1948, **24**, 166-78.

58. SHOCK, N. W., and YIENGST, M. J. Age changes in acid-base equilibrium of the blood of males. *J. Geron.*, 1950, **5**, 1-4.

59. SIMMS, H. S., and STOLMAN, A. Changes in human tissue electrolytes in senescence. *Science,* 1937, **86,** 269-70.

60. SMITH, L. E., and SHOCK, N. W. Intravenous glucose tolerance tests in aged males. *J. Geron.,* 1949, **4,** 27-33.

61. SOLOMON, D. H., and SHOCK, N. W. Adrenal cortical and pituitary function in age. *J. Geron.,* 1950, **5,** 302-13.

62. STEVENS, D. M. Relation between dark adaptation and age. *Nature.* London, 1946, **157,** 376-77.

63. STIEGLITZ, E. J. *The second forty years.* Philadelphia: J. B. Lippincott Co., 1946.

64. ——. *Geriatric medicine.* Philadelphia: W. B. Saunders Co., 1949.

65. TIBBITTS, C. (ed.). *Living through the older years.* Ann Arbor, Mich.: University of Michigan Press, 1949.

66. TODD, T. W. Skeleton, locomotor system, and teeth. In COWDRY, E. V. (ed.), *Problems of ageing.* Baltimore: The Williams & Wilkins Co., 1939.

67. WEIDMAN, F. D. Ageing of the skin. In COWDRY, E. V. (ed.), *Problems of ageing.* Baltimore: The Williams & Wilkins Co., 1939.

Chapter 2

ALTERED ENDOCRINE FUNCTIONING—
SEXUAL AND PSYCHOSEXUAL CHANGES

Changes in Functioning of the Endocrine Glands

Some mention has already been made of the endocrine glands, particularly of the thyroid gland, in relation to the process of aging. The endocrine glands offer a fruitful source of study and one which has captured the imagination of many. In spite of the fact that knowledge of these glands is as yet far from complete, precipitous investigators have tickled the romantic fancies of an aging public with their tales of rejuvenation with endocrine therapy, so that many persons today believe that with an operation of some sort, pills, or injections, they could maintain perpetual youth. Such, according to the consensus of truly scientific investigation, is definitely not the case. Even though it is granted that the endocrine glands are extremely important, and perhaps even that changes in them may prove to be one of the prime factors in the aging process in the human organism, there is as yet no conclusive evidence that true rejuvenation can occur or that youth can be prolonged indefinitely by means of endocrine therapy or transplantation.

As we have already seen, the human organism is so constituted that a change in any part effects an alteration of the total pattern. The organs and systems of the body are so closely interrelated that an acceleration or retardation of the functioning of one results in far-reaching functional changes in other areas. What is true of the different organs and systems of the body holds true also for the body and mind of the human organism, for each is an integral part of the whole rather than something which is separate and distinct. Thus alterations in the functioning glands of internal secretion will result not only in changes in other parts of the body or mind, but changes occurring in other parts of the body or mind will also result in alteration of the functioning of the endocrine glands. For example, cardiovascular changes which result in impaired flow of blood to one or more of the endocrine glands may induce changes in these glands. The changes which would then be found in these endocrine glands would probably not be reversible by means of hormonal therapy, since the basis of the difficulty would be in the cardiovascular rather than in the endocrine system. This example points out the need, in the treatment of the aging process, of studying the whole organism and its interrelated parts and the impossibility of attempting to treat the total organism by means of improving the functioning of one part without first determining the relationship of other functioning areas to the total picture.

In addition to the relationships between the functioning of the endocrine glands and that of other organs and systems of the body, the functioning of these glands, like that of other parts of the body, is also influenced by the hereditary pattern of the organism. The effect of diet, and particularly of vitamin intake, is also of extreme importance. Disease too may attack the endocrine system, thereby altering the functioning of one or more glands, and in the final picture it is often difficult to differentiate the effects of the disease process from the results of a normal aging process.

Other factors which complicate the study of the aging process in the endocrine glands concern the glands themselves and their relationships to each other. Certain glands, for example, secrete several different hormones, and our knowledge of the exact functions of these various secretions is as yet incomplete. Also, the glands work a sort of check-and-balance system against each other, so that the hyper- or hypofunctioning of one gland may result in an under- or oversecretion of one or more hormones of the other glands in an effort to maintain the balance of the system.

The Thyroid Gland

The thyroid gland, located in the neck, has been called by some the "regulator" of the organism, for it seems to affect in varying degrees all the organs of the body as well as tissue building and repair (21). It is thought that the thyroid probably begins to function before birth and reaches its maximum size and function somewhere in the late teens. Its functioning is dependent to a large extent upon the presence of iodine in the food, and its secretion is regulated by one of the hormones of the anterior pituitary gland. Its hormone, thyroxin, is secreted by the epithelial cells and influences salt, protein, and cholesterol metabolism in the cells. Hyperthyroidism increases the basal metabolic rate, with attendant disturbances in certain cells and organs, emotions and thinking, whereas hypothyroidism lowers the basal metabolic rate, with consequent increases of protein, inorganic salts, and cholesterol and a lowering of emotional tone. Some investigators claim that after reaching and maintaining its maximum function through a period in the early twenties, the thyroid gradually begins to show some changes, these changes being evidenced first only in a lowered basal metabolic rate. After forty years of age, structural changes can be seen in sclerosis of the blood vessels, progressively less colloid, and a gradual increase of connective tissue, with later reduction in size of the follicles. These changes are more marked after the age of sixty-five when, in addition, the total size of the thyroid is reduced, the cells are smaller, the colloid is often absent altogether from some of the vesicles, and there is a reduction of iodine and of vascularity. Carlson (4, 5), however, points out that we do not yet know just how far these structural changes can proceed before the thyroid hormonal output falls below the needs of the organism. Certainly the evidence for hypothyroidism and hyperthyroidism with advancing age is conflicting, and many of the evidences attributed to reduced thyroid output (dryness of skin and hair, slower reaction time, weakness of muscles, etc.) could be accounted for by other conditions (25). Carlson concludes that even in very old persons the thyroid, in the absence of disease or iodine deficiency in the diet, is capable of meeting the hormone needs of the organism.

Endocrine Functions of the Pancreas

We have already mentioned the pancreas in connection with digestion and pointed out that there is evidence for decline of pancreatic secretion with advancing age, although many believe that, barring accident or disease, the pancreas has a potentially long life span. Most of the work on the pancreas has been concerned with the reduction of insulin and its relation to the incidence of diabetes, results showing, in general, an increase of initial incidence of diabetes up to the age of fifty and a reduced incidence after the age of sixty. Other more recent studies, however, tend to show that lipocaic (another pancreatic hormone) may be more important than insulin in so far as the aging process is concerned, since it is this hormone which influences fat metabolism, and reduction of fat metabolism is generally found in the aged (5).

Parathyroids

The parathyroids, four or more in number and lying close to the thyroid, secrete at least one hormone which is known to run counter to the thyroid hormone (4, 5). However, information is inadequate concerning the function of the parathyroids and the parathyroid hormones, with the exception of the one involved in maintaining the calcium and phosphorus balance in the body. This hormone is important in the physiology of the bone, but although the bones of old persons are not normal, there is no evidence revealing the part the parathyroid hormone might play in this abnormality. In fact, there is no definite evidence that either hypofunction or hyperfunction of the parathyroids is a significant factor in the impairments of the aged. It is known, of course, that the parathyroid hormone influences bone healing and also that there is a decrease with age in the power of healing of bones, but the relationship between the two has not been scientifically determined. Likewise, the relationship between such nervous instabilities as paralysis agitans, which frequently appears in the aged, and other similar conditions which are known to occur as a result of a deficiency in the parathyroid hormone is purely speculative. It is interesting to speculate too on the possible part the parathyroids might play in the calcium deposits found in many of the tissues of the aged—the lens of the eye and the blood vessels, for example—but to date there is no definite information concerning this.

The Thymus Gland

The thymus gland, located in the chest, is thought to have some connection with calcium balance and sex development in early life, but it involutes early and after adolescence exists essentially as a lymph gland so that it seems to be unrelated to the aging process of the organism as a whole (4).

Adrenals

The adrenals, located near the kidneys, have a part in promoting muscular activity, contribute to the organic state in fear and anger, are related to gonadal function, and influence metabolism, particularly in senescence (2, 15, 28, 31). In senescence the adrenal cortex tends to assume the metabolic activities of the waning gonad.

The adrenal gland is divided into different parts, and these parts secrete different hormones, but the evidence concerning the effect of the hormones on the aging process and the aging of the gland itself is confusing. Some of the evidence points to the possibility of hyperfunction of both the cortex and the medulla as factors in the aging process, whereas other indicia seem to show that medulla hypofunction and adrenocortical failure are causative influences in the aging of the organism. Certainly it is known that the adrenal cortex is indispensable to life and health at all ages and is especially important to the metabolism of the aged. One of its hormones, desoxycorticosterone, controls salt metabolism. Another, with the parathyroid, is concerned in calcium metabolism and may be important in arterial changes, especially those involving calcification in the smaller arteries and renal arterioles. Estrone, progesterone, and testosterone are three of its hormones particularly concerned with gonadal function. The influence of adrenal cortex hormones in other areas can also be seen in the efficacy of the treatment of certain cases of arthritis with cortisone. Carlson (5) concludes, however, that there is as yet no definite evidence that either hypofunction or hyperfunction of the adrenals is directly related to the aging process.

The Pituitary Gland

The pituitary gland, located near the base of the brain at the back of the skull, has three main parts and secretes many different hormones; the exact function of each is not fully known, in spite of the considerable research which has been done in the field (4, 15, 25, 31).

Posterior and Intermediate Hormones.—The posterior pituitary secretes hormones concerned with water balance in the tissues, regulation of blood pressure, and possibly regulation of pigmentation. These factors are all connected with the process of aging.

The hormone of the intermediate pituitary has some influence on metabolism, but again the relationship between the intermediate pituitary hormone and the process of aging is not known.

Anterior Hormones.—The anterior pituitary is known to secrete at least six different hormones from four types of cells.

These hormones are proteins which stimulate growth and tissue repair and influence activity in the ovaries, testes, mammary gland, thyroid, and adrenal cortex. In early life hyper- or hyposecretion of one or more of these hormones results in growth or developmental abnormalities. In adult life hyposecretion of the growth hormone may result in obesity, and hypersecretion in acromegaly (enlargement of the bones and soft parts of the hands, feet, and face). Deficiency or excess of the other hormones may result in disturbances of function of the gonads, the thyroid, or the adrenal cortex or in premature aging, but it is not known if the anterior pituitary hormones under normal conditions of functioning have any direct influence on the aging process. In fact, barring disease or injury, the pituitary gland seems to be a remarkably stable organ which has a potential life span of at least eighty to one hundred years.

On the average, however, there seems to be a slight decrease in pituitary weight after the age of forty in human beings, but the relationship of this to hormone output is not known. It is interesting to note, though, that in fowls Payne (23) found retrogressive changes occurring with age and, correlated with or caused by these degenerations, changes in the thyroid, testes, ovaries, and adrenals.

It will be noted too that pituitary transplantation in cases of young persons presenting features of premature senility has resulted in considerable success, so one cannot but speculate as to the possible efficacy of this measure in some cases of senescents whose decline seems more advanced than their years warrant.

Nevertheless, Carlson (5) concludes that neither the failure of the gonads nor the decreased activity of the thyroid in older persons can be attributed to decreased output of the gonadotropic or thyrotropic hormones of the anterior pituitary. Also, there is evidence to indicate that the anterior pituitary output of adrenocorticotropic hormone (ACTH) is sufficient to maintain the gross functional integrity of the adrenal cortex (28).

The Female Reproductive System

Studies on the female reproductive system (9, 14, 16, 17, 24, 26, 27) show that this highly complex system matures rather late and involutes relatively early in the life of the individual. The whole reproductive period of life of the female is marked by alternating cycles of growth and involution, the final involution and cessation of growth occurring at the menopause. Menopause occurs when the secretion of the ovarian hormone, estrogen, falls below the level necessary for menstrual function. This signifies that the ovaries are no longer able to furnish ova for possible fertilization; in other words the female organism is no longer able to take part in the process of producing offspring.

The menopause is only one of the signs of the aging of the female reproductive system or the female genital organs. There are also other and rather extensive changes which are gradually taking place. Even before the final cessation of menstruation, it is usual to find irregularity of menstrual rhythm, anovulatory cycles (menstrual-like cycles when no ova are produced), and other symptoms which may persist for several years after the final cessation. Perhaps the term "climacteric" would be better to use than "menopause" to denote the end of the reproductive period of life, for this term could include the whole process and also the changes which occur in the male reproductive system during its decline.

The age of menopause varies considerably, and it is thought that climate, diet, and heredity and other factors play a part in this variation. Allen (1) notes a report of a study of the menopause in 1187 English women ranging in age from twenty-three to sixty-five, one of whom continued to menstruate until the age of seventy-three, while 65 per cent ceased to menstruate between the ages of forty-five and fifty-five years. In most women the menopause seems to occur at about forty-seven or forty-eight years of age, although actually the woman's active reproductive life may have ceased before this time in what is sometimes called the "premenopausal sterility period." In this connection, however, it is interesting to recall that in the first chapter of this book note was made of the woman reported by Ripley who supposedly gave birth to a child at the age of one hundred one. Others may recall that not so many years ago a five-year-old girl in South America gave birth to a child.

Few women go through the menopause or climacteric without any inconvenience, but about 15 per cent experience major difficulties (12). Among the most common difficulties are vasomotor symptoms, such as hot flushes, which resemble blushing and may occur in sudden, frequent, intermittent waves over a period of years; irritability, depression, and other emotional instabilities; and headaches, numbness of the extremities, digestive disturbances, and fatigue. It has been claimed by some that unmarried, childless women go through the climacteric earlier and have greater difficulties than married women who have had children and breast-fed these children. This, however, has not been conclusively proved, although one cannot escape the thought that unmarried, childless women are generally less well adjusted in the first place and might therefore be expected to experience greater difficulties in this important area.

Following menopause there occurs gradual but extensive atrophy of the vagina, uterus, breasts, and ovaries. The atrophy of the ovaries is especially important because of the endocrine dominance it asserts over the other female tissues and because of the interaction of the ovarian and pituitary hormones. The decline of the endocrine function seems to be one of the major factors in the aging of the female genital system. The pituitary, to compensate for this decline of ovarian function, secrets an excess of gonadotropins, but the effort to stimulate the ovaries to further action is largely useless. It also stimulates the thyroid and adrenal glands to increased activity in an additional effort to compensate for the ovarian lag. The resultant increased activity of the adrenal cortex may cause an increase of weight because of changes of salt, water, and glucose metabolism.

Finally, the increased adrenal cortex activity results in stabilization of the hyperactivity of the pituitary and consequently also of thyroid and medullary function. This results eventually in stabilization of the nervous system. It is thought that the nervous symptoms, such as tenseness, flushes, sweating, etc., may be caused by the increased secretion of epinephrine or adrenaline by the adrenal medulla.

When the ovaries are removed or damaged by X rays, premature aging of the female genital organs follows. In these cases ovarian therapy will replace the destroyed or deficient endocrine function, induce growth of the genital organs and restore menstrual function. There is much dispute, however, concerning the efficacy of endocrine therapy in normal aging women. Some have pointed to the possible relationship between female genital cancers and the use of endocrines as a warning against the indiscriminate use of endocrine therapy, whereas others consider hormone therapy not only safe in normal persons but important in preventing cancer.

Gregory (13) points out that breast cancer occurs when the female hormone level becomes low and only rarely when the supply is ample. When the female hormone decreases, pituitary activity increases, and if the change is rapid symptoms of menopause will appear. By treating the individual with small amounts of female hormone, these symptoms will be prevented from appearing, and in so doing cancer of the breast will also be prevented. Likewise, cancer of the cervix may be prevented in the same indirect way. For example, in the case of an atrophic cervicitis which tries to heal itself, the cells grow so fast that cancer may develop, and yet the atrophic cervicitis could be prevented or cured by the use of hormones. Nevertheless, Gregory warns that the use of endocrines may be dangerous when cancer is present and that caution in regard to the dose is most important. Endocrine therapy should be undertaken only by an expert.

Others do not view declining ovarian function as primarily

responsible for the aging process in the female reproductive system. Hall (15), for example, reports that the reproductive capacity of the female gonads is lost long before other signs of advanced age or atrophic changes in the accessory structures occur, and states that we cannot blame any single endocrine or group of endocrines for aging since the endocrines themselves are victims of a decreased blood supply resulting from generalized vascular sclerosis. He considers further that a decline in endocrine activity may be a response to slowing bodily functions. He does, however, point out the reciprocal action of the resultant deficiencies on other parts of the body. Korenchevsky et al. (21), treating senescent female rats with sex and thyroid hormones, found that hormonal, especially plurihormonal therapy, stopped and even reversed the aging involution in some organs but also that, because of the impossibility of controlling all factors, there were some harmful effects on other organs. They conclude that although some of the processes of aging appear to be reversible, not all the factors basic to the aging process can be controlled and that, because of possible harmful effects resulting from incomplete knowledge, caution should be exercised in the use of hormonal therapy. They feel that a more normal aging could be achieved by the elimination of those diseases and other factors which complicate the present picture of aging.

Others attach more importance to endocrine factors in aging and are more optimistic concerning the use of endocrine therapy. Benjamin (3), for example, states that endocrine deficiencies always accompany aging. Going on this theory, he treated eighty-eight women between the ages of forty-three and seventy-three with gonadal hormones. In spite of the fact that most of these women were not menopausal cases, he achieved good results with them, finding a positive reaction in 85 per cent of the cases. He obtained his best results by a combined use of estrogen and androgen. Usually a ratio of 85 per cent to 15 per cent proves most effective.

The Male Reproductive System

Like the female reproductive system, the male reproductive system (6, 8, 25, 30, 31) matures rather late, but conversely, the male system does not seem to involute early in life. However, the lack of data and the wide individual differences in the decline of function offer handicaps in the securing of accurate information on the aging process. There is indication of a general decrease in the output of the sex hormones with increasing age, but there is no abrupt cessation of hormonal regulation of genital function in the male as there is in the female. In fact, it would seem that the capacity of the male sex organ to respond to an adequate stimulus is a more important factor in the decline of sexual activity than is the loss of hormonal activation. There is no definite evidence that the involution of the male genital system in old age is due primarily to an endocrine deficiency, and although copulatory behavior generally does decrease with advancing age, there is considerable evidence for copulatory behavior in some very old men. It is not too infrequent, for example, to hear of very old men becoming fathers. In most of the aged men who have been examined, sperm have been present, although reduced in number. It is probable also that they are reduced in vigor.

The testes are composed of two types of tissues—the seminiferous tubules which contain cells which produce and nourish the spermatozoa and the intertubular spaces in which are found blood vessels, lymphatics, loose connective tissue, and specialized interstitial cells which are the origin of one or more male sex hormones. With increasing age some changes are known to occur in the testes, although much information on this subject is still lacking. The interstitial cells show increased pigmentation, but there is no definite evidence for a decrease in the number of the cells. There is also a thickening of the basement membrane of the seminiferous tubules, which it is thought may possibly be due to vascular changes, and a change or retrogression of the spermatogonia (germ cells) into the small, round cells which are generally found in the immature testes.

Structural changes in the prostate are commonly found in older men, and these changes appear to be more pronounced than those in the testes. Prostatic hypertrophy of benign type is found so frequently in men past the age of sixty years that it is thought by some that this may be a true aging process. The cause of this hypertrophy is believed by some to be the decreased output of the male hormone, but it is possible that there may be several contributing causes.

Concerning the male climacteric there is much dispute. Some claim the male climacteric to be an integral, gradual, and normal part of the aging process of the human male organism, something akin to the well-recognized climacteric in the female, while others insist that since not all aged males experience a climacteric, such a process is definitely abnormal. Heller and Myers (18), for example, point out that it affects only a small proportion of those men who live to an old age and that it is probably a pathological accompaniment of the aging process. Minnick et al. (22) reported an increase of copulatory behavior when aged men were treated with testosterone (male hormone) and also when treated with a pituitary-like hormone, and found no difference in the efficacy of the two hormones.

One of the main problems in considering the male climacteric is the difficulty in differentiating a true climacteric from psychic impotence and psychoneurotic conditions. Both may show vasomotor symptoms and emotional disturbances similar to those found in women at the menopause, as well as impotence. Generally, however, the psychoneurotics and cases of psychic impotence do not respond well to endocrine treatment, although they may show response to psychoanalysis or other forms of psychotherapy; the reverse tends to hold true for cases of true male climacteric. There is always the complicating factor, however, that some cases of emotionally induced impotence may, as a result of the effects of suggestion, show a transitory improvement in response to endocrine therapy.

We cannot leave this subject of the male climacteric without a note on Kinsey's report on the sexual activity of the human male. Kinsey (20) reports that there is a steady decline of sexual activity in the human male from a peak in adolescence to old age, and considers that this may perhaps be due largely to a general decline in physical and physiological capacity. He points out, however, that the factor of psychological fatigue—that is, the repetition of the same pattern over and over again without anything new in the way of stimulus or variety—may also play a part. The matter of opportunity is likewise important, for many old men are so unattractive physically to those females who might offer a stimulus to their waning sexual activities that they have no chance to be active sexually. Kinsey found a steady decline not only in the extent of sexual activity but also in all types of sexual activity. He also found an increase of impotence with an increase of age.

Psychosexual Changes

Although we have so far confined ourselves largely to a discussion of the physical changes which take place in the male and female reproductive systems with advancing age, we must rightfully take a psychosomatic approach to the problem of this aspect of the aging process (6, 14, 16, 19, 25, 30). The climacteric is not only a period of changing glandular function and perhaps atrophy of various tissues concerned with genital function, but it is also a period that for many has great psychic meaning and emotional tone. For many persons the climacteric is psychically a change from a life that contained meaning and value to one that appears devoid of both. Of course, this is not true of all persons, for, in the final analysis, the psychic reaction will depend upon the individual—how he evaluates life in general and his life in particular, how much emotional preparation he has had for the change, and how well adjusted he is. If he can view as important not age itself but what he does with the age he has attained, then the climacteric will have greater positive meaning for him and he will accommodate to these changes with the same equanimity that he accepted other changes and vicissitudes of life.

Because psychosomatic unity is so inherent in the human organism, it is usual to find both emotional and physical symptoms accompanying the physiological changes that occur in the reproductive system. Psychosomatic symptoms which commonly occur at the climacteric, and these may be present in men as well as in women, include vasomotor symptoms of various sorts, as previously discussed. Dizziness, dyspnea and palpitation of the heart, also are frequent enough to cause discomfort. Sometimes there is a loss of interest in sexual activity, and sometimes symptoms are referable to other parts of the body. For example, gastrointestinal disturbances, such as gas, belching, constipation, loss of appetite, nausea, and vomiting, or sensorimotor disturbances, such as pains in different parts of the body, headache, tremors, itching, constant fatigue, trouble in sleeping, and restlessness and fidgetiness, may occur. At times these physical symptoms have some basis in hormonal change, but more often they are psychogenic in origin and are either accompanied by or increased by emotional manifestations of various kinds. Both the physical and the psychic symptoms generally occur in individuals who have long shown signs of emotional instability—often in the worried, anxious, moody, overly sensitive person. At the menopause or climacteric, these instabilities become intensified, so that minor ailments and disruptions of the environment become magnified out of proportion to their importance, and the individual reacts with excessive irritability, excitability, or impatience or perhaps becomes very depressed or apprehensive.

The fact that psychosomatic symptoms and emotional instabilities observed at the menopause are commonly found only in those who have previously shown signs of instability has been brought out by various studies. For example, Stern and Prados (29), in studying 50 women with "menopausal syndrome" by means of interviews, social histories, and Rorschach studies, found depression, associated almost exclusively with marriage and reproduction, a common clinical picture, and pointed out that this depression was a reactive depression which presented only an accentuation of a previously existing maladjustment. There was no correlation between the intensity of the physical signs and the severity of the emotional disturbance.

Greenhill (11) also made a rather thorough study of the psychiatric and endocrinological factors in the menopause. He took a group of 100 normal menopausal women without previous or present signs of psychoneurosis and compared them with a group of 50 women referred by physicians for "menopausal syndrome," 50 women chosen at random from hospital records as having been treated for "menopausal syndrome," and 50 women with mild autonomic overactivity but no frank psychoneurotic complaint. He concluded that the normal menopause involves mild autonomic symptoms but that the majority of normal women who have never had a neurosis prior to the climacteric do not experience symptoms during the menopause that might be considered of a psychiatric nature. Furthermore, he found that women who experienced psychoneuroses misdiagnosed as "menopausal syndrome" had been psychoneurotic for all or a large part of their lives, and their psychoneurotic difficulties were merely exacerbated by the menopause in a psychogenic rather than a physiogenic way, as reactions to their morbid interpretations of the ending of their reproductive lives.

Schachter (24), on the other hand, believes that a woman's psychological reaction to the menopausal period depends primarily on her pre-existing vegetative-endocrine constitution, that is, whether she might have been a hyperthyroid or a hyperpituitary case. Schachter states also that single women have more serious psychic difficulties than married women at this period. As indicated earlier, however, this statement is not surprising since it is generally the less well adjusted who do not effect marriage and might therefore be expected to experience greater psychic trauma in response to stress of any kind.

When physical and emotional symptoms appear at the menopause, the use of hormones affords relief in most cases, particularly where the physical symptoms predominate. Where the emotional symptoms predominate and where emotional instability was already present, hormones prove less effective. In fact, Farell (9) warns against the injudicious use of estrogen during the climacteric, as he states that hormonal deficiency is often not the main factor in the difficulty but rather, a malignant disease or mental maladjustment in individuals with a long neurotic history.

Many doctors, however, find their best success in menopausal cases with a combined use of psychotherapy and hormones. Emotional preparation for the menopause is probably the most effective preventive of menopausal difficulties, both psychic and somatic, and few instances of real success with these difficulties will be found without the use of some psychotherapy.

The psychoneurotic manifestations found during the menopause are varied and similar to those found in response to stress in other periods of life, the precipitating and intensifying factor at this time being the loss of the reproductive function. In general, the symptoms of distress, anxiety, and fear are similar to those of "shell shock" and "battle fatigue" found in men emotionally unprepared for war. This, of course, stresses the importance of emotional preparation beforehand for the onset of the climacteric.

Psychotherapy with women at the climacteric (and the same holds true of men, although probably to a lesser extent) reveals many fears connected with the aging process. There is the inevitable recognition of the reality that youth has gone and the fear that, with the farewell to youth, the period between middle age and death is only a period of decline of physical and mental power. The fear of "loss of mind" enters in, with the result that there is an oversensitiveness to slips of memory, absent-mindedness, forgetfulness, and errors of judgment. There is also an oversensitiveness to and exaggeration of illnesses, with the result that there are innumerable physical complaints, often with hypo-chondriacal depression, most of which are manifestations of anxiety and anticipation. These anxieties are connected with fears of being dependent, rejected, helpless, and pain-ridden.

In the experience of the author and associates who have worked with older people, it would seem that to many persons the concepts of death and old age are fairly closely associated, which is probably as it should be since normally death does occur in old age, and to the majority the thought of death—at least of one's own death—is not particularly pleasant. The fear of death is probably always present in our lives, but normally this fear is repressed (32). When factors in aging prevent the successful repression of the fear of death, the morale of the individual declines. Perhaps those who look forward to a life after this one do not find death so terrifying as those who do not share this belief; nevertheless most normal, healthy persons do not welcome the thought of their own death. Yet, faced with the incontrovertible fact of one's own aging, can the thought of death be far away? Since death inevitably follows old age, one's own aging means one's own approach to death. Obviously this arouses fear and the desire to stave off, deny, outwit, or reject the aging process and, of course, the inevitable death just beyond.

According to psychoanalytic theories (10), in youth and even middle age the unconscious belief in the individual's own immortality pushes away ideas and fears of death from the con-sciousness of most normal persons; but declining health and faculties in old age prove too strong external stimuli for the unconscious belief in personal immortality to balance. An awak-ening or a disillusionment develops, which is sometimes rather sudden, and fears of death commence to occupy the thoughts of the oldster. With these fears only psychotherapy, religion, or the development of an improved philosophy of life—and death—can help. The most desirable way, of course, would be to de-velop these concepts early in life.

It has been noted many times that different persons react dif-ferently to the climacteric, that some pass through it with no

noticeable difficulty, whereas others become very upset and distressed, both physically and emotionally. As mentioned earlier,
it is usually those with deep-rooted and long-standing psychoneurotic difficulties who experience the most trouble. Further
study reveals also that it is usually those egocentric individuals,
and this applies both to men and to women, who set the most
store by physical appearance and sex appeal to the neglect of
other potentials, who have the greatest difficulties at the climacteric. For these persons the only value in life is the physical
appeal of one sex for the other, and when that is gone there is
nothing left. These are the women and the men who try desperately to disguise the aging process. They dye their hair,
have their faces lifted, go into frenzies of exercise and diet,
devour endocrine preparations, and play the perennial adolescent
—and it is all pitifully useless. To keep well groomed and to
maintain a youthful outlook on life are both commendable and
desirable, but to refuse to grow up and assume the maturity
consistent with adulthood is a pathetic misplacement of life's
values. Thus, we see the middle-aged men who fear their
waning sexual powers and feel impelled to go to excesses in
order to prove themselves. As it is most important to them to
be attractive to the opposite sex, they usually seek young and
pretty girls and become involved in a series of ever-changing
affairs. They feel important at being seen with a pretty young
companion, are easily stimulated and flattered, and soon are
able to push away the specter of old age and death and delude
themselves into thinking they are as boyishly attractive and
virile as they ever were. The same pattern may be seen in
middle-aged women who, with money, are able to buy the attentions of handsome young men and indulge in excesses with
them, all the while deluding themselves into believing they are
loved for their beauty and charm.

The problem seems to resolve itself into a matter of the personal values these people have or the self-concepts they hold.
When a woman (and the same is true for a man) holds her
greatest and perhaps only attraction to be in the physical and

particularly the sexual areas, she feels lost and ready for discard when these attractions wane, as they inevitably do. She experiences the feeling of being no longer needed, wanted, or useful. The fact that many times around the period of the menopause a woman's offspring have matured, have married, and left the home and no longer have need of her maternal care tends to intensify her feelings of uselessness. The answer to these problems, of course, would be to develop early in life a different set of values and a more worthy self-concept. Changes throughout life must be considered phases of growth, each phase carrying its own values and worth within itself, and each individual must learn to assay his own worth according to the values of the phase of growth he is at present in or about to enter.

The problems of the climacteric are no doubt more acute and far-reaching in women than in men, since many men never experience a climacteric. This period in a woman's life is much more sudden and dramatic and sex life is much more the core of her existence. For a long time men may find excuses for their waning sexual powers and even complacently believe that, given the proper stimulus, they would not be impotent, but with women the fact of the menopause is inescapable. Although some women welcome the menopause as a release from their fear of pregnancy, others view it differently. With the cessation of her menses, the fact is forcibly brought home to a woman that she is no longer able to produce children, that she has reached a partial death, and that perhaps, with these things, her own death is in the not too far-off future. Thus, the menopause is definitely a blow to a woman's narcissism, for she who has been important to herself and her family and in her own eyes the symbol of motherhood, now finds herself no longer of service to the species. She has reached the end of her existence as a bearer of future life, and whether or not she consciously wants more children at this stage of life, the very fact that she cannot have them is destructive of her self-concept. Sometimes a woman's protest against the ending of her usefulness as a female and producer of children results in her having a late baby. Often, in these instances, the protest is entirely unconscious and the having of the baby is against her conscious will and desire. Consciously she may consider that she is too old to have a baby, that it will interfere with her other activities, and that she does not want again to go through the nuisance of caring for a young infant, but in the unconscious her protest against her approaching infertility is so strong that she has the baby. Even to women who do not want to give birth to children, menstruation has a meaning which strikes deep into the emotional foundations, for it affords proof that they are still biologically alive.

However, in spite of the fact that the menopause is basically a blow to a woman's narcissism and the feeling of biological usefulness, it does not follow that all women will react with distress to this phenomenon. Women who have borne many children may welcome this termination of frequent pregnancies as increased opportunity for rest and activity along other lines. Others who, because of their continual hope for a suitable mate and children, have until this time been unable to make the most effective use of their abilities may, when they accept the inevitable, find that they are now free to develop their potentialities more fully and completely.

Of course, the increase of creative and other types of non-biological activity at this time may also be a kind of protest against the menopause and cessation of biological usefulness, but in this case the protest takes the form of a rather healthy sublimation. The woman here is trying to prove that she is still of use to the world, that she is not just a biological being good only for propagation of the species but also a human being with other, equally useful, values to the species. Deutsch (7), from her analysis of many women in this period, reports that libidinous needs tend to become intensified during the climacteric, especially in the preclimacteral period, with the result that many women demand constant signs and proof of still being loved. They want increased attentions and demonstrations of affection from their husbands, and often even these are not enough, so that they seek similar evidences of love from others outside the family group. Usually these are relatively harmless reactions, as most normal women are able to keep the expression of their libidinous needs within the bounds of social propriety. They may sublimate in a more or less constructive manner with only minor demands on husband and family, or they may resort to fantasies. These fantasies are usually similar to those they experienced in early adolescence, the impulses and wishes of which have been sublimated or repressed during the intervening years of maturity, and they may fill much of the waking life, so that the ultimate picture is one of withdrawal to a more satisfying dream life where the dreamer is ever beautiful and loved. The dreams provide a satisfying escape from the frustrations of the climacteric.

Sometimes, though, the libidinous needs become too strong to be bridled, and the woman feels compelled to act out her fantasies, often with embarrassing results to herself and to her family. These reactions are actually a re-enactment of psychological puberty, and they display, often with increased intensity, the same feelings and behavior experienced by the individual at that time.

Occasionally too, a woman's reaction to her own sex shows a change during the climacteric (7), so that former friendships and relations with female relatives tend to become troubled by jealousies, new demands, and quarrels. These result from an intensification of a latent homosexuality which has been well sublimated throughout life: the previous ease supplied by the sublimation is no longer in effect as the needs become stronger, so that the woman now demands all the attention and extra proofs of love from her friend or quarrels with her as a result of unconscious panic over the threatened danger from the homosexual conflict. When the inner homosexual conflict becomes too strong in already maladjusted women during the climacteric, paranoid ideas sometimes develop. These are similar to the temporary paranoid reactions to homosexual danger in puberty, although sometimes they may be the beginning of a chronic psychosis.

In general, the climacteric has a tendency to repeat both the neurotic and the psychotic states of puberty, and neurotic manifestations which may have gone unrecognized before tend to become intensified as in puberty.

It is not uncommon at the menopause to find women with rather severe anxiety states and expressed fear of "losing my mind," "going insane," etc. These anxieties and fears are generally caused by a conflict between the increased libido and the established mores. We have already discussed the intensification of libidinous needs during the climacteric, and it is not too hard to understand how increasingly difficult it becomes to bridle these desires at the menopause. With the menopause comes the cessation of the fear of unwanted or illegitimate pregnancy, with consequent disgrace and rejection by society, so that it becomes less easy to control lawless impulses. Thus, the forces of the id come now into stronger conflict with the superego, with the result that the fear of giving way to these impulses brings on feelings of anxiety. These women often respond well to psychotherapy.

Many of the reactions of women at the menopause, however, depend not only upon the emotional adjustment of the woman within herself but also upon the conditions of her environment, although, of course, the two are inextricably interrelated. A feminine woman who has lived a happy, full, sexually gratifying, married life, borne children which she has been able to bring up as individuals with personalities and lives distinct from her own, and been able to develop spiritual and other values aside from the physical, will adjust to the climacteric without undue stress, develop her potentialities along other lines, and find happiness in areas other than the purely sexual and reproductive. If she has maintained good relationships with her offspring and has been able to give them their freedom, she will find that she can continue her motherhood not only with them but also with their spouses in healthy, mutually satisfying relationships. The mother-in-law is not always and need never be a bugaboo, for a wise mother-in-law can form warm friendships with her new sons and daughters and thus keep alive her motherhood.

Grandmotherhood likewise offers many opportunities for the enrichment of life in the later years, and in many ways may prove even more satisfying than motherhood itself. Assuming she is a normal and well-adjusted person, there is less room for ambivalent feelings on the grandmother's part and on the part of her grandchildren, so that she can both give and receive love more whole-heartedly. There is also less responsibility involved and less need of guidance of the grandchildren, so that the relationship need not be marred by the aggressions and hostilities which frequently beset the mother.

Summary

The endocrine glands, or glands of internal secretion, play an important part in the process of aging of the human organism, but understanding of the part they play and of their relationships to each other is incomplete. There is as yet no conclusive evidence that true rejuvenation can occur or that youth can be prolonged indefinitely by means of endocrine therapy or transplantation.

Endocrine functioning is affected by the hereditary pattern of the organism, diet, vitamin intake, disease, and the functioning of the other glands in the endocrine system.

The thyroid gland, located in the neck, is an important regulator of the body. It affects tissue rebuilding and repair and influences the functioning of other organs of the body. With increasing age changes occur, but it is not yet known how far these structural changes must proceed before the hormonal output falls below the needs of the organism. Some believe that, in the absence of disease or iodine deficiency, the thyroid gland maintains its functional capacity even in old age.

Although the pancreas has a potentially long life span, there is evidence for decrease of insulin and lipocaic output with advancing age. Since the latter is concerned with fat metabolism and this is generally reduced in old age, lipocaic may be an important hormone in the aging process.

The parathyroids may be concerned with the condition and healing of bones in old age, with certain nervous instabilities, and with the calcium deposits found in many of the tissues of the aged, but this has not definitely been proved.

The thymus, as far as is known, seems to be unrelated to the aging process of the organism.

The adrenals are known to be important in the promotion of muscular activity, gonadal function, particularly in senescence, calcium metabolism, and the organic states in fear and anger, and they may also be important in arterial changes in old age. Nevertheless, there is as yet no definite evidence that either hypo- or hyperfunction of the medulla or the cortex is directly related to the aging process.

The pituitary gland has three main parts and secretes many different hormones. The relationship between the posterior and the intermediate pituitary hormones and the aging process is not certainly known. The anterior pituitary secretes at least six different hormones which are proteins known to stimulate tissue growth and repair and to influence activity in the ovaries, testes, mammary gland, thyroid, and adrenal cortex. Disturbances of hormonal functioning are known to be influential in premature aging, but the relationship to normal aging is uncertain.

The female reproductive system matures late and involutes relatively early in life, so that the female organism is able to take part in the reproducing of young for only a short period in the total life cycle. Menopause, one of the first external signs of the aging of the female organism, occurs when the secretion of the ovarian hormone, estrogen, falls below the level necessary for menstrual function. In the majority of women it occurs at about forty-seven or forty-eight years of age.

Prior to and following the menopause, other endocrine and structural changes also take place.

There is considerable dispute concerning the efficacy of endocrine therapy for aging women, but where both psychic and physical symptoms are present, the combination of endocrine therapy and psychotherapy seems to be beneficial.

The male reproductive system matures rather late in life but does not always involute early. There is, in general, a decrease in the output of the sex hormone with advancing age and decline in copulatory behavior, although there are wide individual differences.

There is also evidence for some structural changes in the prostate, and prostatic hypertrophy is common in men past sixty years of age.

A male climacteric does not always occur, but when it does, vasomotor symptoms and emotional disturbances, similar to those commonly found in women at the menopause, are frequently found, as well as impotence.

In general, we might say that aging is psychosomatic and that sexual aging is psychosexual. Some of the symptoms found at the climacteric are physical, but most are psychogenic in origin and due to earlier poor mental hygiene.

Common psychosomatic symptoms occurring at the climacteric are vasomotor disturbances such as hot flushes and sweating, gastrointestinal upsets, dizziness, dyspnea, palpitation of the heart, headaches, tremors, itching, constant fatigue, sleeplessness, and restlessness.

Emotional disturbances such as excessive irritability, excitability, or depression usually occur in those who have long shown signs of emotional instability. The climacteric merely exaggerates those emotional maladjustments which were already present.

Anxiety and fears of becoming useless, of being unwanted, and of death are common at this period. Fears of waning sexual powers and sometimes of one's own lawless impulses frequently result in anxiety.

Adjustment to aging, and especially to aging of the reproductive system, involves an adjustment of one's personal values in life. Rather than aging itself, it is what one does with aging that is important.

REFERENCES

1. ALLEN, E. Female reproductive system. In COWDRY, E. V. (ed.), *Problems of ageing*. Baltimore: The Williams & Wilkins Co., 1939.
2. Androgen therapy. *Therapeutic Review*. Parke, Davis & Co., Nov., 1950.
3. BENJAMIN, H. Endocrine gerontotherapy: the use of sex hormone combinations in female patients. *J. Geron.*, 1949, **4**, 222-33.
4. CARLSON, A. J. Physiologic changes in normal aging. In STIEGLITZ, E. J. (ed.), *Geriatric medicine*. Philadelphia: W. B. Saunders Co., 1949.
5. ——. The thyroid, pancreatic islets, parathyroids, adrenals, thymus and pituitary. In COWDRY, E. V. (ed.), *Problems of ageing*. Baltimore: The Williams & Wilkins Co., 1939.
6. CLARK, L. Sex life in the middle-aged. *Marriage, Fam. Living*, 1949, **11**, 38-60.
7. DEUTSCH, H. *Psychology of Women*. Vol. II. *Motherhood*. New York: Grune & Stratton, Inc., 1945.
8. ENGLE, E. T. Male reproductive system. In COWDRY, E. V. (ed.), *Problems of ageing*. Baltimore: The Williams & Wilkins Co., 1939.
9. FARELL, D. M. Dangers in management of the climacteric. *Med. Clin. N. Amer.*, 1948, **32**, 1523-32.
10. FREUD, S. *Collected papers*. Vol. IV. *Thoughts for the times on war and death* (1915). London: International Psychoanalytical Press, 1925.
11. GREENHILL, M. H. A psychosomatic evaluation of the psychiatric and endocrinological factors in menopause. *5th med. J.,* Birmingham, 1946, **39**, 786-94.
12. GREER, I. The menopause: a pattern repeats. *J. Pastoral Care*, 1949, **3**, 6-10.
13. GREGORY, J. E. Hormone therapy in cancer. *Med. Times,* 1950, **78**, 461-65.
14. HAMBLEN, E. C. *Facts about change of life*. Springfield, Ill.: Charles C Thomas, Publisher, 1949.
15. HALL, C. E. Age and the endocrine glands. *Tex. Rep. Biol. Med.,* 1948, **6**, 321-26.
16. HAMILTON, G. V. Changes in personality and psychosexual phenomena with age. In COWDRY, E. V. (ed.), *Problems of ageing*. Baltimore: The Williams & Wilkins Co., 1939.
17. HARRIS, L. J. Treatment of the menopause. *Canad. med. Ass. J.*, 1948, **58**, 251-55.
18. HELLER, C. G., and MYERS, G. B. The male climacteric: its symptomatology, diagnosis and treatment. *J. Amer. med. Ass.,* 1944, **126**, 472-77.
19. KAUFMAN, M. R. The psychoanalytic point of view. With discussion by S. Atkin. *J. Orthopsychiat.,* 1940, **10**, 73-84.
20. KINSEY, A. C., POMEROY, W. B., and MARTIN, C. E. *Sexual behavior in the human male*. Philadelphia: W. B. Saunders Co., 1948.
21. KORENCHEVSKY, V., PARIS, S. K., and BENJAMIN, B. Treatment of senescence in female rats with sex and thyroid hormones. *J. Geron.,* 1950, **5**, 120-57.
22. MINNICK, R. S., WARDEN, C. J., and ARIETI, S. The effects of sex hormones on the copulatory behavior of senile white rats. *Science,* 1946, **103**, 749-50.

23. PAYNE, F. Changes in the endocrine glands of the fowl with age. *J. Geron.*, 1949, **4**, 193-99.

24. SCHACHTER, M. Profil neuro-endocrine et psychologie de la ménopause. *Sc. Hop.*, Paris, 1947, **23**, 953-56.

25. SHOCK, N. W. Physiological aspects of mental disorders in later life. In KAPLAN, O. (ed.), *Mental disorders in later life.* Stanford, Calif.: Stanford University Press, 1945.

26. SHORR, E. Problems of mental adjustment at the climacteric. Discussion by A. W. Stearns and E. Kahn. In *Mental health in later maturity.* Publ. Hlth. Rep., Wash., 1942, No. 168, 125-37.

27. SICKER, L. Change of life: a psychosomatic problem. *Amer. J. Psychotherapy*, 1949, **3**, 399-409.

28. SOLOMON, D. H., and SHOCK, N. W. Adrenal, cortical, and pituitary function in age. *J. Geron.*, 1950, **5**, 302-13.

29. STERN, K., and PRADOS, M. Personality studies in menopausal women. *Amer. J. Psychiat.*, 1946, **103**, 358-68.

30. STIEGLITZ, E. J. *The second forty years.* Philadelphia: J. B. Lippincott Co., 1946.

31. TURNER, H. H. The endocrine aspects of gerontology. *Geriatrics*, 1949, **4**, 74-78.

32. ZILBOORG, G. Fear of death. *Psychosom. Quart.*, 1943, **12**, 465-75.

Chapter 3

EMOTIONAL CHANGES

Emotional reactions are common to every living human being, but they must be viewed as part of the reactions of the total organism, not as something separate and distinct from the rest of the body and mind.

Emotions—Biological and Psychological

Emotions, first of all, must be considered in relation to the situation which produced the reaction. There are three components of emotion: the conscious state, the accompanying inner organic state, and the overt or postural reactions. It is not just what one feels—joy, love, hate, anger, etc.—but also whether one strikes out, stiffens, runs, or shows some other kind of bodily reaction and what accompanying changes occur in the body during the experience.

We know that the whole body reacts in response to strong emotional stimuli—that the adrenals, for example, pour forth adrenaline for use in emergency states of fear and anger, that the gonads respond to emotions connected with love and sex, etc. These are normal components of emotional reaction, but it is possible that in the aging person they may be modified by the changes which have taken and are taking place in the organs of response within the body. In the absence of pathology, there is no evidence for a change in the excitability of the nerves with advancing age, but, as we have already seen, there are modifications of endocrine secretions and emotions. It seems likely that endocrine changes have some effect upon the emotional reactions of older persons, and we have seen this to be the case at the climacteric, but it is also evident that this action is reciprocal. Actually, much needs yet to be learned concerning the influence of changes in the endocrine glands and other organs upon the emotional reactions of the aging person, and at present few data are available. Nevertheless, as we study emotional reactions and changes in old age, we must bear in mind that with all reactions, and possibly too with all changes, there are accompanying bodily states or conditions within the organism. Physical and psychic changes are inseparable (32).

The emotional changes which occur with advancing age are, in general, closely tied up with the psychosexual changes we have just discussed (8, 17). They are closely connected too with physical, social, and intellectual changes, the whole being an interactive process and all a part of the total aging process. Psychosomatic unity is so much a part of the human organism that we cannot rightfully consider decline in one aspect without also treating deterioration in all other aspects, for truly each one is but a part of the total pattern. As a part of the total pattern, decline in any one aspect will necessarily affect, in turn, decline in the other aspects. Thus, normal or pathological deterioration of one or more organs of the human body will often induce emotional upset or decline. A person may become irritable because he does not feel well, has pain, or experiences fatigue, or he may become apathetic and hopeless because a physical condition renders him helpless and he thinks he will always be dependent and useless. These reactions, as we have seen, frequently accompany changes in the reproductive systems of men and women.

However, the reverse can also occur, so that we find physical complaints, malfunctioning, and even deterioration in various systems of the body caused by emotional maladjustment, disturbance, or deterioration. A similar interaction will be found between emotional decline and social and intellectual, as well as physical changes.

If we look into the psychosomatic reactions of the aging organism a little further, we can see the operation of compensation within the personality. In response to frustration in one area, the old person may seek satisfaction in another area, even though he may be unaware of his motives for doing so. This is a pseudopodiac reaction of the personality wherein when one side is depressed, another side extends its tentacles. For example, somatic adequacy having declined, psychic compensation may be sought along intellectual lines, in social activities, or by the emotional expedient of irritability and cantankerousness in an effort to retain some measure of the power lost through the decline of physical prowess. Again, the unconscious sense of loss which may be induced in the aged person by virtue of his waning physical or intellectual efficiency may result in hoarding and miserliness. Though he may have much money, the old miser cannot spend it. He projects his personal sense of loss onto the monetary field and must hang on to his possessions, since money is symbolic of power. (The same general principle sometimes holds true for certain cases of constipation in the elderly. The individual may retain his feces as a symbolic holding on to something precious to him.)

This brings us logically to the question of the reversibility of the aging process. Is the aging process reversible and, if so, to what extent? We have already learned that there are differences of opinion concerning the efficacy of various kinds of physical therapy, and in particular endocrine therapy, in the retardation or alteration of the aging pattern of the human organism. In some cases, we have seen that a combination of physical therapy and psychotherapy has proved successful in retarding, and occasionally perhaps even in reversing, the aging process, for a time, but we do not yet know which is the more important—the physical treatment or the psychotherapy. We do know, however, and even popular observation will bear this out, that with an improved emotional outlook we find improvement in the general physical condition of the aged person and an increase in his mental alertness (3). When his emotions are healthy, he looks better, feels better, and is more ready to learn and to partake of the life around him. When he is emotionally disturbed, on the other hand, he does not look well, complains a lot, has many aches and pains, experiences difficulty in concentrating and in learning new things, cannot continue normal social relationships with those around him, and seems mentally sluggish. These facts would seem to indicate that with proper hygienic measures (both physical and mental), the aging process might be retarded considerably and even, within limits, since eventual decline and death are inevitable, reversed to some degree when the decline is in advance of biological necessity.

The Life Pattern

It would seem that the life pattern of the individual is one of the most important factors in the rate of decline, particularly of emotional decline, in the aging individual. It has been said that we develop habits, ways of reacting, and patterns of behavior early in life, throughout the period of childhood and early youth, that these become crystallized in the thirties and forties, and that we must then live with them for the rest of our lives (21). This emphasizes the need for developing healthy and adequate patterns of living early in life, and certainly the importance of this cannot be underestimated, for actually very few persons do effect amelioration of their habits and reactions after the thirties or forties. It would, however, be a foolish and needlessly hopeless outlook on the period of later maturity and old age to state that ameliorative changes cannot take place after thirty or forty years of age. It is doubtful if anyone is ever, save when in a state of senile decay, too old to effect a positive change within himself. It is just that because of the greater plasticity of the young organism, changes are more easily made in youth, and oldsters usually do not know how, and often do not want to exert the effort required to change. It is probably for this reason that many psychoanalysts are still so reluctant to attempt analysis of an older person, even though some are becoming more optimistic regarding the outlook with the older patient.

When a normal pattern of living and reacting has been established early in life, the aging process proceeds gradually and smoothly with no major distresses, anxieties, and emotional upsets. Naturally, every person, normal or otherwise, will experience some swings of mood. There are times when he is quite happy and contented and other times when he feels less happy and is not entirely satisfied with the world or himself. In the mentally healthy person these emotional variations are not extreme or prolonged and do not, therefore, seriously affect physical, intellectual, or social functioning. The person who has developed and practiced a healthful outlook on life recognizes the naturalness of the aging process and is prepared to gain satisfactions in the later as in every other period of life. He accepts the fact that the satisfactions of childhood are not the satisfactions of adolescence, those of adolescence not those of adulthood, and those of later maturity not the same as those prized in the prime of life. As in adolescence he did not cling to the behavior patterns and satisfactions of childhood, so in senescence he will not try to be the perennial youth and make himself ridiculous by his adolescent behavior. He will accept later maturity and all it implies and look forward to the adventure of discovering the new satisfactions which are inherent in this period.

Unfortunately, in aging persons, and particularly in those going through the climacteric, we often find an intensification of already existing bad patterns of living and reacting or a reactivation of those adjustment difficulties found at puberty (18). Minor maladjustments to the environment, to the self, and to life in general may have been present for years but kept under control or at least within the bounds of normality until the added stress of aging increases their intensity and forces open manifestation of symptoms. Long-established attitudes of selfishness and egocentricity, which perhaps were not so evident during the periods of life when environmental demands were many, tend to become more marked and open in their display. Anger and lack of control are now more in evidence, since there seems to be less need for hiding or controlling violent and unpleasant emotions. There is now also a marked tendency to project one's faults and difficulties onto others. It is others who are selfish, egocentric, and bad-tempered—others who are so mean and lacking in consideration that they cause one to react in this unpleasant fashion. These aging individuals, since they will not recognize the changes occurring within themselves, cannot accept their own unstable emotional manifestations and must find a scapegoat and a way of justifying themselves.

The tendency which many have always shown to overemphasize illness and other minor things becomes aggravated. A slight illness or injury which to most normal persons would be of little or no significance assumes vast importance and often is dramatized to an abnormal degree. This serves a double purpose: it brings desired attention and solicitude from those in the environment, and it provides an excuse for a general letdown, irritability, and other emotional instabilities. It is a protection against felt inadequacies, the idea being that if one is physically ill, stricken with disease or injury, it is an accident of life which might happen to anyone and an accident for which one can in no way be held accountable. If one is physically incapacitated, others cannot expect things of him which he privately suspects, but will not admit, that he could not do anyway.

If the aging person feels the lack of emotional satisfactions and affection and has no capacity for or practice in healthy sublimation, there often results an increase in the drive for oral satisfactions, taking the form of constant complaining and faultfinding or eating too much. Overeating seems to be a particularly common way of reacting to the lack of needed affection in later years, and the outcome is often unfortunate, for it frequently results in obesity and digestive disturbances which reciprocally aggravate the already present emotional difficulty.

As mentioned earlier, adolescent psychoneurotic and psychotic-like episodes are frequently repeated during the climacteric (8). The patterns of living which are basic to these reactions have probably been present all or most of life, but the reactions themselves could be kept under control until the strain, first of adolescence and then of the climacteric, became too much for the organism to bear.

The way in which a latent homosexuality, always repressed and controlled, may become evident during this period has also been discussed. Although the individual may have been unaware of the tendency and may never have shown any overt manifestations of it, the life pattern again may be seen in his reactions to members of the same or the opposite sex or in his failure to achieve a normal heterosexual life. Psychoanalysts find this eruption of latent homosexuality basic to the development of paranoid thinking at this age. Homosexual reactions being consciously unacceptable to the individual, he begins unconsciously to project his thoughts and feelings onto others, and thus the paranoid beginnings are initiated (10).

Feelings and Attitudes of the Older Person

Generally speaking, the feelings and attitudes of the individual will determine how well or how poorly he will adjust to his own aging process. Those who are normally happy within themselves and who are well adjusted to their environment will usually accept the inevitable in a healthy manner and seek their own satisfactions in areas suited to their needs and period in life. This, of course, they have always done, so that adjustment to them is not a new thing. The adjustment, however, is facilitated when they feel loved and respected by those around them and useful to their environment.

Those whose attitudes and feelings are not healthy or well balanced and who are not happy within themselves or well adjusted to their environment will experience greater emotional difficulties as life advances and the onset of old age becomes an incontrovertible fact. The kind of emotional difficulties they experience, of course, will depend to a large extent upon their lifelong emotional reactions, their feelings about things, and their attitudes toward various areas of life and living. Those, for example, who have always been troubled with feelings of inadequacy and insecurity and who have tried to offset or diminish these feelings by achieving success in some field may be strongly affected by their failing capacities. They have tried for so long to prove to the world and to themselves that they are not as inferior as they suspect that when they face the reality of being unable to achieve or produce, the feelings of inadequacy may become overpowering and result in considerable emotional disturbance. This is probably especially true of those individuals who have placed an overemphasis on physical achievements, and particularly on sexual prowess or appeal, to the neglect of other potentialities. The athlete who finds he tires quickly now and can no longer win championships, and the woman who relied on her beauty and sex appeal and now finds herself discarded in favor of younger, fresher women, both experience great difficulty in accepting the changes attendant upon growing old. The result is frequently seen in an anxiety state, with a combination of psychic and somatic complaints, which is a reaction to an unconscious danger or threat to the personality (2).

Those individuals who have been denied emotional satisfactions by reason of guilt or fear sometimes become panicky at the approaching loss of opportunity to gain these satisfactions and frantically seek compensation before it is too late.

An early example of this can be seen in the case of a respectable woman of thirty-seven who sought help because of her confusion of feelings. She had become distressed and fearful over the idea she might die without ever having had sexual experience, and yet there was no prospect of marriage and her moral and religious principles had always prevented her from having illicit affairs. Finally, she had reached the decision of having an affair, but she became filled with anxiety over the decision she had made. She had even blocked the religious taboo and was amazed when the thought finally occurred to her that she would have to tell of it in the confessional.

With many such persons, feelings of moral guilt in regard to sexual experience and fears of pregnancy may have resulted in failure to achieve emotional satisfaction even in marital life, and in their later years they try desperately to repair this defect, often with unfortunate results. The fact that they need no longer fear pregnancy makes it more difficult to maintain their normal control of their impulses, with the result that they sometimes show temporary rejection of their families and seek undesirable companionship. The reciprocal effect, of course, is a temporary or permanent rejection of them by their families, which again increases the emotional instabilities already present. In these cases unhealthy attitudes toward sex have resulted in too rigid control and repression throughout a large part of life, with a later unbridled outbreak of impulses no longer amenable to the control formerly impressed upon them.

Conservative and reactionary attitudes tend to become intensified as age advances (17), so that it is usual to find a predominance of oldsters in reactionary groups. This seems to be due to the psychic rigidity of the older person, which makes change a challenge and a threat to his personality and existence (18). Old persons tend to be the diehards of tradition and often will cling tenaciously to conservative and even outmoded ideas and customs. Of course, this is not true of all old persons, for it seems that the basic personality makeup plays an important part in the picture. Thus it is that some remain progressive in their outlook until extreme old age, and present-day society finds many revolutionary oldsters in its ranks. Actually, scientific studies of conservatism tend to draw conflicting conclusions in this matter. Fisher (10), in comparing the attitudes of two generations of college students and their parents, concluded that, in the parents, conservative viewpoints were stronger than the more radical and critical ones. On the other hand, Pollak (25), from the results obtained on a market research program, where questions dealt not only with different aspects of new commercial products but also with changes in economic, social, or political organization and government policies, failed to find significantly increased conservatism among the old. Davis and Coombs (7) likewise found no necessary connection between age and conservatism.

Some of the conservatism which is found among older persons may be due to the fact that their long experience in life has tended to make them cautious and thoughtful about accepting untried innovations, but probably results more from habit and from their sense of inadequacy and inferiority as social beings. They tend to cling to long-established beliefs, customs, and practices which affect the environment with which they must interact, because these give them some much-needed feelings of security and support. Things of the past which once gave pleasure tend to be retained when present gratification is restricted. Familiarity of environment makes situations which arise easier to understand and to cope with, thus decreasing the feelings of inferiority which would result from having to deal ineffectually with unfamiliar situations. The fact that it becomes increasingly difficult to learn new things as one grow older makes conservatism easier for older persons. This is in line with Goldstein's findings that, with a lowering of mental energy (such as he finds in schizophrenic and organic mental patients), stereotypy is resorted to, leading to rigidity and conservatism (14). There is not so much challenge, and there is less possibility of failure because of incomplete understanding, when the environment and the things in it remain the same. There is also the emotional need of finding the world unchanging and predictable, for this affords the greater security and confidence the old person so badly needs.

Normal Emotional Needs

The emotional needs of older persons are similar to those of persons in other periods of life (13), but unfortunately this is not always recognized by society as a whole or by the families of the senescents. Too often those who themselves have not yet reached the period of later maturity take it for granted that senescents have no emotional needs. They assume the attitude that when one has lived a long time his emotional needs have vanished—that he has already experienced everything in life he is going to and that now he should leave the emotional aspects of life to younger folk. Even many kind and well-meaning relatives seem to think that so long as the old person's physical comfort is attended to, he should be satisfied to vegetate and contentedly wait for death. However, the viewpoint is no doubt altered considerably when these same individuals reach the later years of life. Although changes occur in the emotions as well as in other areas, the basic emotional needs probably remain essentially the same throughout life. That these are not being fully met is evidenced by the fact that studies tend to show that happiness decreases with increasing age (27) and is positively related to economic independence (12).

Security.—One of the prime needs of all individuals throughout life is security, and this is especially true of the old person. The old person needs security in all areas—economic security so that he can have some degree of independence, security in the position he occupies within his home, and security in affections. Security in these areas is difficult both to attain and to maintain, but without it the old person tends to become irritable, unhappy, and troublesome.

Economic security in old age is so difficult to plan for that only a relatively small percentage of those over the age of sixty-five years are completely independent financially. This is particularly true of women, since such a very small proportion of women of this age are gainfully employed (28). With the high cost of all commodities, the increasing number of years required for school attendance and educational preparation for life, and the retirement practices which demand early discard, it becomes ever more difficult to amass sufficient funds to support a family, educate children, and put away enough money to look after one's self in old age. Also, the fiscal policies of countries, inflation, the government's encouragement to spend, and the threat of war and especially of the atomic bomb all work against the saving of money toward the insurance of financial independence in old age. Social security and old age pensions help a little but are woefully inadequate, especially for those whose work does not provide for either of these protections. Yet financial security, which provides the old person with a certain amount of independence, self-esteem, and freedom, is important to emotional health, and the lack of it is particularly hard for those who have always been self-supporting and independent.

The old person needs also to feel secure in the position he occupies in his home. This is not only security in knowing that there will always be a roof over his head, but security in his acceptance in his own home and in the affections of the others who live in it. If he feels that the other members of the household, whether they be relatives, friends, or strangers, reject him and would like to be rid of him, he will feel emotionally insecure and will usually show this insecurity in a way that will make him still more unacceptable in his environment.

Recognition.—The aging person needs recognition as an individual. He needs recognition for the person he is now, not the person he once was. He needs to feel that these people respect him—respect his ideas, his way of life, his feelings, and his worth as a person. This is a need in every period of life, but it is an especially important need for the older person who has once had recognition in his life. Perhaps it is worse to have something and then lose it than never to have had it at all. Failure to attain recognition in his present period of life often results in the senescent's becoming aggressive and difficult. In order to build up his own importance in the eyes of those around him, he tries to live on his past achievements, to enhance the importance of his accomplishments in bygone days, and in every way to show what a leader or truly great person he was. Through constant repetition of his stories, he finally comes to believe in his former prowess, thus attaining some of the personal satisfaction he so badly needs. Often he struggles to carry over his former leadership or importance (either real or imagined) into his present life situation by trying to dominate everyone around him. The more this is resisted or ignored, the more domineering he becomes in his efforts to force recognition of his authority and hence of his importance. Given normal recognition in his present life situation, he would have no need to develop these defenses which make life difficult both for him and for those with whom he lives.

Self-Esteem.—With recognition from others as an important person in the scheme of things, the oldster can develop and maintain self-esteem, which is another important emotional need in the period of senescence. The physical and intellectual changes accompanying old age constitute in themselves a blow to one's narcissism, and when this is intensified by social disapproval or discard, self-esteem quickly declines. Aggressive or withdrawal reactions, which are defensive in character, may result. Often the old person will react with a hopeless attitude, indicating his belief that, since he is no longer of any use in the world, there is no need to make any further effort for anything. He seems despondent and unhappy, has no interest in anything, will do nothing, and seems to be waiting only to die.

New Interests and New Situations.—It is important for the old as well as for persons of all other ages to find new interests and new situations. Although with increasing age there is decreasing interest in social and active pursuits and an increasing preference for sedentary recreation of a more solitary nature (20), older persons need opportunities to participate actively in life, to see new things, to meet new people, to learn new things, and to absorb new ideas. They need to face new situations in all areas of life—the intellectual, the emotional, and the social. To be emotionally healthy, they must keep abreast of the times and not live in the past so that they resist all new things, and to do this they must have and be ready to take advantage of opportunities in all fields of life. Without new experiences anyone, and particularly the older individual, will vegetate intellectually, emotionally, socially, and probably also physically.

Love and Affection.—Probably love and affection are the most important emotional needs of people at all ages throughout life. This is especially true of the old person, who is already experiencing emotional stress occasioned by his realization of his waning powers and is therefore in need of the support and security afforded by love and affection in his life. This involves the real love of a family, not just toleration. The old person must feel within him that the love of his family is still present, even though his actual usefulness to his offspring is over. When usefulness has gone and care and attention are needed, it is easy to forget the role once played and to discard the old person emotionally and consider him a nuisance. When this occurs, old persons tend to become difficult and demanding. They are unconsciously seeking what is their due and may become troublesome in their efforts to get it.

This brings up the question of marriage in the period of later maturity and old age. The disparity of ages and activities of old and young living together often results in incompatibility and friction, so that it seems impossible to develop the warm, affectionate relationship so badly needed by the old person. In spite of this, society in general and families in particular tend to frown on the very idea of marriage between old folks. They view it as silly or as something not quite nice, and in this connection it is interesting to note the reversal of parent-offspring roles. Whereas it once was the parent who had the dominating role and obstructed the marriage of his offspring, it is now the offspring who object when the aging parent wants to remarry after the death of a spouse. They take the attitude that sex among older persons is or should be nonexistent, a thing of the past reserved for youth alone. Unfortunately, too many older persons, especially women, have accepted this taboo and are ashamed to admit that they have sexual feelings for fear of being considered abnormal or indecent. Yet we know that, despite some decline of sexual activity with age, it is rare to find a man under sixty who is impotent for physical reasons alone, and most women have as great and some even greater interest in sex following the menopause. Why then should those in this period of life be denied the satisfaction of these needs in the normal relationship of marriage? True, it is not possible for all older persons to achieve marriage, and to fail to do so will not result in serious maladjustment provided the person is not already maladjusted, but for those who can it should certainly be encouraged as a normal means of expressing a basic human drive.

This does not imply that marriage or a sex relationship will prevent emotional maladjustment or make a maladjusted person normal, nor does it mean that a sex relationship is the only way to achieve emotional satisfaction in life, for these things are obviously untrue. A later marriage may prove quite unhappy because of illness, financial dependency, or lifelong irksome habits of one or both partners. An extramarital sex relationship may be traumatic for those with moral, ethical, and religious standards, and marriage with a suitable partner may not be possible. Yet without these things many persons adjust satisfactorily and live happily and effectively in their environment. To do so, though, they must effect healthy sublimations, usually in the form of warm, affectionate relationships with family or friends, or of useful or creative activities. Some will do it through love of God or an ideal or through devotion to a cause. They can be either aided or frustrated in their efforts along these lines by their families. If they are aided or abetted, life runs more smoothly for all; if they are frustrated, frictions and tensions arise and life becomes more difficult for all. Clubs for mixed groups of older persons are often very helpful in establishing these much-needed social and emotional relationships, which result in the improved adjustment of older men and women.

Failure to achieve marriage or emotional satisfaction or to sublimate these drives effectively often results in enhanced but distorted interest in the sexual area. With the exception of occasional sex aberrations, the direct expression of the interest is repressed in most cases, but it may find its outlet in an overly virtuous attitude toward sex, a suspiciousness of the activities of others, a condemnation of youth, the "times," and the wildness of the present generation, gossiping, and scandal-mongering. Older persons may even spy on young folks, see evil in everything around them, and become zealots in their efforts to protect others against the sins of sex. This is a projection of their own feelings and desires onto others, and perhaps, too, there is some jealousy, some envy of youth involved. The old are not free of faults and undesirable reactions just because they have lived a long time; in fact undesirable habits tend to become crystallized and intensified as one grows older. It is just that they are less troublesome when one has greater emotional satisfactions in life.

Probably one of the most pitiful things in life is to see the enforced separation of an old couple who have loved each other devotedly throughout a lifetime of marriage. When death occurs to separate an aged couple, it is usually the woman who is left, since women tend to live longer than men, but as death is inevitable and cannot be avoided forever, there is little that can be done about this. There is another practice, however, which seems to be unnecessarily cruel, unkind, and lacking in understanding of basic human needs, and one that could be avoided. This is the practice in some quarters of separating husband and wife, placing one in a men's dormitory and one in a women's dormitory, when they enter an old age home. For two who have lived together in love for many years and known the close companionship that only a happy marriage can bring, a separation of this sort is emotionally traumatic and one that brings with it sorrow, resentment, a feeling of defeat and hopelessness, and real tragedy for the individuals. Surely, when emotional satisfaction is recognized to be the most important basic human need, such a cruel deprivation of this need could in some way be avoided.

The importance of and the interest in association with members of the opposite sex can readily be seen in those old age homes and colonies which admit both men and women. Both the men and the women in these homes take more interest in their personal appearance, in their surroundings, in activities, and in the people around them. Here are formed many close friendships between men and women, and many marriages. Usually, although not always, it is the old person who has previously been married who remarries when he meets a desirable spouse in the old age home. Many, after the death of a spouse in the home, remarry someone else in the group, and some follow this pattern several times in succession. Usually these are the better-adjusted, happier, and more acceptable members of the group.

Emotional Health

Emotional health in later maturity and old age is essentially the same as emotional health at other periods of life. To be emotionally healthy, one must be able to adjust happily and effectively within himself and to his environment and the persons in it, and one must be able to live within the limits of his physical and mental equipment and with other human beings. He must be able to live with others harmoniously, and productively, without making a nuisance of himself. He can do these things only if he is mentally alert, socially considerate, and good-tempered, if he has a sense of humor, and if he has good balance and control in his relationships with others. He must be capable of love and other emotions, but he must not be ready to give unbridled expression to his emotions. He must maintain close contact with reality at all times: he may dream but he must not use his dreams to retreat from life; he may indulge in alcohol and other forms of recreation, but he must not make excessive use of these as an escape from reality. For the aging person who wishes to remain emotionally healthy, it is especially important to avoid rigidity and a feeling of hopelessness and to maintain optimism and a readiness for change. The old person who is emotionally healthy is not too retrospective but maintains a consciousness of the future (9). He does not always live in the past and bask in his previous accomplishments but tries to live in the present and look forward to the future—the future in this life, not only in the next. He is tolerant and ready to participate in new experiences, emotional and otherwise, accepts the aging process as another part of life, and is ready to seek what satisfactions life has to offer in his own period.

Changes in the Self

Using "self" in the common, everyday meaning to include the body-image as well as the individual's image of his own personality in general, without attempting to go into the niceties of any of the classifications of various schools, we might say that changes in the self do occur in all areas. They are an inevitable part of life and, try as we may, we cannot retard them forever. Every individual who lives long enough will some day be old and experience physical, mental, and emotional changes, and some day he will experience death. This is an inexorable law of nature, whether we like it or not, but the way in which we accept this law determines whether we shall be happy and well adjusted in old age or unhappy, disgruntled, and querulous. The important thing is how one accepts the changes which are gradually but steadily taking place with advancing age.

Physical Changes.—The physical changes are important, as we have already seen, but the actual changes are probably of less importance than how these changes are accepted. If the self is accepted purely as a beautiful, wonderful physical specimen, the physical changes which occur will, of course, be more difficult to accept. This by no means implies that we should not attempt to keep the body beautiful, but merely that one must have other values besides the physical ones in life.

Sometimes an emotional lack of acceptance of physical changes results in a complete denial of them. A desperate attempt to justify this attitude or to prove its truth to one's self leads to physical excesses of all sorts. Sexual excesses are probably the most frequent forms of physical overindulgence engaged in by those who would deny physical aging and try to prove to themselves and others that they are still as vigorous and attractive as they once were. Others with higher moral standards but essentially the same basic pattern of denial may overexert themselves in sports and other forms of physical activity, often with resultant heart attacks because of the inability of the organism to stand the extra strain put upon it.

On the other hand, an emotional lack of acceptance of physical aging may take the reverse form of overemphasis. Here the individual overemphasizes all physical changes and illnesses and uses them for his own purposes. Usually the mechanism is unconscious, but it serves its purpose just the same, bringing attention and emotional satisfaction to the selfish old person at the expense of those around him. Physical incapacity makes a wonderful area for rationalization: it serves as a splendid excuse for not doing what one does not want to do. It has such an element of sincerity about it: everyone KNOWS the older person would LOVE to do this or that which his family would like him to do, but he just CAN'T because of his physical condition—his lack of strength, his heart, etc., etc. Sometimes the overemphasis takes the form of a too passive acceptance of inevitable changes: he is old now and therefore of no further use or good in the world, his physical constitution will not permit him to engage in physical activity any longer, and there is nothing left for him now but to sit and rock himself to death. This attitude usually breeds intense dissatisfaction and depression, and yet it is very difficult to pull the old person out of it. He sits too much, eats too much, and gets too fat, and then the real troubles begin. Other physical symptoms develop, both real and fancied, thereby intensifying to him the reality of his decline and bringing still further depression and dissatisfaction.

Even more often, the overemphasis on physical changes is used to control the environment. The old person becomes preoccupied with his own health and problems and uses real or imagined illness to control those about him. The minute things are not to his liking or someone contemplates doing something of which he does not approve, he becomes ill, thus focusing attention upon himself and forcing others to do his bidding. Of course, the pattern for this type of behavior is laid down early in life, so that we may find it at all ages, but it is a pattern that often becomes acute and especially difficult for the family during the middle and later years when unhealthy reactions are intensified. Actually it is a form of aggression which the aging person is using to retain his hold over his loved ones. The mechanism is usually unconscious and often accompanied by a pious, long-suffering, self-pitying attitude, with a subtlety of implied accusation against loved ones for causing this distress.

The operation of this reaction can be seen in the following case:

A woman, about fifty years of age, was in the menopausal period. She was married and had one daughter to whom she was very much attached. She had been babied and spoiled as a child, and her husband continued the pattern after their marriage, so that she never matured emotionally. He waited on her hand and foot, catered to her every whim, and was overly concerned when she was ill. Although there was nothing organically wrong with her, she became invalided by the menopause at periods when it was convenient for her to do so. These spells usually came on when her husband showed any interest in attending club meetings or going anywhere without her, and especially when her daughter gave indications of wanting to live a life of her own. Mrs. L. had been a beauty in her day and was still attractive and young-looking for her years. She enjoyed traveling around with her daughter and was more than pleased when anyone remarked that they looked more like sisters than mother and daughter. When her daughter began going out with young men, she was very coquettish with the youths, but as soon as one man would become more than mildly interested in her daughter, she immediately became bedridden and in need of constant care for long periods of time or until she felt the danger to be safely past. After a few such experiences, the daughter ceased to tell her mother anything concerning her social life or her feelings until she finally decided to get married. When she announced her plans to her mother, Mrs. L. took to her bed with a heart attack and remained there, proclaiming her imminent danger of death, until the day following her daughter's marriage. Then, her plans having failed, she got up and resumed her usual household duties. She still continues with her pattern of illness to control her environment, but now there is only her husband to control, as her daughter has sensibly moved out of the neighborhood.

The normal attitude toward physical aging involves a real acceptance of the changes which are occurring. The emotionally healthy aging person recognizes that physical changes are to be expected, and, while he may not be delighted that they are occurring to him, he neither overemphasizes them nor permits them to incapacitate him. He finds, for example, that he cannot run as fast as he once did, but instead of becoming depressed or emotionally upset over the fact, he views it realistically and objectively. He recognizes that it is of relatively little importance, for actually he has no need of winning foot races. He knows that in spite of the fact that he cannot run fast, he can still walk, and usually in a sprightly manner, if he so desires. He has no need of risking a heart attack by overstraining himself to prove that he is as quick as he ever was, nor has he the need of making his slowdown an infirmity by lagging and shuffling along. If he is a sensible person, he will take normal care of himself physically and neither overeat nor overstrain himself, but he will not be overly concerned about his health and make it the topic of all his conversations and thoughts. He will exercise in moderation and with judgment and keep his body as fit as possible.

Intellectual Changes.—The intellectual changes which occur are likewise important, but again it is the way in which they are accepted that is of the greater importance. Some changes do occur with advancing age, as we shall see later, but it is likely that much can be done either to accelerate or to retard these declines. The individual's emotional attitude toward the changes probably determines, in large part at least, the rate of decline of his intellectual functioning.

A normal attitude toward the intellectual changes which are taking place will involve a normal compensation and effort to retard decline. The emotionally healthy aging person will, for example, recognize his tendency to forget recent events and his slower learning of new things, and he will make an effort to offset these declines in various ways so as not to let them interfere with his work, his avocations, or his social relationships. He will practice learning new things, recognizing that although learning is slower, it will decline even faster with disuse. He will try to learn something new each year, and he will make every attempt to keep abreast of the times. He may even develop various devices to help himself to remember those troublesome, important little things he finds himself constantly forgetting. For example, he may carry a little notebook and jot down important things to be remembered and then review them at leisure, or he may pay special and careful attention to the name of a new person he meets and then make it a point to repeat the name several times both to himself and to the person to whom he is talking. When, in spite of everything, he does forget things, he will accept it as unfortunate but will not become upset emotionally by placing undue stress upon it.

Unfortunately, however, not all aging persons can accept their intellectual changes philosophically or objectively, so that many unhealthy reactions can be seen. Some take a passive, defeatist attitude and will make no effort in any direction. When they start to forget things, they immediately take the attitude that they are gradually "losing their minds," that they are too old to learn anything new, and that they can no longer be expected to remember anything. They use their age as an excuse for not doing what they do not want to do: they do not want to make the effort to learn anything new or to remember most of the things going on around them, so they use their declining intellectual functioning as an excuse to relieve them of the bother. It is interesting to note that these same persons have little difficulty in remembering those things they want to remember and that others usually want them to forget!

Others react with a complete denial of any decline. These persons claim that they remember better than they ever did and tend to project their own lacks in this area on to others. Probably one of the most common reactions of this sort among older persons is their frequent accusation against others of stealing the things they mislay. They put a precious thing away carefully and then forget where they put it; being unable to admit even to themselves their forgetfulness, they believe someone stole the thing from them. Often, when faced with their error, they still cannot admit their decline and persist in the belief that someone stole it and probably put it back again when in danger of being caught. This belief is often intensified when the old person senses the hostility of those around him. The feeling of loss engendered is a blow to narcissism, the result of which is to enhance the insecurity of the ego with its accompanying need for self-love; as a measure of protection against this, the blame is projected onto others.

Some resort to fabrication and distortions to hide their forgetfulness. They remember only parts of something, but, being unable to put forth a fragmented story, they fill in gaps with bits from their own imagination. Often too, their forgetfulness results in distortions in varying degree. These tendencies may be seen mildly in many old persons, but the more severe the emotional maladjustment and the lack of acceptance of aging, the greater the fabrication and distortion. The extremes of these tendencies can be seen in cases of senile dementia. The stories told are, of course, in accord with the emotional needs of the individual.

Changes in the Ego and Libido.—The ego tends to become more rigid with advancing age (18). There is a lack of elasticity in the personality, and this can be seen in a clinging to the old and a resistance to the new and in an unwillingness to accept changes in the self or the environment. This serves as a defense against anxiety, which is aroused when changes occur that the individual does not understand or that he is unable to cope with. One of the functions of the ego is synthesis and organization which leads to integrated behavior. When the ego is functioning efficiently, behavior is well integrated and adjustment to life situations proceeds smoothly. In old age, however, there is a decrease in the efficiency of ego-organization, with the result that adjustment to changing conditions and situations becomes increasingly difficult. Instead of following the earlier life series of adjustment and readjustment, the individual now tends to react to the new with hostility, irritability, suspicion, and fear and to cling to the old automatized and habitual patterns of behavior. With the old, he was able in some measure to achieve gratification of his instinctual drives and mastery of his environment, and therefore he would like to maintain this status. With the new he cannot be sure, so that it is more advantageous from every standpoint to hold on to the old. Thus, he manifests his psychic rigidity by his conservatism and traditionalism. This psychic rigidity of some aged persons and the stereotypy of their emotions are often expressed outwardly by their stereotyped gestures. That stereotyped gestures are usual among the old is common knowledge and is evident also when we reflect on how much easier it is to caricature an old than a young person.

The libido tends to withdraw back into the self in old age, and this is threatening to the integrity of the individual, both physically and psychically, and creates oversensitivity to all stimuli. This oversensitivity is the source of many characteristics of old age, ranging from irritability to hypochondriacal fears.

Tensions and Frustrations.—Stresses and eruptions coming from within the self and occurring also in the environment result in various manifestations of emotional maladjustment.

Aggression, which may occur in the form of open hostility or in more subtle, masked form, is frequent. So also are anxieties of many forms, irritability, and anger. The constant complaining, tears, and self-pity of many old persons are too well known to require further note. We have already mentioned the real or fancied illnesses so common to this period.

Personality Studies

Personality studies of older persons reveal more clearly the changes which are taking place within the self. In 1946 Klopfer (19), using the Rorschach method of personality diagnosis, made a study of fifty persons between the ages of sixty-two and ninety-three, the average being seventy-four years. Thirty of his subjects were institutionalized, and twenty were not. In general, he found intellectual impairment in these individuals, inability to make full use of their inner resources, and some loosening of intellectual ties to reality. He also found that they experienced difficulty in forming satisfactory social relationships, partly because of a reduction in their responsiveness to the finer emotional nuances in their environment.

In 1947 Padros and Fried (26), also using the Rorschach, studied the personality structure of thirty-five subjects between the ages of fifty and eighty years. These investigators found, in general, a progressive impoverishment of creative intellectual faculties with increasing age. Those between fifty and seventy years of age tended to react with anxiety to an awareness of their own intellectual inadequacy, whereas those over seventy tended to become resigned to this inadequacy. The capacity for emotional responsiveness became relatively shallow, and there seemed to be little inner conflict. They also found that, with increasing age, control over the instinctual demands tends to disappear and some of the primitive manifestations of childhood tend to reoccur.

Chesrow, Wosika, and Reinitz (5), likewise studying aged persons (white males in this instance) by the same method, found delayed responses, a reduced number of responses, stereo-typed thinking, constriction in the emotional sphere, and impotence.

Grossman *et al.* (16) also used the Rorschach to study a selected group of fifty institutionalized persons between the ages of sixty and ninety years. These individuals showed a low level of functioning and decreased productivity, reasoning, imaginative capacity, and motivation. Thinking was generally rigid and vague, and emotional life tended to be rigid, shallow, and unadapted, with difficulty in forming satisfying social relationships. Individual differences in this group were marked, however, and some showed healthy, well-integrated personalities. Although more unstable emotionally, more women than men were responsive, flexible, productive, and sensitive to the environment.

Summarizing these emotional changes found in the personality of some elderly persons by means of the Rorschach, we might say that we find reduced and shallow emotional responsiveness, efficiency, and productivity, little inner conflict, reduced control of instinctual demands, constriction, impotence, and a recurrence of the primitive manifestations of childhood.

Emotional Reaction to Environmental Stress

Although thus far we have dealt only with the emotional reactions and changes taking place within the individual, we cannot, as mentioned earlier in this chapter, consider emotions apart from the situations which produce them. While recognizing that the individual will react to stress in accordance with his basic personality makeup, his life pattern of reacting, and the changes which have taken place during the aging process, we must also recognize that there are many situations of real environmental stress to which those in later maturity are subject and will react emotionally. For example, the loss of one's job and the strain of seeking another when one is too old to be readily marketable in the employment field, or retirement from gainful employment, may result in considerable emotional trauma to some persons. Of course, the attitudes of the person being retired and the specific causes of the retirement will largely determine the subsequent state of mental health of the older person, but the stress to some may be the precipitating cause of serious emotional upset (6). To be discarded from a job, whether by enforced retirement or by discharge, carries with it the implication that one is no longer of any use. In effect, it says to a man (or woman) that he is now inadequate and cannot keep up with his juniors and that therefore he must now be relegated to the rocking chair. With the decline it implies, this serves as a definite blow to one's narcissism. Feelings of inadequacy and unworthiness, which may have been present before, become intensified with this seemingly objective proof of inferiority. Interest in the external world lessens and tends to become concentrated on one's self, one's ailments and declines, and the ill treatment one has suffered at the hands of others.

Fears of Dependency and Loss of Status.—With these feelings come also the fears of possible dependency—the worry that savings or pensions will not be enough to keep a man, and possibly his wife, independent and provide for their needs. There is the fear among those who have always been independent that they may have to accept charity from strangers or from their offspring or that they may become ill and not have enough to see them through. There is an especial worry about dependency upon offspring among those whose relationships with their offspring are strained, and this often happens with those overprotective, overcontrolling, dominating parents who now find the parent-child roles unpleasantly reversed.

There is also the matter of "losing face" with one's family, friends, and associates when one loses his job or retires from it. With retirement, this is offset to some extent by the tributes paid to one on his retirement day and by one's own protestations of pleasure at not having to work any longer, but the loss of power and prestige soon becomes evident. There is the loss of the leadership, real or implied, that goes with having a job and being head of a family, and there is the felt decline of importance in the eyes of one's family and friends. The reaction is worse, of course, in those individuals who have developed no other potentialities outside their regular job. If the retiring person has hobbies, interests, or avocations to which he anticipates devoting his time, the transition will probably not be too difficult, but if he has done nothing except go to and from work each day and spend his evenings with the newspaper, he will no doubt get bored very soon. Many have noted that death frequently comes early to those who retire and have nothing further to interest them in life. In the personal experience of the author, this has been found often to occur within six months or a year. Again we can see the psychosomatic unity of the aging human being and the impossibility of understanding him by viewing only one facet of his makeup.

The change in one's status within the family group is likewise an emotional stress to which many aging persons are subjected, and this is true of both men and women. The father, as head of the family and chief provider, has under normal conditions been the leader of the group, looked up to, respected, and needed. Other members of the family have been dependent upon him and, if he has been harsh in his treatment of them, afraid of him. Now, when his children have matured, secured employment, and started families of their own, he is no longer the head of the household or the leader of the group. He is no longer feared, and, because his psychic rigidity forces him to cling to the old customs and habits, he may no longer even be respected. This is especially true in the American culture where, in general, the role of the father is mainly that of the provider and carries with it relatively little of the respect and awe shown to fathers in a European culture (15). He may even, if he is retired, become an unwelcome dependent in the household of one of his offspring. This is a difficult role for the old father to accept, and if he has insufficient outside interests and emotional satisfactions in life, he may try to continue his domination in his new home and make life miserable for others by the irritability and temper outbursts he shows in his efforts to get his own way and rule his environment.

A similar situation holds for women who have raised a family of children. As mother, the woman has been more or less the center of the household. She it is who has had the most to do with the care and training of the children and the care of the home. She is the one who has bathed and dressed the children, bound up their wounds, listened to their woes, scolded them, and cooked their meals; and she is the one who has had the major responsibility for the care and decoration of the home. Now, when her children have matured and married, she must take a back seat. She is no longer the center around which the household revolves: her daughters and daughters-in-law have taken over that role, and she is not now needed as she once was. If she finds it necessary to give up her own home and go to live in the home of one of her offspring, she may feel the change in status even more keenly than she would have had she remained in her own home. If she is basically a selfish or emotionally maladjusted woman who has insufficient satisfactions in life, she may present the usual mother-in-law problem in her new home, struggling to dominate, to have things remain in the old ways to which she is accustomed, and to retain her control over her offspring. Of course, given a wise and healthy mother and daughter or daughter-in-law, these problems need never arise, for the mother will seek her own emotional satisfactions in a more normal way than by trying to dominate her family and the daughter will give her mother opportunities to feel needed, useful, independent, and wanted.

The death of a spouse is frequently the major cause of the change in residence which brings to the foreground the real change of status that has occurred in the case of the aging parent. Thus, the adjustment problem becomes doubly difficult. Not only has the aging person to relinquish his role as leader and head of the family to take a back seat in the household of another where he only too often feels unwanted, but he must also adjust to the loss of a partner to whom he was attached and to whose ways he had become accustomed. This question is discussed further in Chapter 5.

The frustrations attendant upon these changes in family status result in anxieties, irritability, and general emotional upset. Often the aging person is not conscious of the reason for his dissatisfaction and emotional disturbance but just knows that he feels restless, tense, and uneasy, that he is worried, has vague psychosomatic symptoms, gets upset easily, and generally feels cranky.

Aggressive Reactions.—Some form of aggression (as is discussed more fully in Chapter 5) is a common reaction to these frustrations, and this aggression may be turned toward others or inward toward the self. When aggression is external-ized, it can be seen in the efforts of a parent to continue his or her power over the offspring. This may be expressed in many different ways: it may take the form of illnesses which occur at convenient times when the need to control is strong; it may be expressed in a kind of clutching dependency; or it may show up in a constant plea for gratitude—"I am the good father (or mother); I have worked my fingers to the bone for you; you should love me and appreciate all I have done for you." These are more or less masked forms of aggression and are often employed by persons who on the surface seem meek and mild, but they are forms of aggression just the same. When aggression is internalized and is sufficiently strong, it may result in self-destruction.

When aging parents and adult offspring reside in the same household, and particularly if the home happens to belong to the offspring, we often see a reversal of the parent-child relationship, so that the offspring now assumes the directive role once held by the parents. Interestingly enough, this may result in a re-enactment on the part of the parent of his earlier feelings toward his own parents. He now unconsciously views his offspring in the same way he once viewed his parents and reacts to them in the same way he reacted to his parents when he was young. Sometimes the early unresolved conflicts the aging person had with his own parents and destructive feelings repressed for many years may be relived in his reactions toward his offspring. He may show open hostility, become contrary and resistive to direction or suggestion, indulge in verbal abuse, and show ambivalence in his fluctuating attitudes of love and hate. The attitudes he had toward his parents at puberty and during adolescence are especially likely to be revived at this time, and as it was in adolescence so also in this period ambivalence is common.

Loneliness.—Another emotional stress for older persons occurs when friends or contemporaries die. When one hears of the death of one after another of those of his own age, the thought inevitably comes that perhaps his own death is imminent, or at least not very far away. This tends to intensify feelings of futility, hopelessness, and depression. The sense of loneliness and isolation also increases as one gradually comes to realize that there are progressively fewer persons of his age in the world. The loss of his friends strikes especially close to him because the older one gets the harder it is to make new friends.

The problem of loss of friends seems to be particularly difficult for older women who are more often left without a mate and who, having been occupied for years with the raising of a family, have nothing to fall back on now that their children have grown up and gone away. These are the women who have been the mothers and homemakers, who have stayed close to their homes and family life to the exclusion of outside interests and friends, and who, when husband and children have gone, seem to have nothing left in life. Many have lost the art of making friends and look upon themselves as too old to start anything new.

Oldsters need companionship with others of their own age. They need opportunities for friendly relationships with both sexes. Marriage, of course, is desirable when it can be achieved, but even when it cannot, companionship between men and women will always prove stimulating and satisfying to those who are normal. In many communities this need for mixed companionship has been met by clubs and recreational centers for older persons.

When the income of aging persons is limited or a spouse has died, there always arises the problem of living arrangements, and this is a great problem indeed, particularly in cities and areas where there is a housing shortage. Living arrangements may be one of the most important factors in the loss of friends, the inability to make new friends, and the tensions and frictions between parents and offspring. Often, in city apartment living, there is not enough room for the aging parent (even if he does have a bedroom to himself) and he seems always to be under foot. Perhaps he does not fit in well with the group when his offspring entertain, and yet he has no place except his small bedroom to go and get away from them all. He himself has no place in which he can entertain his own friends, so he soon gives up and loses touch with them, thereby becoming more dissatisfied than ever with his life. Usually it is better for an aging parent not to live in the home of a son or daughter if it can be avoided. It is more advisable to live in his own home if it is in any way possible, and this is particularly important when relationships have been a little strained. However, when it seems absolutely necessary for the two generations to share a home, it is desirable for the older person to have his own apartment in the home, so that both can have some measure of independence and privacy. In smaller communities where space is not at such a premium as in the city, some very satisfactory arrangements have been worked out whereby the older person has his small cottage on the same lot or the next lot to that of his child. In this way he can be looked after in case of need and can feel close to his family and at the same time retain his independence. In his own apartment or house, no matter how small, he can have a place for entertaining his own friends and developing his own hobbies and interests. When each generation has its independence, harmony is much easier to achieve and to maintain. The aging person then has the choice of staying young in spirit and active in life or growing old in a rocking chair.

The following brief case studies are examples of some of the reactions of persons to the aging process and to the stresses attendant upon it.

Mr. T., aged sixty-eight years, was a dependent type of person who had leaned on someone all his life. His mother babied him when he was a child, so that as an adult he remained emotionally immature. When he married, his wife continued the same pattern, doing everything for him, babying him, helping him with his business, etc. Shortly before his sixty-eighth birthday, his wife died suddenly after a brief illness. He was overwhelmed by the shock, retired from business, and refused to go out to see his old friends or to have anyone come to his home. He did nothing all day long but cry and wander from one room to the next. He engaged in no gainful employment, did nothing around the house, and did little for himself. He even refused to have a maid come in to clean his house and insisted that his married daughter come from a neighboring town to do it for him. He remained melancholy and depressed and refused to do anything to help himself. Within the year he died, although according to the medical report, there was nothing wrong with him physically.

In contrast to this, we find a more successful picture of aging in the following case.

Mr. A., aged seventy-five, has been a pretty well-adjusted person all his life and has always been active in club work. He was forced to retire on a pension at the age of sixty-eight, although he was still active and quite capable of continuing his work. He did not particularly like the idea of retiring but decided to make the best of it and get what fun there was left in life for him. Unfortunately, his wife became ill a short time after he retired, and he assumed the major burden of her care until her death five years ago. Now he is alone but seems to be enjoying life and gives the general impression of being younger than he was five years ago. He is faithful in his club attendance, travels, and even has a "girl friend" some years younger than he who is very devoted to him.

The following is an example of aggression and psychoneurotic reactions occurring in a woman who probably had a basic psychoneurotic personality all her life.

Mrs. B., a widow, aged fifty-eight, was a high-school teacher. She had been married rather unhappily but had no children, and her husband had died many years previously. For many years she had not only taught school but had the care of her ill, aged mother and her ill sister. She apparently accepted these responsibilities well and could always be depended upon to carry out her duties with the utmost efficiency. During a vacation period, she sustained a slight injury to her arm and immediately took to her bed and stayed there for weeks in spite of the fact that the doctor told her there was nothing wrong with her arm. When she finally did get up, she insisted on keeping her arm in a sling until atrophy of the muscles started. Her mother, now that the need has arisen, is up and about and doing things around the house that she had not done for years and seems to be enjoying her activities. There is nothing further that can be done for Mrs. B. physically, but she is in much need of psychotherapy. At the present time, the secondary gains of her illness—less responsibility and much attention and sympathy from everyone—are too great for her to get well. This is the second attack of this kind that Mrs. B. has had, the first one having occurred several years ago. At that time she gained much attention and sympathy and might have continued in her invalided state had it not been for the sudden serious illness of her sister and the need for her to take care of the sick person. Although she has always accepted responsibilities with apparent willingness and docility, actually she has considerable hostility and aggression in her personality, and this is evident in her present reactions. She is punishing her mother, her brother, and her sister for her own dissatisfactions with life.

Summary

Emotional reactions are common to every living human being, but they cannot be considered apart from the reactions of the total organism or from the situation which produced the reaction.

Emotional reaction consists of a conscious state, an inner organic state, and postural reactions.

There are indications that with proper hygienic measures (both physical and mental), the aging process might be retarded considerably and even reversed to some degree when the decline is in advance of biological necessity.

The life pattern of the individual is one of the most important factors in the rate of his or her emotional decline.

Bad patterns of living already existing tend to become intensified with age. In the later period of life, we often find a re-enactment of adolescent psychoneurotic and psychotic-like behavior. Selfishness, irritability, and lack of control are common. The tendency to overemphasize illness becomes aggravated, often as a protection against felt inadequacies.

The attitudes and feelings of an individual will, in general, determine how well or how poorly he will adjust to his own aging process. The person who is happy and well adjusted to his environment is able to accept the inevitable in a more healthy manner than the one who is basically dissatisfied with himself and his environment.

Those with feelings of inadequacy and insecurity which they earlier succeeded in balancing and those who place an overemphasis on the physical, and particularly on the sexual, side of life generally find the changes most difficult to accept.

Those who have been denied emotional satisfactions by reason of guilt or fear reactions sometimes show anxiety and panic reactions and frantically seek compensation before it is too late.

Conservative and reactionary attitudes frequently result from a growing sense of inadequacy and inferiority and the need to find security in seeking an unchanging, predictable, less challenging world.

The emotional needs of older persons are basically the same as those of persons at other periods of life and include security— both financial and in regard to the position in the home, recognition as an individual, self-esteem, opportunity for new experiences, and love and affection. Without fulfilment of these needs, the old person may become difficult to live with and tend to vegetate intellectually, emotionally, socially, and possibly also physically. In addition, he may frequently show suspiciousness of the activities of others and an overly virtuous attitude toward sex and may become a gossip-monger.

Marriage among older persons of suitable temperament is desirable if it can be achieved, and every effort should be made not to separate older married couples when circumstances force them to enter old age homes.

To be emotionally healthy in later maturity, as well as in earlier periods of life, involves being able to adjust happily and effectively within one's self, to the environment, and to the persons in it and to be able to live with other human beings harmoniously, productively, and without being a nuisance. The old person especially must avoid rigidity, hopelessness, and retrospection and maintain optimism, readiness for change, and a consciousness of the future.

Changes in the self occur in all areas; rather than the changes themselves, the important thing is how these changes are accepted by the individual.

The normal attitude toward physical changes is to recognize them and take normal care of one's self but not to be overly concerned about them or let them incapacitate one.

Some intellectual changes will occur, and the normal reaction will be to recognize these and try to compensate for them in a healthy way.

The ego tends to become more rigid with advancing age, and the libido tends to withdraw back into the self. The lack of elasticity in the personality makes adjustments and readjustments to life situations difficult, so that the individual tends to cling to those habits, traditions, and customs which are familiar and give him some satisfaction and to react with hostility, irritability, and fear to those new things which arouse anxieties and tensions in him.

Tensions and frustrations coming from within the self and from the environment often result in aggression, anxieties, irritability, anger, complaining, weeping, and illnesses.

Personality studies of older persons show, in general, reduced and shallow emotional responsiveness, efficiency, and productivity, little inner conflict, reduced control of instinctual demands, constriction, impotence, and a recurrence of the primitive manifestations of childhood.

The older person is also subject to much real environmental stress to which he will react emotionally in accordance with his basic personality makeup, his life pattern of reacting, and the changes which have taken place during the aging process.

Environmental stresses include retirement or loss of a job, change in family status, and loss of friends.

Frustrations attendant upon these stresses result in anxieties, irritability, and general emotional upset. Aggression is frequently seen in the efforts to keep control over offspring by means of illnesses, pleas for gratitude, or clutching dependency. If the aggression becomes internalized, self-destruction may occur.

The offspring's assumption of the directive role in the family may result in a reliving on the part of the old person of his earlier, unresolved, destructive relationships with his own parents, particularly those feelings he experienced around the period of adolescence.

It is desirable for older persons to retain their independence, maintain their own friendships, and develop their own hobbies and interests. This makes life and living much easier for all concerned. Feeling loved, secure, wanted, and useful is most important for the older person's happiness and adjustment.

REFERENCES

1. BARKER, L. F. Physical changes in old age and their effects upon mental attitudes. In LAWTON, G. (ed.), *New goals for old age*. New York: Columbia University Press, 1946.
2. BENNETT, E. O. The anxiety state. *Post grad. med. J.,* 1946, **22,** 375-78.
3. BOURLIÈRE, F. Excitability and aging. *J. Geron.,* 1948, **3,** 191-95.

4. CAVAN, R. S., HAVIGHURST, R. J., BURGESS, E. W., and GOLDHAMMER, H. *Personal adjustment in old age.* Chicago: Science Research Associates, 1949.

5. CHESROW, E. J., WOSIKA, P. H., and REINITZ, A. H. A psychometric evaluation of aged white males. *Geriatrics,* 1949, **4**, 169-77.

6. CUSHING, J. G. N. Problems of retirement. Paper delivered before 2d International Congress of Gerontology, Abstract *J. Geron.,* 1951, **6**, 76.

7. DAVIS, K., and COOMBS, J. W., JR. The sociology of an aging population. In New York Academy of Medicine, *The social and biological challenge of an aging population.* New York: Columbia University Press, 1950. Pp. 146-70.

8. DEUTSCH, H. *Psychology of women.* Vol. II. *Motherhood.* New York: Grune & Stratton, Inc., 1946.

9. FISCHER, A. L. Charakteristika der seelischen Gesundheit im Alter. *Gesundh. u. Wohlf.,* 1945, **25**, 197-204.

10. FISHER, S. C. *Relationships in attitudes, opinions, and values among family members.* Berkeley, Calif.: University of California Press, 1948.

11. FREUD, S. *Collected papers.* London: International Psychoanalytical Press, 1925, Vol. III.

12. GARDINER, L. P. Attitudes and activities of the middle-aged and aged. *Geriatrics,* 1949, **4**, 33-50.

13. GARDNER, W. P. Psychiatry in geriatrics. *Minnesota Medicine,* 1950, **33**, 353.

14. GOLDSTEIN, K. *The organism.* New York: American Book Co., 1939.

15. GORER, G. *The American people.* New York: W. W. Norton & Co., Inc., 1948.

16. GROSSMAN, C., WARSHAWSKY, F., and HERTZ, M. Rorschach studies of personality characteristics of a group of institutionalized old people. Paper delivered before 2d International Congress of Gerontology. Abstract *J. Geron.,* 1951, **6**, 97.

17. HAMILTON, G. V. Changes in personality and psychosexual phenomena with age. In COWDRY, E. V. (ed.), *Problems of ageing.* Baltimore: The Williams & Wilkins Co., 1939.

18. KAUFFMAN, M. R. The psychoanalytic point of view. Discussion by S. Atkin. *Amer. J. Orthopsychiat.,* 1940, **10**, 73-84.

19. KLOPFER, W. G. Personality patterns of old age. *Rorschach Res. Exch.,* 1946, **10**, 145-66.

20. KUHLEN, R. G. Psychological trends and problems in later maturity. In PENNINGTON, L. A., and BERG, I. A. *An introduction to clinical psychology.* New York: The Ronald Press Co., 1948.

21. LAWTON, G. *Aging successfully.* New York: Columbia University Press, 1946.

22. LEWIS, N. D. C. Mental hygiene in the senium. *Ment. Hyg.* London, 1940, **24**, 434-44.

23. *Mental health in later maturity.* Publ. Hlth. Rep., Wash., 1942, No. 168.

24. *Mental hygiene in old age.* New York: Family Welfare Association, 1937.

25. POLLAK, O. Conservatism in later maturity and old age. *Amer. soc. Rev.,* 1943, **8**, 175-79.

26. PRADOS, M., and FRIED, E. G. Personality structure in the older age group. *J. clin. Psychol.,* 1947, **3**, 113-20.

27. SHOCK, N. W. *Trends in gerontology*. Stanford, Calif.: Stanford University Press, 1951.
28. ———. Gerontology (later maturity). In STONE, C. P. (ed.), *Annual Review of Psychology, 1951*. Stanford, Calif.: Annual Reviews, Inc., 1951. Vol. II.
29. STIEGLITZ, E. J. *The second forty years*. Philadelphia: J. B. Lippincott Co., 1946.
30. TIBBITTS, C. (ed.). *Living through the older years*. Ann Arbor, Mich.: University of Michigan Press, 1949.
31. VISCHER, A. L. Weltanschauung und Lebensalter. *Schweiz. z. Psychol. Anwend.*, 1943, 1, 171-79.
32. ———. *Seelische Wandlungen beim alternden Menschen*. Basel: Benno Schwabe & Co., 1949.

Chapter 4

INTELLECTUAL CHANGES

Interest in the decline of intellectual functioning with advancing age has existed for a long time and although much still remains to be learned, there has already been considerable scientific investigation in this area (8, 36, 40). In general, the investigations have proceeded along the lines of measuring the decline in intelligence test scores or the decline in specific intellectual functions.

Intelligence Test Scores

Prior to the development of intelligence tests as we know them today, there had been some data gathered on the intellectual functioning of old persons, but little attempt had been made to measure any changes which might have taken place. However, the growth of the intelligence testing movement, particularly in this country, served as a spur to studies in this area. These tests, especially at first, consisted largely of administering intelligence tests either to unselected normal groups of wide age range, to selected groups of wide age range, to special groups of older persons, or to presumably matched groups of older and younger persons. One study used a retest method. These researches led gradually to the development of the present-day widespread interest in the problem of mental deterioration as such—mental deterioration in both normal and psychotic old persons.

One of the earliest applications of intelligence tests to wide age-range groups of normal persons occurred in 1928 when Jones, Conrad, and Horn (35) reported on a psychological sur-

vey which was being made on individuals between the ages of
ten and sixty years in a number of small New England villages.
Reporting on completion and multiple choice tests, they found
a continued improvement in test scores up to the early twenties
and a marked decline after the age of forty-five years. By the

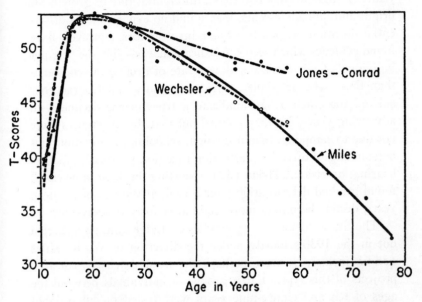

Fig. 3. Mental test scores as related to age. From L. A. Pennington and
I. A. Berg (eds.), *An introduction to clinical psychology*, p. 226. Copyright,
1948, by The Ronald Press Co.

age of fifty-five years, the median scores had dropped below the
thirteen-year-old average. Variability, however, increased in
the upper years. The investigators considered the inferiority
of the older groups to be "not due to speed handicap, nor to
factors involving interest in pictures, visual acuity, or education."

Later Jones and Conrad (34), reporting from the same survey, gave the results of the Army Alpha administered to 1,911
persons, also between the ages of ten and sixty years. The
growth curves found in this survey were similar in form to those

found by other investigators and showed a linear growth to the age of sixteen, with negative acceleration to a peak between the ages of eighteen and twenty-one years. Decline set in gradually and proceeded more gradually than growth, but a recession to the fourteen-year-old level was found by the age of fifty-five years. Although they reported a differential rate of growth for bright and dull adolescents, they found no evidence for a differential duration of growth. Later investigators, however, have found evidence which seems to indicate that possibly the brighter individuals tend to show a slower rate of decline in senescence than those who are duller. Evidently Jones and Conrad considered that their results indicate a true mental decline with advancing years, for they pointed out that the differences were not due to sampling, administration, schooling, motivation, understanding of directions, attention to action vs. speed, practice, hearing, or vision. Hsiao (32), reporting on these same cases, found gradual deterioration after a peak at the age of eighteen years, decline becoming more rapid after forty to forty-four.

The Stanford University Studies on Later Maturity, carried out in the 1930's mostly under the direction of W. R. Miles (58-65 inclusive), were perhaps the most extensive research projects of this type. Large groups of individuals between the ages of ten and eighty-nine years were tested on all sorts of abilities. In general, the results showed a maximum scoring ability, whether general intelligence or a specific ability was under consideration, between the ages of eighteen and forty-nine years, usually in the earlier half of this period. A gradual decline then set in, but 10 per cent to 25 per cent of those in later maturity and old age were found to do as well as the average in middle maturity or at the peak of ability. Then too, the decline seemed to vary with the ability being tested. Some abilities, such as imagination, for example, seemed to be ageless. The drop between the ages of eighteen and eighty-five years was found to be 62 per cent of the original score, which would mean a decline of seventy months in the mental age level. This means that an individual who would rate at the 93d percentile of the tested population in his youth would rate at the 50th percentile by the eighth decade of life. As mentioned earlier, certain abilities showed more resistance to decline than others, and of course this corroborated similar indications from earlier studies. Verbal associations, generalizations, interpretations of meaning, and recognition of relations showed marked resistance to decline with age, whereas speed, organization and recall of unfamiliar material, and difficult logical procedures involving wide immediate memory span showed speedier decline. It was felt that the decline evidenced by the older persons was shown in a diminution in reaction speed and in the sum of energy available for new work types rather than in intelligence; in other words, it was correlated with physiological rather than psychological deterioration. It was noted, however, that feelings of inferiority and insecurity handicapped individuals in their test performances. From the studies it was concluded that appropriate training and practice, persistence, and other stable personality factors are assets to mental longevity.

An early application of intelligence tests to a selected group of wide age range occurred when Weiss (84), reporting from Germany in 1927, studied the test scores of several hundred unskilled workers, railway guards, and locomotive engineers between the ages of twenty and sixty. He found the intellectual performances of these individuals declined steadily from the age of thirty years on, but their sensory performances and performances on tasks requiring dexterity remained fairly constant until the age of forty-five or fifty, following which there was a sharp decline.

Others—for example Pintner (69)—noted the gradual decrease beyond the twenties on the Army Alpha when this test was given to U. S. Army officers.

Using more restricted groups, Mursell (66) gave a number of institutionalized individuals the Kuhlmann-Binet and the Kuhlmann-Anderson tests and reported a gradual decline in ability between the ages of fifteen and forty-four years, a more marked decline between forty-five and fifty-four, with again a more gradual decline after the age of fifty-five. However, as all these individuals were institutionalized, we might assume that the selection was of maladjusted and probably natively inferior individuals.

A special group of older persons was studied by Beeson (2), who, in 1920, examined twenty individuals between the ages of fifty-five and ninety-three years, average age seventy-five, in a home for the aged. He used the 1916 Stanford-Binet Intelligence Test and found the average I.Q. to be 83. Beeson considered this indication of dull normal intelligence to be due largely to a decline in mental processes at senescence. Interestingly enough, he found no deterioration with advancing age, since the older half of the men proved to have higher scores than the younger half. However, the author felt that this might be due to the possibility that the more intelligent tend to remain independent and to avoid charity longer than those who are duller. On the subtests in the scale, the old persons did best by far in the vocabulary tests. The greatest deterioration occurred in memory for digits and words, immediate visual memory or perception, analysis and synthesis, inventiveness and ingenuity, imagination, numbers, and arithmetical reasoning.

Werner (85) likewise studied a small group of individuals in a home for the aged on Knox cubes, digit span, Porteus mazes (10-14), substitution, and paired associates and found that, whereas the group equaled the Army group on the first two, they declined somewhat on the mazes and markedly on substitution, and they failed completely on the paired associates. The author considered that the group was probably originally above the mean of the Army group but had declined.

Groups of older and younger psychotic individuals were studied by Foster and Taylor (17) in an attempt to determine the age changes which occur normally and those which occur when one is affected by mental disorder. They administered the Yerkes-Bridges Point Scale to these groups and found the normals to show a gradual falling off with advancing age, the least decline being in very easy tests and the greatest in dissected sentences, making drawings from memory, giving words in sentences, and giving words in three minutes. The older psychotics excelled the younger in comprehensions, absurdities, and abstract definitions but were inferior in the construction of sentences and in making drawings from memory. The authors suggested as possible reasons for the deterioration found in the older persons some falling off of ability, as shown especially in the drawings, some lack of practice, as in sentence construction, and the fact that older persons tend to be less adaptable and interested, and the tests require rapid adjustments. They considered the older persons to be superior in the problems of life requiring the experience of years. Another interesting point in this study was the authors' stress on the importance of comparing only those of the same level of intelligence and their suggestion that the mental condition of the older person could more accurately be determined if two mental ages were given, one which would compare him with his normal contemporaries and one which would compare him to his own adolescent level of intelligence or that of normal young people. As will be seen later, there were subsequent attempts to make both these comparisons.

Highly selected but different types of persons were studied by Sward (79) who matched forty-five university professors between the ages of sixty and eighty years with forty-five younger academic men between the ages of twenty-five and thirty-five years and subjected both groups to a rather exacting and diversified mental test. Results showed few unambiguous signs of decided psychological decline in these bright, successful senescents. The individual differences on the tests were wide and far more impressive than the differences due to age alone. On six of the eight tests there were significant score differences in favor of the younger group, but the author considers the losses found in the older group to be due largely to disuse and to be an artifact of the particular test used. The senescents were uniformly superior to the younger group in general vocabulary. Sward concluded that age impairs the rate more than the quality or accuracy of mental operations and that, although there may be some real decline with age, decline cannot be held to be the rule for psychological operations at large.

Using a retest method, Garrison (22) studied a group of men and women on the Yerkes-Bridges Point Scale after a ten-year period and found that, whereas those under thirty on the second testing gained considerably, those over thirty lost in about the same degree, and variability increased.

The Problem of Mental Deterioration

These researches and the development of newer techniques in measurement led to an interest in the problem of mental deterioration as such in the aged. That some mental decline was the normal accompaniment of advancing age and that this decline was more marked in some functions and in some persons than in others had already been shown by the investigations carried out, but the development of techniques for the measurement of mental deterioration in psychotic individuals offered new possibilities for research among the aged. It was recognized that research into the normal mental decline expected with advancing years was important not only for itself but also because deterioration measures of psychotics could not be valid unless the age factor were controlled and the normal deterioration to be expected were known. Much research in this area has been done, and much remains yet to be done.

Gilbert (24) administered the Babcock Test for the Measurement of the Efficiency of Mental Functioning to 175 persons in the sixties and 185 persons in the twenties, matching the two groups for intellectual level. [The Babcock Test (1) estimates the original intellectual level by means of the Terman vocabulary, vocabulary (score) having been found to be one of the best single indices of intellectual level and remarkably resistant to the deteriorating effects of age and mental disorder.] She found an average efficiency index of −4.5 for the older group in contrast to the average efficiency index of 0.0 for the group in the twenties, the differences showing marked evidence of the decline of efficient functioning in senescents. No young person of the group studied scored an E.I. as low as the mean of the older group, and only two of the older group reached the average E.I. of the twenty-year-old group. There was also a decrease of E.I. from the early to the late sixties, indicating progressive deterioration within this decade. As with other studies, however, the decline of functioning was found to be differential, the amount of deterioration varying with the test used, although all tests showed some decline. The amount varied from 57 per cent loss in the learning of paired associates to only 12 per cent loss in the giving of general information. The average indices were lower than those found by Babcock in her work with psychotics, but it was pointed out that Babcock used no age control with her psychotic groups. The wide individual variation in decline was also noted, and particularly the fact that the very brightest individuals tended to show both relatively and absolutely less decline.

Except with individuals with a special language handicap or too deteriorated to cooperate, the Babcock Test is a valuable instrument to use in the measurement of deterioration, especially when it is used for research purposes. For practical and clinical use, however, it is rather long and cumbersome in its present form, and many old persons will not cooperate for long periods of testing. Its value would also be enhanced if norms were available for the different decades of life so that we could determine in a particular individual whether his obtained E.I. is normal or better or worse than should be expected for his age group, as well as what the E.I. is compared with that of normal young people or the subject's own presumable peak. Brody (5, 6) in England has suggested a shortened Babcock, consisting of the discrepancy between a brief vocabulary and five other tests, for the measurement of deterioration in psychotics, and it is possible that this may be applicable also to the measurement of old age deterioration. Rapaport (74) likewise has condensed the functioning part of the test into three groups with a total of seven tests. The present author sometimes reduces the number of tests to ten which are included under four of the six functioning groups, but again these variations have not yet been standardized according to decades of life. Rabin (72, 73) in his use of the Babcock Test has also pointed out this need of age standardization of the test.

The Shipley-Hartford Conceptual Quotient Scale (77), a differential loss scale patterned somewhat along the lines of the Babcock Test, was originally designed for use with psychotics but has also been used successfully to measure deterioration in the aged. The scale measures the discrepancy between the vocabulary score and the abstraction or conceptual thinking score, this latter score being divided by the vocabulary score in a manner similar to that used in determining the I.Q. In general, a lowering of C.Q. is found with advancing age. The main difficulty with this test is that it is not suitable for use with those individuals who are of natively inferior intelligence.

Wechsler (83), in standardizing the Wechsler-Bellevue Adolescent and Adult Intelligence Scale, found that the total scores showed a progressive decrease with advancing age, the decline being sharp after the age of forty years. He considers that intellectual deterioration is part of the general organic process and begins at a relatively early age, perhaps in the late twenties. Wechsler points out that curves show a close parallelism between loss of brain weight and decline of mental ability with age. He believes, therefore, that it is only fair that we should compare older persons with others of their own age group as we do with those younger, and in his adult scale he takes account of the age factor in measuring adult intelligence. Thus, he has I.Q. norms for each decade of life up to the age of sixty years, with provisions for extrapolation after this age. Wechsler points out that the measurement of mental deterioration involves the present functioning level, the previous level of functioning, and the difference between these two in quantitative terms. Noting then the differential decline of abilities, he separates his tests into two groups: the "Hold Tests," consisting of information, comprehension, object assembly, picture completion, and vocabulary; and the "Don't Hold" tests consisting of digit span, arithmetic, digit symbol, block designs, and similarities (picture arrangement). In practice he uses four tests from each group—information, object assembly, picture completion, and vocabulary from the first group, and digit span, arithmetic, block design, and digit symbol from the second group—and calculates the ratio between the scores on the two groups to get a percentage of loss and an efficiency quotient. If for example an individual attains a score of 40 on the hold tests and a score of 32 on the don't hold tests, his deterioration loss is 20 per cent and his efficiency quotient 80. The percentage of loss expected in normal individuals ranges from 1 in the semidecade of twenty-five to twenty-nine years, to 8 in the forty to forty-four year period, 11 at forty-five to forty-nine years, 14 from fifty to fifty-four years, and 16 from fifty-five to fifty-nine years. Corresponding deterioration quotients would be 99, 92, 89, 86 and 84. Thus, if a person should have a deterioration quotient considerably below the norm for his age, we might suspect his deterioration to be abnormal. Wechsler finds that impairment or loss of function is best revealed by measuring speed of response, learning, and ability to perceive new configurations, especially spatial ones.

Others working with the Wechsler-Bellevue Scale report difference in their findings regarding these hold-don't hold test groups, some of the investigations tending to be in agreement with and some differing from Wechsler's results. For example, Madonick and Solomon (54), examining twenty-nine women and twenty-one men over the age of sixty in a denominational home for the aged, found the order of performances on the subtests to be in agreement with Wechsler's findings. These individuals performed best on the information and comprehension subtests and poorest on the picture arrangement and digit symbol material. This, however, was a rather selective sample in as much as the subjects had been successful professional and executive persons, and their I.Q.'s were above average. Rabin (73), working on hospitalized seniles between the ages of fifty and eighty-four, and Chesrow, Wosika, and Reinitz (7), working on subjects between the ages of sixty-four and eighty-three, did not find results in complete agreement with those of Wechsler for the hold-don't hold tests when the relative positions on the subtests were compared, although the general results were not too dissimilar. On these studies, however, the object assembly test was found to be among the most difficult items for the older persons.

On the other hand, Boehm and Sarason (4) do not believe that the Wechsler hold-don't hold system will differentiate mental deterioration from mental deficiency. Also, Hunt (33) in studying the means and standard deviations of different age groups, concludes that as only the information and comprehension tests hold up well with age and only the block design and digit symbol decline with age, normal deterioration could better be measured by using only these four tests. Chesrow et al. (7) also found no correlation between Wechsler-Bellevue and Rorschach indications of deterioration. Magaret and Simpson (55) likewise found little agreement between the Wechsler-Bellevue and the Shipley-Hartford scales with regard to indications of deterioration with psychotics between the ages of forty and forty-nine and little agreement of either with psychiatric ratings.

Lorge (50-53 inclusive), comparing the results of different age groups on the Intelligence Scale CAVD (a power test with unlimited time allowance), the Army Alpha, the Otis Self-Administering Tests of Mental Ability (twenty-minute time allowance), and the Thorndike Intelligence Examination for High School Graduates, found a decline with increasing age on all except the CAVD tests, indicating the loss to be one of speed, not of power. He warns against this confusion of speed and power in tests and also against the selective samples on which adult tests are often standardized. Although admitting the value of short methods to get a quick estimate of ability when this is necessary, he warns that such methods should be used and interpreted cautiously because they are less reliable and valid.

Foulds and Raven (18, 19, 75), again using a differential loss method of investigation, studied several thousand individuals of varying ages and occupations by means of the Raven Progressive Matrices Test and the Mill Hill Vocabulary Scale. Results in general showed a rise in scores on the matrices to about age fourteen, where they remained constant until about twenty-five, after which they showed a gradual decline. The vocabulary scores, on the other hand, showed a rise to about the age of thirty, with little decline to the age of sixty years. These investigators conclude that the average person's ability to form comparisons and to reason by analogy increases rapidly during childhood to reach a maximum at the age of fourteen years, after which it remains constant to the age of twenty-five; after the age of twenty-five years, there is a gradual and constant decline to the age of sixty, and an even greater decline between the ages of sixty and eighty years, so that by the age of eighty the ability to reason by analogy is comparable to that of the average eight-year-old child. On the other hand, the ability to recall information increases steadily to at least the age of twenty-five years, where it remains constant for the next twenty-five to thirty years.

Eysenck (13, 14), using Raven's Progressive Matrices tests to study 100 male senile dements, average age seventy-three years, found their average scores comparable to those of an eight-year-old child or the lowest 3 to 4 per cent of the adult population. Essentially their errors showed no differences from those of normal adults save in the matter of speed. Later, making a factorial study of twenty different tests given to seventy-five senile dements, Eysenck found a general factor and three group factors, mainly concerned with speed, memory, and physical strength, running through the tests. She found decline to be most marked in abstract reasoning and least on those tests involving old experience and knowledge. She notes that the organization of mental abilities in the senile dements differs markedly from that in the normal adult because of the differential deterioration in the abilities of the seniles.

Halstead (29, 30), after experimenting with eighty tests, finally used a battery of twenty-five tests for the measurement of deterioration in twenty seniles between the ages of sixty-eight and eighty-three years. He found that this group experienced difficulty in revising old habits and in retaining visual and auditory material of a meaningful kind. They showed inelasticity, perseveration, and impairment of judgment, planning, and spatial discrimination. They performed better at tests of rote memory and those involving old associations and best at those of simple motor ability, immediate visual recognition, and early acquired habit patterns. Vocabulary held up well, but Halstead warns against the use of vocabulary with those who are illiterate or of natively low intelligence. He also points out that tests of comprehension and vocabulary should be short and simple. This battery of tests proved to be effective in differentiating between normal seniles and cases of senile dementia.

As mentioned earlier, Rorschach studies tend in general to show some intellectual impairment with loosening of intellectual ties to reality and impoverishment of creative intellectual faculties (38, 70).

From the discussion thus far, we might assume that the curve of intellectual impairment parallels in reverse the earlier growth curve of intelligence, declining gradually but regularly from a peak in early youth to a theoretical zero point at some unknown time in extreme old age. This, however, would be purely speculative, as there have been insufficient studies of extreme old age and no one has yet found the age at which the theoretical zero point of intelligence is approached by normal old people. There are, on the other hand, some indications (based on unpublished research by the author) that after a fairly regular decline in senescence, a plateau of decline is reached and that this plateau may be maintained for some years. No research has yet been published on this, though, and further investigation is needed before definite conclusions can be reached.

A point to be remembered too is that on examination, an old person may rate considerably above the average with respect to intelligence test scores and yet, in reality, be much deteriorated—that is, deteriorated below the level he had once attained. An example of this can be seen in the case of an octogenarian whom the author has had occasion to examine for research purposes over a period of years. This individual is a brilliant man who has had, and is still having, an interesting and useful professional career. His I.Q. is now in the 120's, indicating very superior intelligence. However, seven years prior to attaining this I.Q. he attained an I.Q. of 143, and it seems likely that had he been examined still earlier in his life, his I.Q. would have been still higher. This man's scores also serve as an illustration of the above-mentioned plateau of decline which may be reached, for over a period of five years his intelligence test scores have remained practically constant.

From these many, and sometimes extensive, investigations into the matter of intellectual impairment with advancing age, we can see that there is a decline in intelligence test scores in senescence. All studies are in agreement on this point, but the studies also show that the decline is differential and a function of the test used, the greatest loss usually being found on tests involving speed and learning of new things and the least on tests such as vocabulary and general information. Just what the relationship is between intellectual decline (i.e., both general and differential impairment) and general physical decline or perhaps differential impairment of various areas of the brain is uncertain, but it seems probable that the two cannot be entirely separated. Studies agree, however, that individual differences in decline are marked and that emotional or personality factors play an important part in success on the tests (42). Motivation, drive, persistence, and practice through the years are important factors in determining whether the individual will do well or poorly on the tests, and these are factors which are not easily measurable. It is felt, however, that when these factors are on the positive side, they may help retard the deterioration process.

It has been mentioned several times that intellectual impairment with advancing age is a matter of differential loss and a function of the test used. Therefore, it is desirable to study the decline on separate intellectual functions.

Psychophysical Capacities—Motor Performances

Psychophysical capacities tend to show a gradual decline with advancing age, and this can often be noted by casual observation as well as by scientific investigation (11, 12, 23, 27, 40, 56-65, 67). No doubt most of us have noted that old persons usually slow up, seem less vigorous and strong than they once were, and tire more easily.

Actually, there is a decline of gross physical strength and speed after the twenties. Athletes, such as prize fighters, tennis players, professional football players, and track men, reach their peak of performances between twenty-five and twenty-nine years and thereafter show rapid decline (46). The capacity for endurance and for recovery after exertion also declines after this age. The strength of muscles decreases from the twenties onward (82), and this decrease of strength is most evident in the flexors of the forearm and in the muscles which raise the body. Strength of grip and strength of pull show similar decline.

Reaction time to light and sound stimuli reaches a peak of speed in the twenties with a gradual decline of efficiency thereafter, so that by the age of sixty men may show a 75 per cent increase in reaction time to light stimuli and a 95 per cent increase in reaction time to sound stimuli. Women of comparable age show a 70 per cent increase in reaction time to light stimuli and a 110 per cent increase in reaction time to sound stimuli.

Motility of various types also shows a decline with advancing age, reaching a peak in young adulthood, usually the late twenties, with decline thereafter, the decline becoming steeper from the sixties onward. There are, however, wide individual differences and overlapping in the younger and older groups. The same general picture for peak of efficiency and decline holds good for digital extension-flexion, rotary motility of the preferred and nonpreferred hand, and manual reach and grasp.

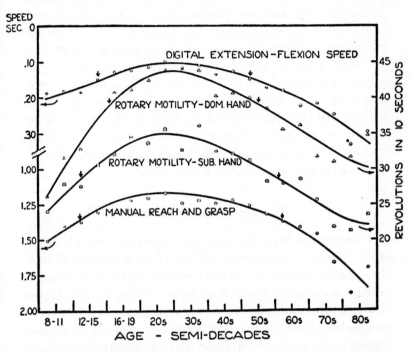

Fig. 4. Age differences in certain motor abilities. From L. A. Pennington and I. A. Berg, *An introduction to clinical psychology,* p. 223. Copyright, 1948, by The Ronald Press Co.

Results on manual ability tests show a decrease of efficiency on such tasks as dotting and stringing beads but no clear decline on such activities as tapping, cutting, and others with which the individual is familiar. The decline begins later and is less with the more intelligent individuals. An interesting point in connection with the decline in manual ability is that the decline seems to occur first and to be greater in the finger and wrist than in the coarser movements, indicating a possible reverse parallel to the earlier development from the coarser to the finer movements.

In general, we find that skilled hand or foot movements, speed of reaction, and strength of grip or pull decline gradually from a peak in early adulthood, but there are wide individual differences, and some old persons do as well as the average young person. It would appear that experience and use tend to retard decline in motor performances, so that the decline in one's own field of motor endeavor often is not so great and is frequently compensated for by better judgment and greater care. This is seen in the case of automobile drivers and certain factory workers and is a practical point for industry to consider in the employment of older workers. The loss in motor performances seems to be greatest when the learning of a new motor skill interferes with old, well-established habits (76).

Perceptual Performances

Perceptual ability shows progressive changes with advancing age. Speed of perception, flexibility in the perception of relations, and the amount which can be appreciated in a single act of perception decrease steadily from decade to decade, but it is possible that some of this decline may be compensated for by experience and persistence in practical situations. Normal old persons show a marked tendency to make false identifications of objects when these are presented to them pictorially, part of which may be due to difficulties of perception and part of the senile attitude of repugnance for the new and the compulsive tendency to make stereotyped responses to any external situation (28). "Sufferers from senile deterioration tend to perceive and define objects in terms of mere utility rather than of composition or construction; these persons become interested in individual parts of an object to the exclusion of the total pattern; they largely ignore color; their preconceptions cause them to ignore inconsistencies and even to distort the present material" (31). Decline in speed is the most marked perceptual change with advancing age in both normal and abnormal senescents (3, 13, 24).

Comprehension

The decline in comprehension with advancing age seems to be more a matter of decline in speed of comprehension rather than decline in the actual ability to comprehend if given sufficient time—again a question of power vs. speed. The newness of the activity is also an important factor, as the old person seems to experience greater difficulty in comprehending when the material is entirely new or out of his usual field of knowledge.

Learning and Memory

The inability to learn new things and to remember are the difficulties most frequently complained of by the old. Learning and memory, however, are of many different types. For example, we often find that although the ability of an old person to learn new things is greatly impaired, his memory for childhood events may be fairly intact. Also, in the learning of new things, initial comprehension and perception are involved as well as effort and motivation. Often an old person can learn but his motivation is not sufficiently strong to stimulate him to make the effort required to do so. Emotional factors may facilitate the learning process or serve as a block to further learning, and this may be evident in old age as well as in any other period of life. Lack of practice in vigorous learning may also result in some disability in this area among older persons (78).

Immediate repetitive ability, or memory span as it is often called, involves the ability to concentrate long enough to receive new impressions, and this, of course, is basic to the learning process. Performances in this area can be tested by memory span for digits (forward and reversed), immediate repetitions of words and sentences, and Knox cubes. Investigations show slight to moderate loss of this ability in senescence (16, 24, 26, 39). Kubo, for example, in studying rote memory for words in a group of 355 individuals between seventy and 100 years, found no sudden drop until the age of eighty-two, when a rapid decline set in. Repetition of digits, it will be recalled, is one of the Wechsler "don't hold" tests, and Wechsler notes that decline in this ability occurs but not so much as in some other tests and concludes therefore that the old have other things than memory loss of which they might well complain (83). It will be seen, however, that when meaning is involved the memory loss is markedly greater than when it is simply a matter of memory span.

Immediate memory and initial learning show marked impairment with advancing age, and this has been noted popularly as well as scientifically. Failure to remember recent events and to learn new things are among the most noticeable characteristics of the aged, in contrast to the relative ease with which they recall events of their childhood or many years past. Scientifically a marked loss of both verbal and nonverbal memory and learning ability has been noted in old age (16, 24, 26, 40, 76, 83). For example, persons in the sixties are, on the average, able to reproduce designs from memory little better than half as well as they could in their youth. Likewise, in motor learning with direct vision there is a 16 per cent loss in the sixty-plus age group and a 47 per cent loss with mirror vision in the same group, showing again that there is the greatest deficit when tasks tend to conflict with well-established habits. Simple verbal memory, such as that involved in the immediate reproduction of a paragraph, shows a marked loss by the time the sixties have been reached, and the learning of entirely new material, which involves the formation of new associations that may run counter to old established habits of thought, shows an even greater loss. Decline in this latter type of learning may range from 40 per cent to more than 58 per cent (24, 26).

Retention of recently learned material varies from a loss of more than 39 per cent on the delayed reproduction of a paragraph to more than 60 per cent on the delayed recall of newly learned, unfamiliar material (24, 26).

Briefly then, we might say that older persons on the average show some but relatively little decline in their ability to receive new impressions but suffer greatly in their ability to integrate new data and to form the new associations necessary to the learning of entirely new material, whether this material be of verbal or of nonverbal nature. Also, although they remember bygone events readily, they experience difficulty in retaining recently learned material. The learning process of the aged suffers from decreased flexibility and adaptability. Old persons can and do learn new material, but learning for them is laborious and the results are less satisfactory than when they were young and at the peak of their efficient functioning. The very brightest individuals tend to retain the efficiency of their learning process better than those who are not so bright. While the real reason for this is not known, one might postulate the theory of organismic superiority. It is also possible that interest, practice, greater flexibility, and continued activity in the intellectual field are important factors in the maintenance of the efficiency of the learning process.

Reasoning and Judgment

Reasoning and judgment tend to develop slowly both in general and in specific areas. Scientific studies of these functions in the aged (24, 40, 41, 58, 61, 62, 63) reveal some interesting points. For example, reasoning and judgment are among the latest of all abilities to reach their peak, and they are among the last to go. This fact probably accounts in large part for the fewer industrial accidents, less spoilage, and less waste of materials found among the older age groups in spite of their slower speed and learning ability. When speed and flexibility are involved in reasoning and judgment, decline is seen. In general, verbal associations, generalizations, interpretations of meaning, and recognition of relations show marked resistance to age. However, abstractions and conceptual thinking of the type measured by the Shipley-Hartford Test of Conceptual Thinking show decline (77). It must be remembered, though, that this is a completion type of test, and tests of this sort involve flexibility of thinking, which, as we know, declines with advancing age. Reasoning and judgment are found to be especially well maintained where experience is involved. For example, in one's own field where experience has been accumulating over a period of many years, there is little evidence for any decline with the years, at least until extreme old age is reached. This can easily be seen in the continued excellent work of many aged judges, doctors, philosophers, etc.

General Information

General information is another ability which holds up well with advancing years (83). This, it will be recalled, is one of Wechsler's "hold" tests, and the findings of other investigators tend also to support his contention that general information does not readily decline in old age.

Vocabulary

Vocabulary has long been considered one of the best single indices of intellectual level we have. Terman found a high correlation between vocabulary score and general intelligence and considers this to be the best of his subtests on the 1937 Terman-Merrill Revision of the Binet-Simon Intelligence Tests (80, 81). O'Connor (68) found a high correlation between vocabulary score and success and also found that vocabulary tends to increase as long as one stays in school, but that it does not increase by more than two school years between the ages of twenty-three and fifty years. Mention has already been made of numerous investigations of general intelligence in the aged the results of which tend to show that vocabulary is one of the best-retained abilities. Also, it has been noted that vocabulary retention forms the basis for the differential loss tests, such as the Babcock and the Shipley-Hartford, which are used to measure deterioration or mental impairment. Tests made specifically on vocabulary changes with age likewise tend to agree that vocabulary holds up well with age and is remarkably resistant to impairment. As Feifel reports in his study of vocabulary (15), Green, using 110 persons between the ages of nineteen and eighty-four, found no significant change beyond the early twenties. Shakow and Goldman, studying 302 adults with the 1916 Terman vocabulary and equalizing them by using representative educational samplings for each decade, found no change in vocabulary from the age of eighteen years through the sixth decade, although a slow decline set in after this latter period. In a later study Roe and Shakow reported similar results on a group of sixty-nine normal adults. Thorndike and Gallup, using a vocabulary test taken from items of the Intelligence Scale CAVD, found no age differences in vocabulary scores until the "over sixty" age group was reached. Fox (20), comparing thirty individuals between the ages of seventy and seventy-nine with a similar group between forty and forty-nine years old, noted no statistically reliable differences in vocabulary between the two groups. Fox and Birren (21), using Wechsler's vocabulary and Seashore and Echerson's English Recognition Vocabulary Test with a group of 216 institutionalized persons, average age 71.3 years, reported no relation between vocabulary and age or length of institutionalization and only a low positive correlation with education. Vocabulary in this group was not significantly affected by visual or auditory defects. Lewinski (49), in studying 1,000 males between the ages of seventeen and sixty-two years, likewise found no significant vocabulary change with age increase. Rabin (72, 73), in studies using the 1916 Terman vocabulary and the 1937 Terman vocabulary, found a slight tendency for vocabulary scores to be slightly higher at the older age levels.

Different theories have been advanced to account for the fact that vocabulary does not seem to increase materially after young adulthood has been reached and shows such resistance to impairment with advancing age. One of these theories (Babcock) is that the earliest learned material is the last to be forgotten and that words remain as indicators of the ability one once had, since some kinds of words cannot be learned by persons of inferior intelligence and the type of word one can learn is highly correlated with intelligence as measured by the criterion of ability to succeed in school and college work. This theory has been criticized on the grounds that the reason vocabulary SEEMS to show resistance to impairment in contrast to the impairment shown on other tests is that in vocabulary one usually has a wide choice of responses, whereas in other tests the choice of response is narrowed, so that in defining a word, even if the more difficult conceptual organization has deteriorated, the correct response can still be obtained on a lower conceptual level or even on a completely concrete one.

Going on to the supposition that if qualitative differences were considered in the scoring of vocabulary, this function would also show impairment, Feifel (15) studied 370 abnormals and normals between the ages of fifteen and eighty years, matched and divided into the age groups fifteen to twenty-nine, thirty to forty-nine, and fifty to seventy-nine. He found that abnormals generally selected more inferior types of responses at all ages, but that the tendency was more pronounced in older than in younger abnormals, these individuals tending to select the inferior explanation, illustration, repetition, and demonstration types of responses. There was also some suggestion of a similar tendency for older normals to use types of responses common to children, but there was nothing clear-cut or definite with these individuals as there was with the abnormals. Kaplan (37) likewise, in a longitudinal study of older morons, found qualitative changes in vocabulary, although the actual vocabulary scores were generally maintained.

Creative Imagination

Creative imagination has generally been considered to be ageless, and much of this belief has come about through the knowledge of the many excellent creative works of aged persons. However, there have also been some scientific studies of this area of functioning. W. R. Miles (64), for example, studied creative imagination by means of the kinephantom, which is rather like an animated ink blot. He used 1,203 subjects, found no relation to age by decades, and therefore considered creative imagination to be truly ageless. Dorland, Lehman, and others believe that creative contributions can be made at practically every age level beyond early youth, but it seems that a good emotional adjustment is essential to continued efficient use of one's abilities. Lehman, in a series of studies on creative activity in later years (44-48) found that the age of producing one's most important work varies with the task, the oldster finding his greatest success in the fields of business and politics. For example, the peak for political achievement is fifty to fifty-nine in contrast to the peak of twenty-five to twenty-nine for tasks involving physical prowess.

In contrast to this, we recall the previously mentioned Rorschach studies which have tended to show impoverishment of creative intellectual functions in old age (38, 70).

In this connection, Dorland's studies of master works are of interest (9, 10). Dorland made a study of the average age at which individuals in various fields of endeavor produced their master works, and it will be noted that in none of them was the peak of ability supposedly reached in early youth. It will also be noted that the age of producing masterpieces varies with the type of activity. Chemists and physicians, e.g., reach their peak at forty-one, dramatists at forty-four, novelists at forty-six, explorers and warriors at forty-seven, actors and musical composers at forty-eight, artists and divines at fifty, reformers and essayists at fifty-one, physicians, surgeons, and statesmen at fifty-two, philosophers at fifty-four, astronomers, mathematicians, satirists, and humorists at fifty-six, historians at fifty-seven, and jurists and naturalists at fifty-eight.

The creative achievements of numerous aged individuals in various fields of activity throughout the ages likewise lends credence to the contention that creative imagination may be ageless, provided one has creative imagination to start with. However, we must not forget in evaluating the creative achievements of older persons that not only were most of the works completed long before they reached the public, but also that they necessarily were the result of the accumulation of earlier reading and thought over a period of years.

To cite a few examples of creative achievements of older people, Michelangelo was writing sonnets at the age of seventy-nine and continued his creative work until his eighty-ninth year. Lamarck dictated his *Histoire Naturelle* until his death at the age of eighty-five. Alexander von Humboldt started writing the *Kosmos* at seventy-four and was writing at the age of ninety when he died. Russell Sage, the philanthropist and banker, died at his desk at eighty-five. Victor Hugo did his best writing between seventy and eighty. Voltaire likewise did much of his best work in the last ten years of his life, even though he was ill most of the time and died at the age of eighty-four. Immanuel Kant, although frail, worked until a few months before his death at eighty. In our own times, Lillien Martin, psychologist, did much of her best work after her "old age" retirement from a professorship at Stanford University. She not only opened and ran a child guidance clinic but started the first old age clinic in the country, developed her own methods of rehabilitating the aged, wrote several books, learned to drive an automobile, traveled, and kept actively engaged in LIVING until her death in her early nineties. Sigmund Freud was revising his theories constantly up to the time of his death at the age of eighty-four, in spite of suffering occasioned by his exile and illness (cancer). George Bernard Shaw, one of the greatest contemporary literary figures, was active and delighting the world with his quips until his death at the age of ninety-four. Winston Churchill, now in his late seventies and currently Prime Minister of Great Britain, is still active in writing and painting. "Grandma" Moses never did anything with art until the period of later maturity, but she has created quite a stir with her appealing "primitives." Ruth St. Denis, world-famous dancer, is still actively engaged in her profession, although admittedly "somewhere between seventy and eighty years old," and from all accounts she has energy far exceeding that of women many years her junior.

Numerous other examples could be given of individuals who have either continued their creative activities or initiated them in later maturity and kept active and productive until their death at a very advanced age, but just a sample of these should suffice. However, the fact that there are individuals who do not start their creative activities until later maturity arouses interest in the possibility that many other individuals may also have untapped sources of creative ability—creative abilities which have not been developed because of the pressure of life. It seems quite possible that many individuals may have sources of creative ability which they have not developed because they have been too busy earning a living, raising a family, etc. In the period of later maturity, when more time should be available for these creative abilities, it may be possible to tap these sources and develop worth-while talents previously hidden.

Motivation

Motivation is the mainspring of life. It is motivation which determines, within the limits of one's capacity, what tasks will be accomplished and what goals achieved, and yet motivation is something which cannot easily be measured. Undoubtedly it has considerable influence on the deterioration process. When one has not the motivation to keep mentally and physically healthy, decline more readily sets in. Also, if the old person is content to vegetate in a rocker for the remainder of his life, there is little that anyone else can do about it, for it is he himself who must have the drive to move forward if any change is to be effected. It used to be accepted as a truism that, just by virtue of their age alone, old people could not change. Now we know that this is not so; assuming normal physical and mental ability, anyone CAN change at ANY age provided he has sufficient motivation to do so. Unfortunately it too often happens that there is insufficient motivation to change, for change requires effort on the part of the individual himself, and this many persons cannot or will not exert. For these persons a change would be acceptable if someone else did all the work, but for them it requires too much effort to change themselves, to keep up to date, and to learn new things. Learning is possible; but, because it takes a longer time, requires a greater effort, and gives results which are not always as satisfactory as desired, it is often not attempted. In short, little retardation of the aging process or rehabilitation of the aging individual is possible unless the person involved has the motivation to change himself and to develop.

The operation of the factor of motivation can readily be seen in the lives of men of genius. These men seem to possess stronger impulses and the ability to canalize their energy into specific fields, and therefore they continue to produce even in old age and in spite of weakened intellect.

Summary

Results of numerous intelligence tests given to many individuals at various periods throughout the life span agree fairly well in showing that after reaching a peak of performance somewhere in the teens or twenties, there is a gradual decline in test scores from early to late maturity.

There is some evidence for a decline from the early to the late sixties and also a possibility that at some time in senescence a plateau of decline may be reached and maintained over an indefinite period of time.

Intellectual decline is differential and largely a function of the test used, separate abilities apparently declining at different rates. Some tests, such as the Babcock, the Wechsler-Bellevue, and the Shipley-Hartford, make use of this differential loss principle in measuring individual intellectual impairment.

Probably the best picture of individual intellectual impairment with age could be obtained by comparing the aged person both with his contemporaries and with what was presumably his own peak of mental functioning.

Individual differences in decline of abilities are wide, and there are indications that the very brightest, on the average, tend to show both relatively and absolutely less decline than those who are less bright.

Intellectual impairment is inextricably bound up with physiological, emotional, social, and personality traits and cannot rightfully be considered apart from them or from changes which occur in these areas also with advancing age.

Psychophysical capacities, including gross physical strength and speed, reaction time, motility, and various types of manual ability, decline gradually from a peak in early adulthood, but individual differences are wide and some old persons do as well as the average young person. Experience and use, particularly in one's own field, tend to retard decline in motor performances.

Perceptual changes with advancing age can be seen mostly in the decline of speed and flexibility.

Decline of comprehension is found for the most part when speed is involved, although newness of activity is also an important factor.

The greatest deterioration occurs on tests of learning which involve the formation of entirely new associations or integration of new data and facility of perceiving relations, and this is true whether the learning be of verbal or of nonverbal nature.

Immediate rote memory declines, but not as much as meaningful memory, and simple meaningful memory not as much as learning involving the formation of new associations which may run counter to old, well-established associations.

Although the old retain bygone events readily, they experience marked difficulty in retaining recently learned material.

The learning process of the aged suffers from decreased flexibility, adaptability, and motivation. Although their learning takes longer, is more difficult, and gives less satisfactory results, the old can and do learn new things, and by continued activity in the intellectual field, they may do much to retard the decline of the learning process.

Reasoning and judgment, when speed and flexibility are involved, tend to decline with advancing age. However, when verbal associations, generalizations, interpretations of meaning, and recognition of relations are considered without regard to speed, there is indication of a marked resistance to age. Where experience such as one would have in his own field of endeavor is involved, reasoning and judgment are especially well maintained.

General information does not readily decline in old age.

Vocabulary tends to hold up with age better than other abilities, and because of this and its high correlation with general intelligence, vocabulary is used on some tests as the measure of original intellectual level.

There is a possibility that vocabulary may decline in certain qualitative aspects, but the evidence for this is inconclusive and seems to hold for the abnormal rather than the normal old persons.

There is considerable evidence for the belief that creative imagination, provided there was any present in the first place, is ageless. Creative works have been produced by persons in all ages of maturity up to and including the nineties.

Motivation plays an important part in intellectual decline with advancing age, for when motivation is absent, we find waning interest in things and a decrease of intellectual activity and use of intellectual abilities. The result of this disuse, of course, is accelerated decline. Motivation seems to decline in many aging individuals, but it is not something which is easily measurable. Motivation on the part of the aging individual is necessary not only to maintain the status quo but also to effect any change in the process of rehabilitation of the aged.

REFERENCES

1. BABCOCK, H. *An experiment in the measurement of mental deterioration.* Arch. Psychol., N.Y., 1930, No. 11.

2. BEESON, M. F. Intelligence at senescence. *J. appl. Psychol.*, 1928, **4**, 219-34.

3. BELLIS, C. J. Reaction time and chronological age. *Proc. Soc. exp. Biol. and Med.*, 1935, **30**, 801-3.

4. BOEHM, A. E., and SARASON, S. B. Does Wechsler's formula distinguish intellectual deterioration from mental deficiency? *J. abnorm. soc. Psychol.*, 1947, **42**, 356-58.

5. BRODY, M. B. The measurement of dementia. *J. ment. Sci.*, 1942, **88**, 317-27.

6. ———. A survey of the results of intelligence tests in psychoses. *Brit. J. med. Psychol.*, 1943, **19**, 215-61.

7. CHESROW, E. J., WOSIKA, P. H., and REINITZ, A. H. A psychometric evaluation of aged white males. *Geriatrics*, 1949, **4**, 169-77.

8. DONAHUE, W. Changes in psychological processes with aging. In TIBBITTS, C. (ed.), *Living through the older years.* Ann Arbor, Mich.: University of Michigan Press, 1949.

9. DORLAND, W. A. M. The triumphs of maturity: I. The age of the master work. *Welfare Mag.*, 1927, **18**, 1307-29.

10. ———. The triumphs of maturity: II. The achievements of maturity which the world might have passed. *Welfare Mag.*, 1927, **18**, 1444-66.

11. EHRINGER, G. Age et déclin des aptitudes. *Arch. de Psychol.*, 1927, **20**, 318-23.

12. ———. Déclin des aptitudes avec l'âge. *Arch. de Psychol.*, 1931, **23**, 67-73.

13. EYSENCK, M. D. A study of certain qualitative aspects of problem-solving behavior in senile dementia patients. *J. ment. Sci.*, 1945, **91**, 337-45.

14. ———. An exploratory study of mental organization in senility. *J. Neurol. Psychiat.*, 1945, **8**, 15-21.

15. FEIFEL, H. Qualitative differences in the vocabulary responses of normals and abnormals. *Genet. Psychol. Monogr.*, 1949, **39**, 151-204.

16. FOSTER, J. C. Significant responses in certain memory tests. *J. appl. Psychol.*, 1920, **4**, 143-54.

17. FOSTER, J. C., and TAYLOR, G. A. The application of mental tests to persons over fifty years of age. *J. appl. Psychol.*, 1920, **4**, 39-58.

18. FOULDS, G. A. Variations in the intellectual activities of adults. *Amer. J. Psychol.*, 1949, **62**, 238-46.

19. FOULDS, G. A., and RAVEN, J. C. Normal changes in the mental abilities of adults as age advances. *J. ment. Sci.*, 1948, **94**, 133-44.

20. FOX, C. Vocabulary ability in later maturity. *J. educ. Psychol.*, 1947, **38**, 482-92.

21. FOX, C., and BIRREN, J. E. Some factors affecting vocabulary size in later maturity: age, education and length of institutionalization. *J. Geron.*, 1949, **1**, 19-26.

22. GARRISON, S. C. Retests on adults at an interval of ten years. *Sch. & Soc.*, 1930, **32**, 326-28.

23. GIESE, F. Erlebnisformen des Alters: Umfrage-ergebnisse uber Merkmale persönlichen Verfalls. *Dtsch. Ps.*, Halle-Marcbold, 1928, **5**, No. 2.

24. GILBERT, J. G. *Mental efficiency in senescence.* Arch. Psychol., N.Y., 1935, No. 188.

25. ———. Senescent efficiency and employability. *J. appl. Psychol.*, 1936, **20**, 266-72.

26. ———. *Memory loss in senescence. J. abnorm. soc. Psychol.*, 1941, **36**, 73-86.

27. GOLDFARB, W. *An investigation of reaction time in older adults and its relationship to certain observed mental test patterns.* Teach. Coll. Contr. Educ., 1941, No. 831.

28. GRUSZECKA, A. Zafalszowania rzeczywistosciw wiekn starczym. *Kwart. Psych.*, 1930, **1**, 273-87.

29. HALSTEAD, H. A psychometric study of senility. *J. ment. Sci.*, 1943, **89**, 363-73.

30. ——. Mental tests in senile dementia. *J. ment. Sci.*, 1944, **90**, 720-26.

31. HIRSCH, E. Uber senile Denk und Sprach-starungen. *Psych. Forsch.*, 1928, **10**, 358-92.

32. HSIAO, H. H. "The performance on the Army Alpha as a function of age." Master's thesis, Columbia University, 1927.

33. HUNT, W. L. The relative rates of decline of Wechsler-Bellevue "hold" and "don't hold" tests. *J. consult. Psychol.*, 1949, **13**, 440-43.

34. JONES, H. E., and CONRAD, H. S. The growth and decline of intelligence: a study of a homogeneous group between the ages of 10 and 60. *Genet. Psychol. Monogr.*, 1933, **13**, 223-98.

35. JONES, H. E., CONRAD, H. S., and HORN, A. Psychological studies of motion pictures: II. Observation and recall as a function of age. *Univ. Calif. Publ. Psychol.*, 1928, **3**, 225-43.

36. JONES, H. E., and KAPLAN, O. Psychological aspects of mental disorders in later life. In KAPLAN, O. (ed.), *Mental disorders in later life.* Stanford, Calif.: Stanford University Press, 1945.

37. KAPLAN, O. Mental decline in older morons. *Amer. J. ment. Def.*, 1943, **47**, 277-85.

38. KLOPFER, W. G. Personality patterns in old age. *Rorschach Res. Exch.*, 1946, **10**, 145-66.

39. KUBO, Y. Mental and physical changes in old age. *J. genet. Psychol.*, 1938, **53**, 101-18.

40. KUHLEN, R. G. Psychological trends and problems in later maturity. In PENNINGTON, L. A., and BERG, I. A. (eds.), *An introduction to clinical psychology.* New York: The Ronald Press Co., 1949.

41. LAWTON, G. Mental abilities at senescence: a survey of present-day research. *J. appl. Psychol.*, 1938, **6**, 607-19.

42. —— (ed.). *New goals for old age.* New York: Columbia University Press, 1943.

43. ——. *Aging successfully.* New York: Columbia University Press, 1946.

44. LEHMAN, H. C. The creative years in science and literature. *Sci. Mon.*, N.Y., 1936, **43**, 151-62.

45. ——. The creative years: best books. *Sci. Mon.*, N.Y., 1937, **45**, 65-75.

46. ——. The most proficient years at sports and games. *Res. Quart. Amer. phys. Educ. Ass.*, 1938, **9**, 3-19.

47. ——. The creative years: medicine, surgery and certain related fields. *Sci. Mon.*, N.Y., 1941, **52**, 450-61.

48. LEHMAN, H. C., and GAMERTSFELDER, W. S. Man's creative years in philosophy. *Psychol. Rev.*, 1942, **49**, 319-43.

49. LEWINSKI, H. J. Vocabulary and mental measurement: a quantitative investigation and review of research. *J. genet. Psychol.*, 1948, **72**, 247-81.

50. LORGE, I. The evaluation of mental status. Mental test, with discussion by J. G. GILBERT. *Amer. J. Orthopsychiat.*, 1940, **1**, 56-61.

51. ———. Intellectual changes during maturity and old age. *Rev. educ. Res.,* 1941, **11**, 553-61.

52. ———. Intellectual changes during maturity and old age. *Rev. educ. Res.,* 1944, **14**, 438-45.

53. ———. Intellectual changes during maturity and old age. *Rev. educ. Res.,* 1947, **17**, 326-32.

54. MADONICK, M. J., and SOLOMON, M. The Wechsler-Bellevue Scale in individuals past sixty. *Geriatrics,* 1947, **2**, 34-40.

55. MAGARET, A., and SIMPSON, M. M. A comparison of two measures of deterioration in psychotic patients. *J. consult. Psychol.,* 1948, **12**, 265-69.

56. MILES, C. C. Influence of speed and age on intelligence scores of adults. *J. gen. Psychol.,* 1934, **10**, 208-10.

57. MILES, C. C., and MILES, W. R. The correlation of intelligence scores and chronological age from early to late maturity. *Amer. J. Psychol.,* 1932, **44**, 44-78.

58. MILES, W. R. Measures of certain human abilities throughout the life span. *Proc. nat. Acad. Sci.,* Wash., 1931, **17**, 627-33.

59. ———. Change of dexterity with age. *Proc. Soc. exp. Biol. and Med.,* 1931, **19**, 136-38.

60. ———. Correlation of reaction and coordination speed with age in adults. *Amer. J. Psychol.,* 1931, **43**, 377-91.

61. ———. Abilities of older man. *Person. J.,* 1933, **11**, 352-57.

62. ———. The maintenance of our mental abilities. *Sci. Mon.,* N.Y., 1933, **34**, 549-52.

63. ———. Age and human ability. *Psychol. Rev.,* 1933, **40**, 99-123.

64. ———. Age and kinephantom. *J. gen. Psychol.,* 1934, **10**, 204-7.

65. ———. Psychological aspects of ageing. In COWDRY, E. V. (ed.), *Problems of ageing.* Baltimore: The Williams & Wilkins Co., 1939.

66. MURSELL, G. R. Decrease in intelligence with increase in age among inmates of penal institutions. *J. juv. Res.,* 1929, **13**, 197-203.

67. NICHOLSON, T. F. "The increase and decline in speed and control of voluntary motor ability with advancement in age." Unpublished Ph.D. thesis, Indiana University, 1929.

68. O'CONNOR, J. Vocabulary and success. *Atlantic Monthly,* Feb., 1934.

69. PINTNER, R. *Intelligence testing.* New York: Henry Holt & Co., Inc., 1931.

70. PRADOS, M., and FRIED, E. G. Personality structure in older age groups. *J. clin. Psychol.,* 1947, **3**, 113-20.

71. RABIN, A. I. The relationship between vocabulary levels and levels of general intelligence in psychotic and nonpsychotic individuals of a wide age range. *J. educ. Psychol.,* 1944, **35**, 411-22.

72. ———. Psychometric trends in senility and psychoses of the senium. *J. gen. Psychol.,* 1945, **32**, 149-62.

73. ———. Vocabulary and efficiency levels as functions of age in the Babcock method. *J. consult. Psychol.,* 1947, **11**, 207-11.

74. RAPAPORT, D. *Diagnostic psychological testing.* Chicago: Year Book Publishers, Inc., 1945. Vol. I.

75. RAVEN, J. C. The comparative assessment of intellectual ability. *Brit. J. Psychol.,* 1948, **39**, 12-19.

76. RUCH, F. L. The differentiative effects of age upon human learning. *J. gen. Psychol.,* 1934, **11**, 261-86.

77. SHIPLEY, W. C., and BURLINGAME, C. C. A convenient self-administering scale for measuring intellectual impairment in psychotics. *Amer. J. Psychiat.*, 1941, **97**, 1313-24.

78. SORENSON, H. Adult ages as a factor in learning. *J. educ. Psychol.*, 1930, **21**, 251-57.

79. SWARD, K. Age and mental ability in superior man. *Amer. J. Psychol.*, 1945, **58**, 443-79.

80. TERMAN, L. M. The vocabulary test as a measure of intelligence. *J. educ. Psychol.*, 1928, **9**, 452-56.

81. TERMAN, L. M., and MERRILL, M. *Measuring intelligence.* Boston: Houghton Mifflin Co., 1937.

82. UHLAND, J. M. Einfluss des Lebensalters, Geschlects, der Konstitution und des Berufs auf der kraftverschiedener Muskelgruppen: I. Mitteilung über den Einfluss des Lebensalters auf die Muskelgruppen. *Arbeit. Physiol.*, 1933, **6**, 653-64.

83. WECHSLER, D. *The measurement of adult intelligence.* Baltimore: The Williams & Wilkins Co., 1944.

84. WEISS, E. Leistung und Lebensalter. *Indus. Psychotechn.*, 1927, **4**, 227-45.

85. WERNER, H. M. "Some psychological tests of the aged." Master's thesis, Columbia University, 1932.

Chapter 5

CHANGES IN SOCIAL RELATIONS

Social changes found in the aging population are obviously part of the aging process of the individual and are inextricably bound up with his physical, intellectual, and emotional decline. In general, with increasing age there seems to be an increasing deprivation of earlier activities and satisfactions. Most persons want to live on, to continue active with their group, either vocationally or socially, and to maintain the position they have acquired (12). They want to hold the affection and esteem of those around them and to feel accepted, wanted, and needed. These are normal desires of persons at all ages, but they may be desires which are more difficult to achieve as one grows older, not only because of the changes which have taken place within the individual but also because of the changing attitude of the environment in which he lives. With advancing age, changes will take place in the social area, as well as in the physical, intellectual, and emotional areas, but the direction these changes take will depend to a large extent upon the culture in which the individual resides (28).

Attitudes in Different Cultures

Treatment of the aged varies widely in different cultures, and this is true of both primitive and civilized societies (7, 21, 32, 54). Some opportunities for the aged to gain prestige are found in all types of cultures. Likewise, some neglect of the aged is found in all types of cultures, and, in some primitive societies, we even find abandonment and killing of the aged. It used to be the custom among certain Eskimo tribes to abandon or to kill outright those aged who were no longer able to look after themselves and keep up with the tribe (53). This was an accepted custom and not necessarily carried out with disrespect or in any spirit of cruelty; rather, it was a matter of necessity when the burden of the old became too great for the other members of the family or tribe to carry. Among the Melanesians, the old who were incapable of work were buried alive. In Tierra del Fuego, during times of hunger, the members of the tribe would kill and eat an old woman before they would kill their dogs, the explanation being that "dogs catch seals, women can't" (32). Similar customs of neglect and abandonment are frequent among certain African and other primitive tribes where the aged are considered a liability rather than an asset to society.

On the other hand, in some primitive cultures the aged gain prestige as chiefs, religious leaders, or medicine men, keeping their people subject by their wisdom and magic. In some of the Australian tribes, for example, there is a regular gerontocracy wherein the aged really rule the society and are venerated and often feared. As Simmons has shown in his interesting book on the subject (52), some early primitive societies, such as the Aztecs and Incas, had organized systems of old age assistance, and other groups cared for their aged by the roles of hospitality and communal responsibility. Food taboos often resulted in the aged getting the delicacies. In many tribal societies the old had property rights and held considerable prestige, although this prestige held only for an age period which fell short of decrepitude. In most, the elderly men were more favored than the women, although in some groups the reverse held true. Some occupations and functions were essentially the prerogative of the older members of the tribes, and these included such things as midwifery, leading in games and ceremonies, dispensing genealogical and other information and traditions, solving human problems, healing, instructing in arts and crafts, advising on the supernatural and the elements, etc. Their major field for social participation was in the political, judicial, and civil areas, particularly if they had been prominent earlier, but success in these areas was dependent upon ability, initiative, and a favorable combination of social and cultural conditions and sex, men being more favored in this respect than women. In spite of these useful roles, however, the aged were reported by Simmons to be essentially dependent upon the family and to have a need of the younger tribal members.

In China the traditional attitude toward the aged is one of reverence and respect. As Chandler (4) has pointed out, the Oriental ideal of filial piety gives authority, security, honor, and a sense of immortality to the older generation. The old are considered wise because of their long experience. The Chinese conception of happiness in terms of tranquility, parental pride, and aesthetic appreciation of the finer things tends to favor the aged. The classic writings of the Chinese, for example, emphasize the joy of a calm, tranquil life, wherein one has time to contemplate and reflect, to enjoy the growth and development of children, and to give to others the pearls of wisdom acquired through a lifetime of study and experience. These attitudes automatically bring with them veneration of the aged. A personal communication to the author by a student of Middle East culture reports that, among certain Moslem groups, the older and less efficient a person becomes, the more is it a religious duty to revere him and obey him blindly.

The attitude toward the aged in American culture varies with the section of the country, but in general the attitude is negative and one of indifference and neglect. It is not an attitude of neglect in the sense of abandonment, although this too often occurs in a disguised form when families place their aged members in old age homes regardless of the wishes of the old person himself or the comfort of the institution he enters, but rather an attitude or habit of ignoring the old person and his problems. An exception to this attitude is seen among the Hutterites, a religious sect living in the western United States and Canada (14). Although this is essentially a young group, the aged fare well and maintain good mental health. They keep their prestige, are not forced to retire, are provided with adequate physical and medical care, and have complete economic security. Their religious beliefs and their faith in the hereafter reduce their fear of death.

In rural areas, among static agricultural and familistic societies where he can often be an asset in the home, the aging individual can frequently adjust quite happily (8). In crowded city areas, where space and the usefulness of the aged are limited, the oldster is all too often ignored, neglected, and unwanted. Generally speaking, we find that where mutual dependency is low and where space is limited or the culture nomadic, the old person is neglected. An industrial economy makes adjustment more difficult for older persons (55). With the exception of the Chinese culture, which seems to have a different philosophy of life and living (and this, of course, would hold true of other cultures with a similar philosophy of life), the more useful the old people are (or can make others think they are), the more they are revered; the less useful they are, the less they are respected or wanted. As others have noted, modern society, by means of improved living conditions, better control of disease, etc., has added many years to life, but it has done little to make these years worth living.

However, it is interesting to speculate upon what future changes may take place in the American attitude toward the aged in view of the ever increasing numbers of aged in our population and the interest which is developing in this area (36, 43, 46). Will we eventually, by sheer weight of numbers, develop a modern, civilized gerontocracy of our own—a gerontocracy wherein the old, by reason of the political power of their vote, will dictate the policies of the government? Will our culture be one essentially of conservatism because of the advanced age of its leaders? Industry already has many aged directors; will it be forced to extend the policy to its ranks and employ more old people in order to lessen the dependency load on the middle-aged group? As the old become more numerous in our culture, will they also become more vocal and demand more rights and privileges for themselves? Will they be forced to maintain their flexibility in order to hold their rightful place and compete in the changing American scene, or will our active, youthful culture become less ready for change and become willing to accept some of the rigidities imposed by a society with a rising age level? These changes are all within the realm of possibility as the population shift continues toward the upper ages. When we consider that in 1947 there were 1,200,000 persons over the age of sixty-five years in New York State and that in 1950 it was estimated that 8 per cent of the population of the United States was over sixty-five and that these numbers are showing a steady increase, we can readily understand that changes in the social structure, in social attitudes, and in social behavior will necessarily take place. When we consider too that the life expectancy has risen from about twenty-one years in the era of the Greeks, twenty-five years in the time of Christ, and a figure in the forties during the last century to better than sixty-seven years today, we can expect the increasingly large older group to become more vocal in demands for privileges.

Euthanasia

It is appropriate at this point to say a few words about euthanasia, since this problem is widely discussed today (16). Those who would hasten death for suffering persons beyond the hope of medical science think they have a wide field among the aged for their proselytizing. They take the view that since the aging process itself is irreversible, any incurable and painful disease of the aged makes the whole picture so hopeless that it is useless to bother with the burden of these persons. The advocates of euthanasia maintain that the infirm aged should be hastened to a painless and easy death because it is only humane not to let them live and suffer. Many of the aged themselves agree with this view, especially when they suffer from illness, social rejection, and lack of love, so that they feel there is nothing left in life worth living for.

Of course, these points carry with them a strong emotional appeal based on humanitarian motives and a certain appearance of logic from a materialistic point of view. But there are those whose firm religious beliefs and sound moral philosophy negate the taking of human life. Those holding these views believe that man has not the moral right to take the life of another human being or of himself and that efforts would better be spent in trying to alleviate the physical, social, and emotional suffering of these unfortunates. Furthermore, there is always the hope that the morrow may bring new medicines and techniques for the alleviation of pain and the prolongation of life. In addition, the power of life and death is certainly a potent weapon to put into the hands of any person, particularly when there are some who may be unscrupulous enough to use it for their own gain. Likewise, such power in the hands of the doctor would place a great strain upon effective doctor-patient relationships, particularly if the old person, as so many are, happened to be at all inclined toward suspiciousness.

Effects of Personal Attitudes on Social Acceptance

It has already been indicated that social changes are dependent in large part upon the changes which take place within the aging individual—physical, intellectual, and emotional changes—as well as upon the situation or environment in which he finds himself. It is the individual's reaction to the disruption of his habit patterns brought about by the change in environmental pressures which is important, and this reaction will, of course, depend upon his physical, intellectual, and emotional state. For example, the bright individual who is both physically and emotionally healthy will, when environmental pressures occasioned by his aging threaten to disturb the even tenor of his way, find opportunities for satisfying substitutes and leisure-time activities (49). Because he faces the problem realistically and does something constructive about it, the environmental pressures ease and his social adjustment proceeds smoothly. Others,

whose physical, intellectual, and emotional decline has advanced
more rapidly or who were maladjusted in the first place, will
react to the pressures in an unfavorable manner and strive to
keep control of the situation by whatever means seem possible
to them, with the result that they induce unfavorable reactions
in those around them and thus hasten the social decline. Many
of these persons can, however, respond to therapy and social
help (48).

The attitudes of the aging individual are most important—
the individual's attitude toward himself, toward growing old,
toward his family, toward social responsibility, activity (19),
and usefulness, toward loss of friends, and toward death. The
senescent's attitude toward the aging process and the meaning
of the symptoms of aging will depend to a large degree upon his
personal experiences in life and upon his cultural setting (59).
As we have already seen, emotional attitudes and habits of
living are long in developing. They are dependent in part upon
the innate personality makeup of the individual and in part upon
the environmental experiences to which he is subject (22). In
senescence these emotional attitudes are largely crystallized, so
that the individual will react to environmental change and stress
in accordance with his habitual pattern. As Diethelm (10) has
pointed out, insecurity develops when confidence in one's body,
earning power, and social desirability is shaken. If emotional
habits include facing problems realistically and seeking the best
solution possible under the circumstances, successful adjustment
to this insecurity will take place. On the other hand, when
emotional patterns of living have not been so healthy, the feelings of insecurity may lead to protective devices of various sorts
which further interfere with successful adjustment. One of the
most frequent reactions is anxiety expressed in somatic symptoms and apprehension concerning the future.

The aging individual's attitude toward himself and toward
his own personal aging will depend in part upon his self-concept
and in part upon the experiences he has had with the old and
with society's attitude toward the old. As mentioned previ-

ously, if he sets great store by his physical prowess and appearance or sees himself as a tycoon among men, he will be inclined to view his aging with alarm and distress because he does not see the worth of other values which might be developed in the period of later maturity. Likewise, if in his experience he has found old persons to be dependent, cantankerous, demanding, domineering, and given to constant illness or has seen them ignored, neglected, or relegated to an inconspicuous corner with their opinions despised or ridiculed or observed the burden and nuisance they are so often considered, he may view with fear and anxiety what appears to be his own approach to this state. On the other hand, if he views himself as a maturing individual whose declines are a normal and inevitable part of life but who can compensate in other ways for the losses he cannot avoid, he may be able to see the period of later maturity as another adventure in life. Also, if he has known charming, active, peaceful old people who have been well regarded and loved by their families and associates, he will be more inclined to accept with equanimity the approach of this period in his own life.

The aging person who has maintained healthy family relationships throughout his life will find old age easier to accept than the one whose family relationships have been unhealthy or destructive. The person who has always dominated his family and prevented his children from emancipating themselves in the normal manner may, when he sees his power waning, strive by various and devious ways to maintain control, often using illness, threats, temper outbursts, and bids for sympathy in his efforts to keep his place as leader and head of the household. Likewise, as we have already discussed, if he never succeeded in resolving his own conflicts in regard to his feelings toward his own parents or siblings (26), he may reactivate the early destructive, hostile feelings toward them in his behavior toward his offspring when the parent-child relationship is reversed. Sometimes real damage and destruction of family life can be brought about by an unhappy, maladjusted old person. Conversely, the aging individual who has lived with his family in mutual respect and affection, who has permitted his offspring to mature as individuals in their own right, and who has maintained his own emotional independence will, in all probability, continue to function happily within his family group as old age approaches.

Acceptance of Responsibility.—The acceptance of responsibility and usefulness to society as part of the duty and privilege of every individual, and something which will vary in character with the age of the person, will aid adjustment to the aging process, provided, of course, that the oldster is given the opportunity to exercise this privilege. There must be, though, an understanding of one's changing role in the matter of responsibility and usefulness as one grows older. As childhood is not expected to be the time of major social and economic responsibility for the family, so also old age should not be expected to assume these major responsibilities. The amount of responsibility which can be expected of the old person will vary with the individual, being dependent upon his physical, intellectual, and emotional capacity. It must be recognized that some can continue until death with full responsibility not only for themselves but for other members of the family as well, whereas others can do little more than take responsibility for the care of themselves. Whatever the individual's capacities may be, the social responsibility of being pleasant enough to live with and of contributing something to the happiness of other members of the family should be accepted.

Loneliness.—Loss of friends is inescapable as one grows older and contemporaries die. To miss these friends and to mourn their loss is normal, but rather than become depressed by seeing in it his own early demise, the person who would age successfully will combat his loneliness by having many friends and being ever ready to make new ones.

The attitude toward death tends to become philosophical as one grows older, but many older persons carry with them not only the fear of death itself (18), but also the fear of what will happen, after their death, to the responsibilities they carry now. They worry about what will happen to their families for whom they may not have provided sufficiently, whether there will be enough money to bury them, and whether they will have a long period of suffering before death finally releases them. These anxieties naturally do not lend themselves to successful aging and smooth social living.

Loss of Social Interests.—Attitudes in general seem to become less social as age advances. Interests tend to become narrow and to center around the self. The aging individual tends to become self-centered and introspective and to live in the past. He shows a return to childhood concepts (9). A certain amount of this can be normal and not troublesome, but too much can result in constant reminiscence, an inability to live in the present and look to the future, and a withdrawal from society. The concept of time and its importance then seems to change markedly. There is also a demand for quiet that makes it very difficult for the aging to live amicably with children and young adults. The interests having turned inward toward one's self, there is a reduced tendency to consider the interests of others. These attitudes, however, can and should be combated, and they are reversible to a large extent.

Both the attitudes and the needs of aging persons vary with the individual. Most prefer to live alone and not with their offspring. They also have a desire to be independent and to manage their own affairs. Illustrations of the attitudes of older persons at different cultural levels can be seen in the studies by Morgan (33) and Gardiner (20).

Morgan studied the attitudes and adjustment of persons receiving old age assistance in upstate and metropolitan New York. Although this study was completed prior to the outbreak of the second World War, there is reason to believe that the findings would hold true for similar groups today. Morgan did an interview study of 381 men and women from seventy to over ninety years of age and found individual differences related to cultural, economic, and educational levels and to sex. She found the following factors associated with good adjustment and happiness in old age: (*a*) good health and freedom from physical disabilities, and this seemed to be more important to the men than to the women; (*b*) next in importance were pleasant social and emotional relations with friends and family, and social life and contacts held more significance for the women than for the men; (*c*) hobbies and outside interests were also found to be important to successful adjustment, and Morgan felt in this connection that adult education offers possibilities for creative interests. Most old people too felt the need of the quiet, privacy, and independence of action provided by living in their own homes, although this was more important to those of American birth than to those born in Europe, who seemed to desire a closer family solidarity. To force many old persons to live with their offspring aggravated family maladjustment. Some form of work or useful activity, not merely a recreational hobby, was deemed most important to those groups of American culture, although not quite so significant for those of European culture. Morgan concluded that aging individuals need independence, a certain amount of power and authority, and suitable activities to fill their hours. She also noted that the differences in attitudes reflected the cultural differences in values relative to family life, economic independence, and individualism.

Gardiner, in studying the attitudes and activities of the middle-aged and the aged, apparently chose a group culturally and economically superior to Morgan's group, as 64 per cent of her group were either partially or wholly independent economically. She interviewed 193 individuals between the ages of sixty and 102 regarding their attitudes and activities. Four fifths of these individuals lived with relatives and reported strong social interests, although two thirds or more spontaneously remarked that they felt unwanted and in the way. Most stated that they were happy, but their happiness bore a strong positive relationship to their economic independence. Health was generally good, but many talked about medicines and their aches and pains. Most felt their dispositions had remained unchanged but admitted that their worst faults were irritability and quick temper and reported that family criticism dealt largely with their interference in family affairs and their personal habits. Most indulged in some daydreaming about the past, but their best-liked activities were visiting, reading, and listening to the radio.

Other studies seem to indicate that those of higher socio-economic status are better adjusted and more dependent upon themselves for leisure-time activities whereas those of lower socioeconomic status tend to depend upon others for their leisure-time satisfactions. The majority of the aging do not look forward to retirement, and those who do look forward to it with pleasure do so because they are planning more pleasurable activities, the use of skills already acquired, and the gratification of other interests (5).

Interest in the Church

Interest in the church varies with the individual in later maturity, as it does in other periods of life (31). It also varies with the cultural setting and with the religious training and habits which have been built up throughout life. With some groups there is a lessened interest with advancing age and a tendency to develop a fatalistic attitude toward aging, death, and dying. Nature seems to be kind in the matter of death, and it has been observed by many that most persons die without fear. Their senses become dulled, and suffering is really not felt. With others, however, there is a heightened interest in the church and in religious activities. Many aging persons, in striving to achieve peace of mind, become more interested in the life hereafter and in developing a philosophy of living and dying. For them, death is often seen as bringing with it a rebirth wherein a new life is begun. Death then becomes not only more tolerable but something to be looked forward to, since it is envisioned as the beginning of a more perfect future life.

There is some indication that the greater the degree of religious adherence in old age, the better is the apparent adjustment (38). However, despite lessened or heightened interest in the church, there is certainly a wide field for pastoral work with the aged. Looking at the situation realistically, we know that in many cases the environment in which he lives makes it impossible for the aging person to achieve normal emotional and social satisfactions. Pastoral work here, in addition to its spiritual value, can do much to alleviate stress by dealing directly with the aging person and with those with whom he lives, helping both to develop healthier attitudes and a better relationship and giving the oldster something to look forward to. Group activities within the church setting can also do much to help the successful adjustment of the aging individual by providing him with suitable, useful, and interesting activities and giving him an opportunity to meet with congenial contemporaries and thus feel accepted, wanted, and useful.

Social Maturity and Deterioration

In discussing social changes and adjustment with advancing age, it is important to know something about the level of social maturity of the individual and also whether and to what extent he has deteriorated socially. Lillien Martin (30), the real pioneer in the field of rehabilitation of the aged, used two qualitative measures of social deterioration, as she felt that knowledge in this area was prerequisite to the beginning of rehabilitation of the individual. The first of these, Fernald's Ethics Test, consists of a list of misdeeds, and the subject must grade the offenses listed from greatest to least according to their seriousness. According to Martin, this "gives quick and decisive knowledge of the subject's sense of values, of his attitudes toward himself and the community." The second is a test of suggestibility devised by Martin herself. It consists of a simple, highly colored picture on the back of which are twenty questions devised to challenge the observations of the subject and intended to determine the stability of his views when another person attempts to influence him. Martin felt that the individual's defensive attitude could be seen either in his indiscriminate acceptance or indiscriminate rejection of every suggestion. Although she found that the old generally did poorly on both these tests, she felt that the responses they gave provided invaluable information concerning the aging person's social deterioration and the direction of his social inadequacies.

The Vineland Social Maturity Test, devised by Doll, has been given to both normal and feeble-minded adults of all ages. The results show marked individual differences, some individuals increasing in social maturity between the ages of twenty-five and fifty and showing little appreciable loss to the age of eighty, some (both normal and feeble-minded) staying the same throughout these years, and some declining gradually but steadily in their social competence with advancing age. Doll in a preliminary study in this area concludes, "Since social competency is a function of mental and physical integrity (we might add emotional integrity), we need not be surprised that the present exploratory study suggests that decline in social effectiveness is related to the later years chiefly as such decline reflects waning vigor" (11).

Cavan and her coworkers (3) have developed an Attitude Inventory and an Activity Inventory for the study of persons past sixty years of age, the aim of the inventories being to secure data on the attitudes and activities of this group in areas such as health, family, friends, work, and economic security. Several thousand persons have been studied by means of these questionnaires, and some of the trends found with age include increased feelings of economic security in spite of lowered income, an increase in religious activities and dependence on religion, and a decrease in feelings of happiness, usefulness, zest, and interest in life. In general, women tended to feel somewhat more secure than men economically and to have more religious activities and interests but to report more physical symptoms and to be less happy.

Criminality Among the Aged

Evidence of social deterioration and maladjustment can be seen in the relatively high incidence of first offenders among those criminals who are fifty years of age and over (41, 42). Sex crimes against children are the most common offenses, and these are generally committed without violence and with a lack of foresight. Criminality in this group is more prevalent among men than women, among Negroes than whites, and among those who are alone in the world than those whose marriages are unbroken. These facts again emphasize the importance of the lack of personal satisfactions in an unsympathetic society in creating social maladjustment and deterioration.

Adjustment then can be considered as the degree of integration or imbalance between the satisfaction of personal needs and the meeting of society's demands. Although there is considerable imbalance and consequent maladjustment among the aged (13), there are many older persons who achieve and maintain integration and are well adjusted. For example, in a study of 533 middle-class normal and problem old people, Pressey and Simcoe (45) found many well-adjusted individuals and considered their success to be due to their many interests and activities and to their continued usefulness to others. They noted that the successful aged had developed a sound philosophy of life and a related mellow quality of character. They feel that successful adjustment among the aged can be helped by the development of abilities, interests, and friendships, all of which can be facilitated by means of workshops, clubs, and other recreational outlets.

Old Age and Family Relations

The emotional aspects of the oldster's family relations have already been discussed in Chapter 3. *Success and happiness in life* with advancing age depend upon both inner and outer resources—the inner resources of the individual and the outer resources of his environment (2). The inner resources of the individual will be present as a result of habits and patterns of thinking and feeling which have been built up throughout life, and these will undoubtedly affect the attitudes of others and the resources found in the environment. In like manner, the resources of the environment will influence the inner resources and attitudes of the individual. The character of the aging person's dependencies and hostilities will determine how well he can adjust to other persons, and particularly to those within the family group. Probably everyone has emotional dependencies, but when these are used destructively in such a way as to prevent the normal growth and living of the individual himself or those around him, they cease to be within normal limits. Also, those hostilities which the individual has never been able to work through may prove most destructive to a healthy family relationship. With sufficient pressure from healthy resources of the environment, the effect of these dependencies and hostilities may be minimized or lessened (44), but even with skilled help, they cannot be eliminated save through the efforts of the individual himself. Contrariwise, undesirable tendencies can be intensified and even healthy inner resources stifled by a destructive environment. Successful family living involves a healthy, emotionally satisfying environment and sufficient resources within the aging individual to make effective uses of the outer resources which are available (35). For happiness in living, there must be a re-evaluation of the roles of young and old in the household and mutual tolerance (3). Each must recognize that the other has rights of his own and habits, attitudes, interests, and abilities which vary with age and the individual, and each must be ready to accept these in the other. There are, however, certain environmental and personal difficulties which make the aging person's adjustment to family life difficult for him and for those with whom he lives.

Questions of money and space, for example, are most important in present-day living. Less than a third of the aged are self-supporting at the present time, and in times of depression when jobs are scarcer the number is even less. This creates a dependency upon offspring often distasteful to both the parent and the offspring (47). The loss of prestige and the feelings of uselessness, inadequacy, and inferiority which this dependency causes are often traumatic for the aging person. The necessity which forces him to be in this position and to relinquish his former role of leader may arouse resentment in him which results in hostile, aggressive reactions toward the members of his family. These reactions will be intensified if he feels that those around him resent his dependency, begrudge the things they must do and get for him, exclude him from their activities, or do not want him. The result, of course, will be further rejection until the situation becomes unbearable for everybody.

The problem of living space is often acute, particularly in congested areas, and crowded living quarters are especially difficult when three generations must live together. In the country, on a farm, or in a large house, three generations can sometimes live together without too much stress and strain, because there is enough space so that each one can have some independence of action without getting too much in the way of the rest. On the other hand, in a city apartment where one extra person constitutes overcrowding and an extra room costs a great deal, the situation can be not only difficult but intolerable unless all persons are well adjusted and considerate. The idle oldster who seems to be always under foot and who, for want of something better to do, constantly complains of his aches and pains, the children's behavior, and the evils of the present generation can make life very unpleasant for those around him. Then too, he himself can be unhappy and hence become difficult when he has no privacy, no place to keep his own things, no place to entertain his friends, and nothing to do. As previously discussed, it would seem that no matter how small his home may be, the old person is better off if he can have a place of his own. It may be a place entirely apart from his family or it may be in the same household, but it should be a place where he can have privacy and entertain his friends. He also needs something to do—something useful and interesting which will make him feel that he is a part of the life around him. When individual roles, duties, rights, and privileges in a three-generation family are clearly understood, adjustment is facilitated and life tends to run more smoothly.

Personal Changes and Family Living

Personal difficulties and peculiarities of the aging person sometimes make adjustment to family life hard to achieve. Personality differences are inevitable in any group, and these differences are more likely to lead to clashes when individuals live together in such close quarters that they are forced to be in constant contact with each other. We know that earlier personality difficulties tend to become more evident with advancing age, perhaps because of the personal rigidity and the tensions and frustrations that accompany the aging process, and they may loom ever more important as one has less and less chance of getting away from them. Much of the satisfying or unhappy family relationship with an aging person in the home will depend, of course, upon the psychological ties which have been built up earlier in life. If there is a genuine bond of affection which is not stifling or selfish on either side and mutual respect exists, the relationships will probably be healthy and satisfying alike to young and old. If, on the other hand, there is too much emotional dependency on one side or the other or there are resentments, either on the part of the young because of having the burden of an aging parent to carry or on the part of the oldster because of his enforced dependency and feeling of being unwelcome, relationships will no doubt be strained.

As mentioned previously, the loss of power and an enforced dependency role (15) are often very difficult for an aging person to accept, especially if he has once held a position he considers important or has at one time held despotic authority over his children. He may then try desperately and by various and devious means to maintain or regain his power and to assert his independence. If he has newly come to live in the home of his son or daughter, he may immediately try to assume the role of head of the house, his position when his offspring were children. He will not accept the fact that they are now adults and no longer subject to his domination and even though he may be dependent upon them for his living, he will still try to exert his authority and tell them what to do, how to raise their children, and how to run their affairs. Naturally this creates friction, especially if the younger persons in the household have insufficient tact and understanding to do anything constructive about the situation. A situation of this sort needs patience on the part of the younger ones and efforts to give the oldster a greater feeling of emotional security and more satisfying, ego-building activities. If the offspring can understand the feelings of the aging parent and try to make him feel wanted and important, he will have less need to assert his authority and independence and to show hostility and resentment. As we have already seen, sometimes the conflict over the dependency role may result in a reactivation of the oldster's own unhealthy attitudes toward his own parents. This is a very difficult problem to deal with, and one which requires more than just understanding on the part of the offspring; the oldster himself needs help in understanding his own behavior and in clarifying his own feelings. This is particularly true in certain cultural groups. For example, often among some Jewish groups in certain parts of the world the aged father finds it impossible to accept the dependency role with his offspring, even though the relationship may always have been bound by affectionate ties. He may prefer to go to an institution for the aged and accept the charity of strangers rather than to take the beneficence of his son, who may not only be able to afford it but also desirous of rendering it (24).

Carelessness and Untidy Habits.—Young persons often complain of the carelessness and untidy habits of some of the aged. Obviously, this is not universal, but neither is it rare. Many old persons do not like things changed and will resist having the furniture moved or their things disturbed for cleaning. Having insufficient present satisfactions, they hoard useless bits of things which have some meaning for them, usually some remembrance of a pleasant past, and will resent any suggestion that they "get rid of the junk" or put it away where it won't collect so much dust. Some old persons do not bathe or change their clothes often enough, so that there is about them an unpleasant odor which is the source of much embarrassment to other members of the household, particularly if one of them happens to be a young adolescent. This situation can be compared with that of the youngster who refuses to wash as a form of resistance to his family. The extremes of this kind can sometimes be seen in senile psychotics. One such nonagenarian known to the writer became so upset whenever her daughter attempted to clean her room or wash her clothes that she finally retired to her room and refused her daughter admittance. She would not emerge for toileting or for meals and opened her door only long enough to get the food her daughter placed outside. She would not wash, refused the use of toilet facilities, and wrapped her feces in bits of paper and secreted the little parcels in various parts of the room. Finally, the stench from her room pervaded the whole house and became so unbearable that the daughter was forced to take steps to have her removed from the house to an institution. Every now and then, we read about an aged hermit whose death brings the revelation that his home is a veritable junk pile. These tendencies can be a great trial to young persons who must live in the same household. Unless they are halted in their very beginnings, it seems almost impossible to do much about them. Even in the beginning it requires much tact, patience, and firmness to deal with the problem adequately. The practical aspects of the problem must also be taken into consideration, particularly the physical effort it takes to bathe regularly and the fact that some old persons do not take baths because it is difficult for them to get into and out of a bathtub and they fear falling and hurting themselves. A little praise for pleasant appearance and a few new clothes will often prove to be of tremendous help.

We have already mentioned the tendency to hoard things and its emotional implications, and this tendency is usually present when there seems to be little left of value in life, so that mementos serve as reminders of things that were once gratifying. The inclination to mislay and to lose things is closely allied to this hoarding drive. Sometimes the old are so certain that someone has stolen their treasures that they treat other members of the household with a thinly veiled suspicion or make open accusations. In either case, the results are strained family relationships.

Interference in Others' Affairs.—Younger folks also complain frequently that the aging person in the home is troublesome and interfering. They say that he finds fault constantly and is always interfering with the running of the household and the raising of the children, that he either spoils or nags his grandchildren, that he criticizes their friends, etc. These things, of course, are not conducive to harmony within the home, but if the younger persons can understand that by these reactions the oldster is merely trying to hold or to regain his former role of importance and leadership, they may be able to cope more adequately with the problem. If they try to make him feel that he is an important member of the household and that his opinion is sought because of its value and wisdom, they will usually experience less fault-finding, criticism, and interference.

The presence of foreign-born grandparents in the home sometimes creates a problem in the American culture. In a culture where English is the accepted language and it is not commonplace to be fluent in other languages, children growing up often view with disfavor someone in the family who speaks only a foreign tongue. Sometimes, through unhealthy attitudes and influences, children become ashamed of the language of their forebears and refuse to speak it, losing the knowledge of it they once had. The ultimate result of this is that we may find persons in the same household and of the same family who actually are unable to communicate with each other adequately, since neither knows the language of the other. This situation is aggravated by the tendency of the aging increasingly to use their original mother tongue and sometimes to forget completely the other languages they learned as adults. Naturally this breeds misunderstanding and discontent. The cultural differences too are often so wide that it is difficult for persons of considerable disparity of age to understand one another even when they speak the same language; when they cannot speak the same language, it is practically impossible to hope for a common ground of understanding. The aging person who comes from a foreign land where the culture is rigid often finds it hard to understand the apparently free and easy standards of Americans and is inclined to view with alarm certain behavior which we consider quite normal. The younger folk, of course, will not accept the old country's rigid standards of many decades ago and insist on doing the same things other youngsters do, with the result that the old person becomes worried, critical, and full of dire predictions regarding the future of the younger generation and, in particular, the younger generation of his family. The conflict has begun! Of course, this situation does not always hold, for it is frequently found that the third generation may actually be less rejecting of the foreign culture than the second generation. The result then may be a banding of the first and third generations against the second generation, with considerable conflict between the two groups.

The curiosity of many aging persons is another trait which often makes family living a trial. Curiosity is a normal trait in itself and one which is basic to the acquisition of knowledge and the conducting of research; but when it is excessive and directed toward individuals and private affairs, it can become irksome. This is what happens in the case of many aging persons who have nothing else to occupy their minds. Having no affairs of their own, they may become concerned with the affairs of those around them, want to know all about everything that goes on, and feel they must play some part in everything that happens. When they know they are not told everything, they may become suspicious and feel that things are being deliberately hidden from them for some important secret reason, usually an unfavorable one. Sometimes they fill in the gaps in their knowledge with fabrications which may distort the whole picture. Generally, in instances of this sort, the tale is filled with the teller's suspicions of wickedness or sin. Curiosity of this sort leads to gossip, and, as we have already seen, this gossip usually reflects the intrinsic desires of the teller projected onto someone else's life screen. This tendency, of course, can be minimized when the aging person has more interesting things to occupy his time and mind or can be induced to redirect his curiosity into more constructive channels.

One mistaken kindness on the part of offspring which often leads to conflict and unhappy family relationships is the coddling of aging parents (17). Often in the spirit of gratitude for all that has been done for them, young offspring will decide to take Papa and Mama into their home and see that they "have a well-earned rest and a life of ease." Papa must retire, for there is no longer any need for him to work; he must not tend the furnace or take out the ashes, for that work is too hard for him; he must just rest and take it easy and have fun. Mama has done housework all her life, so she shall have no more of that; she must no longer clean, wash, iron, or cook; she must just take it easy and rest. Of course, this gives Papa and Mama no independence, nothing to do and no interests, with the result that dissatisfaction soon becomes evident. Papa and Mama become irritable, cantankerous, and hard to please, and the loving offspring wonder how their parents can be that way when so much is being done for them, so much to make them happy. This kind of treatment of parents shows a complete lack of understanding of the normal aging process and of the emotional needs of older persons, particularly, the need to feel useful. After a busy and useful life, older persons feel lost and useless when they have nothing to do, no interests and constructive activities to occupy their time and minds. /The author has heard many normal, healthy, elderly women living in apparent harmony with loving relatives tell how they would love to be permitted to do a little work around the house and to cook a meal once in a while. They express feelings of uselessness because of not being permitted to do any of the things they have done all their lives and show resentment at being relegated to the scrap heap while they are still healthy and alert. The same situation obtains with men.

Loss of the Marital Partner

Loss of the marital partner is often traumatic for the aging person and creates difficulties for him as he tries to adjust to a new kind of family life. When two persons have lived together for many years, they get used to each other's ways, habits, and peculiarities and make some kind of mutual adjustment to them. The habit of living together is so strong that often, regardless of the depth of affection, the one partner will feel an irreparable loss when the other has died. If the relationship between the two was good, the loss will be more keenly felt, and much substitution of interests will be necessary if the remaining partner is to effect any kind of satisfactory life adjustment. In some instances, the surviving spouse may idealize the deceased, withdraw into isolation, and become hostile toward relatives and friends (56). Another may tend to cling more to his offspring and others around him and to depend too much on them emotionally, which, of course, may prove to be emotionally unhealthy for both parent and offspring. Many aging persons who knew happiness in their marital life will soon seek another partner after their dear one has died, and this should be encouraged rather than discouraged, for probably in this way the aging widow or widower can find the greatest happiness and contentment.

On the other hand, if the marital relationship was bad, the remaining partner may take out on others the hostilities he formerly vented on his partner. If he has been fighting all his life, the habit is probably so strong that he will continue fighting even when he no longer has the need to do so. His hostilities, aggressions, and resentments, which he has carried for so long, will probably not be dispelled by the mere fact of the death of the one toward whom he expressed these feelings. They will in all probability be redirected toward someone else in the environment, usually someone with whom he identifies his deceased partner.

Obviously then, in the adjustment of the aging person to a new family life there are many hazards and difficulties to be overcome. Many cannot manage these, so that unhappiness and disruption of family life result; many, however, can and do surmount the obstacles to successful family living and manage to adjust happily to social life within the family group.

Social Implications of Employment and Retirement

Employment and retirement constitute one of the most serious problems of an aging population (37). The common practice of retiring persons who reach the age of sixty or sixty-five years, regardless of the desires of the individual and without consideration of his health, abilities, or capacity for work, is destructive not only to the aging person (25) but to society as a whole. There may be some persons who are ready to retire before reaching the sixties, but there are many others who are physically, mentally, and emotionally capable of continuing work for years beyond the usual retirement age and are most desirous of doing so. The war years alone showed how useful these older persons can be and what a sad waste of manpower it is to discard them on the basis of age alone. Individual differences in aging are too wide to permit us to believe that, on the basis of chronological age alone, one person is fit to work and another to retire. Also, in view of the fact that the very brightest tend to decline at a somewhat slower rate than others, it seems to be particularly unfortunate and wasteful that many professional positions carry automatic age retirement plans. In addition to the economic waste involved in not making effective use of potentialities, there is also the economic problem to the individual himself. After being forced to attend school until well into adulthood and to educate his children in the same manner, he has hardly time to get on his feet financially before he is forced to retire. There has been so little time to put away enough money to look after himself and his wife in old age that he usually finds it necessary on retirement to be either partially or fully dependent upon his offspring. It has been estimated that, unless something is done about the economic aspects of this situation, we may soon find that every employed person in middle life will have, in addition to his own dependents, one additional dependent of sixty-five years of age or more.

According to Clague (6), while there has been an increase of total life expectancy, there has been no corresponding increase in the working life span of the individual. In 1900 the age of retirement and the end of the life span were closer together, so that an average of only three years was spent outside the labor force. In 1940 the discrepancy had risen to five and a half years; and it is estimated that by 1970, if the same trend continues, aging persons, male and female, will average ten years outside the labor force. These figures point out clearly the need of an extension of the working life in order to ease the economic burden of dependency.

It is the biologic and social duty of the individual to work as long as he is physically and mentally able to do so. All evidence points to the fact that the potentialities for the usefulness of the aging population have been greatly underestimated. The aged can produce much and should not only be permitted but encouraged to do so. Many can continue adequately at their own jobs, and many can serve effectively at other full-time or part-time jobs. When one considers the war record of the aged in industry and the many outstanding accomplishments of senescents, the answer is obvious : let everyone work as long as he wants to and as long as he is capable.

Employers tend to reject aging persons for employment for many reasons, personal and economic, real and imagined. The economic reasons offered against employment of older personnel include the expense of pensions and compensation. It is true that it might prove a heavy burden to provide pensions for the old who might be employed by a firm for only a few years. The matter of compensation is controversial, for although it is true that the older employees tend to have fewer accidents, it is also true that it generally takes them longer to recover from the accidents they do have.

Employers also claim that they want to make way for the younger persons and that the old do not work as well—that they learn and perform more slowly, that they get in a rut, and that they resist changes, new ideas, and new methods. In normal times when there is an overcrowding of certain fields of employment, it is the old and the incompetent who are discarded first.

Employers also complain about the appearance of older employees—that they are personally careless, dowdy, and unattractive. They insist, too, that they are trouble-makers, too personal in their reactions, intolerant, cantankerous, bossy, and lacking in initiative. There is some truth in these accusations, and the aging person who would continue effectively at his chosen work must guard against the development of these undesirable characteristics of personality.

On the other hand, the older employee offers many advantages to his employer. On the whole, the older employee is more stable, loyal, conscientious, and devoted to his job. Because of his long experience in a job, he often shows better judgment, wisdom, and strategy in his work (57). Also, he generally has more patience and control in emergencies. In industrial work it has been found that among the older employees there is less turnover, absenteeism, breakage and spoilage of material, fewer accidents, and fewer outside distractions, than found in the younger employees.

Retirement from a job to nothing contributes to biologic parasitism and to degeneration of human society. It is a waste of good manpower and a drain on society, both of which are indefensible. To take a biologically sound specimen of humanity, discard him solely because he has lived a certain number of years, and then provide him with no way to sustain or to occupy himself makes him an unhappy parasite, resented by the very society which forced him into the burdensome position of dependency.

Retirement to another activity, however, may be beneficial both to the individual and to society (29). The majority of aging persons both want and need activity, useful activity which will keep them occupied and interested, and this seems to bring them greater satisfaction than do their relationships with their children and grandchildren. Hobbies are important in the period of later maturity, particularly hobbies of a creative nature. These may be lucrative or nonlucrative, although it is usually better if they can be lucrative, since this tends to give the older person a greater feeling of security and importance.

In general, we might say that work and activity are important in all periods of life, and that the period of later maturity is no exception to this. Older persons should not be retired on the basis of chronological age alone but rather on the basis of their desires, abilities, and usefulness. Every person who thinks of retirement should plan to retire to something rather than just to retire from a job, for useful activity is important as long as one lives. As shown by the "Fossils," a rather selective group of retired government and professional men in Washington, good adjustment can be achieved in retirement, although much of this will be dependent upon financial security, late retirement, and good living arrangements (23).

Financial Provision for the Aged

The dependency of the majority of the old has already been mentioned. Investigations show that most persons have not sufficient resources to support themselves entirely in their old age; either they have spent all their money, or they have lost their savings, or their savings did not last, or are not enough to support them. Fortunately, efforts are being made to ease the situation. In January, 1952, it was estimated that 62.3 million persons in the United States were covered by federal old age and survivor's insurance (60). Nevertheless, this leaves a considerable number of persons still unprovided with this protection.

Federal Social Security Payments.—Old age insurance payments under social security vary with the size of the original income up to a yearly income of $3,600, but the recipients of these benefits are permitted to earn no more than $75.00 a month in wages (as of September, 1952). This is payable at the age of sixty-five years, and a wife may receive two thirds of her husband's benefits in the event of his death, provided she has reached the age of sixty-five. The average amount paid in January, 1952, was $42.00 a month.

Old Age Assistance.—Old age assistance varies with the state and community, and on this some old people fare relatively better. In New York City through the Department of Welfare, employed men and women requiring supplementary aid may receive the difference between the income and the estimated budget, have their rent paid according to housing needs, and have special care or housekeeping services if these are necessary. Unemployed and incapacitated persons may receive the full estimated budget. However, the recipient must let the Department of Welfare take a lien on all valuable assets, with the exception of $250.00 insurance. Elsewhere, allowances are less generous, so that the amount received on old age assistance in 1950 averaged only $44.50 a month for all the states (60).

This is pathetic when we consider all the money which is spent for wars and the fact that under Point 4 of the Marshall Plan we are endeavoring to develop the backward areas of the world. The recipients of these inadequate sums obviously must live with relatives or receive supplementary aid from somewhere. In spite of this, many of the old in low-income groups who receive these allowances do adjust satisfactorily. According to one study (50), their good adjustment is based primarily upon their family relationships, health, leisure-time activities, religion, and self-concepts.

Because of the inability of most old persons to maintain their own homes in their accustomed manner, various plans have been tried out to provide more satisfactory living conditions for them. Of course, the most common plan is to place them in the homes of relatives when this is possible. However, as it is not always possible or desirable, other plans must frequently be considered. Sometimes, when the aged person's problem is mainly one of health, he may be kept in his own home and provided with a housekeeper to look after him, a plan that has proved satisfactory in some instances. In other circumstances, particularly when family adjustments have not been good, institutionalization may be necessary. This institutionalization may have either a deleterious or an ameliorative effect upon the oldster's adjustment (39, 40).

Summary

Social changes found in the aging population are part of the aging process of the individual and inextricably bound with his physical, intellectual, and emotional decline.

Treatment of the aged varies with different cultures. It would seem that, although civilization has added more years to life, it has done little to make these years worth living. There may be an enforced change of attitude, however, as social and economic problems increase with increase in the number of the aged.

Social changes are dependent in large part upon the changes

which take place within the individual—changes which are responsible for his reaction to environmental pressures.

The aging individual's attitudes are important to his social adjustment—his attitudes toward his own aging, his family, his social responsibility and usefulness, loss of friends, and death. These, of course, are dependent upon his experiences in life and the changes which are taking place within himself.

Needs vary with the individual, but most aging persons prefer to live alone, to be independent, and to manage their own affairs.

Interest in religion varies with the individual and his culture, but there are some indications that the greater the degree of religious adherence in old age, the better the adjustment.

Although there are many unhappy, maladjusted old people, there are also many who are socially well adjusted. Attempts to measure social adjustment and deterioration have been made by means of Doll's Social Maturity Test, Fernald's Ethics Test, Martin's Test of Suggestibility, and the Attitude and Activity Inventories developed by Cavan and a group of collaborators.

A large part of the social adjustment of later years involves adjustment to family life, and this, in turn, depends upon the inner resources of the individual, the outer resources of his environment, and the character of his dependencies and hostilities.

Living space and the financial resources of the family are important determinants of the success or failure of family living. Dependency on offspring usually brings about in the aging person feelings of inferiority, uselessness, inadequacy, a loss of prestige, and resentment. Offspring likewise often show resentment and hostility over the dependency and the enforced cramped living.

Personal difficulties of the aging person and personality clashes between old and young are more frequent when the two must live in too close quarters and when unhealthy ties have been formed earlier in life.

Personal difficulties of the aged which often create clashes are resentment of the dependency role and the reversal of parent-child relationships, carelessness and untidy habits, hoarding, mislaying or losing things and then blaming others for it, general troublesomeness and interference in family affairs, language and cultural differences when grandparents are foreign-born, curiosity, and gossiping.

Coddling the aging person breeds dissatisfaction because it deprives him of needed activities and interests.

Adjustment to the loss of the marital partner is difficult for the aging person and may result in a projection of the feeling once held for the spouse onto another person or persons in the environment.

Employment and retirement of aging persons constitute a serious social and economic problem, for the working life has not kept pace with the increase of the total life span. Enforced retirement is a social blow to the individual and an economic burden to those who must support him in those years when he is not permitted to work.

It is a biologic and social duty to work as long as possible, and there is no doubt that the potentialities for work of the aged have been grossly underestimated.

In spite of the opinion of many employers, there is evidence for the view that to the employer the advantages of employing older persons outweigh the disadvantages.

Retirement should be *to* an activity, lucrative or not, for retirement *from* activity leads to vegetation.

Social care of the aged includes provision for their support by means of insurance, pensions, and old age assistance, all of which are inadequate. Relatively few are completely self-supporting.

REFERENCES

1. *Birthdays don't count.* State of New York: Joint Legislative Committee on Problems of the Aging. Leg. Doc. No. 61, 1948.
2. CAVAN, R. S. Family life and family substitutes in old age. *Amer. sociol. Rev.*, 1949, **14**, 71-83.

3. CAVAN, R. S., BURGESS, E. W., HAVIGHURST, R. J., and GOLDHAMMER, H. *Personal adjustment in old age*. Chicago: Science Research Associates, 1949.

4. CHANDLER, A. R. The traditional Chinese attitude toward old age. *J. Geron.*, 1949, 4, 239-44.

5. ——. Attitudes of superior groups toward retirement and old age. *J. Geron.*, 1950, 5, 254-61.

6. CLAGUE, E. The working life span of American workers. *J. Geron.*, 1949, 4, 285-89.

7. *Conference on social treatment of the older person.* New York: New York School of Social Work, 1947.

8. DAVIS, K., and COOMBS, J. W., JR. The sociology of an aging population. In New York Academy of Medicine, *The social and biological challenge of our aging population*. New York: The Academy, 1950.

9. DENNIS, W., and MALLINGER, B. Animism and related tendencies in senescence. *J. Geron.*, 1949, 4, 218-21.

10. DIETHELM, O. The aging person: psychological and psychopathological aspects of aging. *N.C. med. J.*, 1944, 5, 583-85.

11. DOLL, E. A. Measurement of social maturity applied to older people. In *Mental health in later maturity*. Publ. Hlth. Rep., Wash., 1942, No. 168. Pp. 138-45.

12. DONAHUE, W., and TIBBITTS, C. (eds.), *Planning the older years*. Ann Arbor, Mich.: University of Michigan Press, 1950.

13. DUNHAM, H. W. Sociological aspects of mental disorders in later life. In KAPLAN, O. (ed.), *Mental disorders in later life*. Stanford, Calif.: Stanford University Press, 1945.

14. EATON, J. W., and PLAUT, T. Social factors in the adjustment of the aged among the Hutterites. Paper delivered before 2d International Conference of Gerontology. Abstract in *J. Geron.*, 1951, 6, 82.

15. FISHER, G. Mental hygiene problems as they emerge in old age security. In Family Welfare Association of America, *Mental hygiene in old age*. New York: The Association, 1937. Pp. 27-31.

16. FOLSOM, J. K. Old age as a sociological problem. Discussion by LAWRENCE FRANK. *Amer. J. Orthopsychiat.*, 1940, 10, 30-42.

17. FOX, F. Family life and relationships as affected by the presence of the aged. In Family Welfare Association of America, *Mental hygiene in old age*. New York: The Association, 1937. Pp. 1-13.

18. FREUD, S. *Collected papers*. Vol. III. *Thoughts for the times on war and death* (1915). London: International Psychoanalytical Press, 1925.

19. FRIED, E. G. Attitudes of the older population groups toward activity and inactivity. *J. Geron.*, 1949, 4, 141-51.

20. GARDINER, L. P. Attitudes and activities of the middle-aged and aged. *Geriatrics*, 1949, 4, 33-50.

21. HAVIGHURST, R. J. Old age—an American problem. *J. Geron.*, 1949, 4, 298-304.

22. ——. Problems of sampling and interviewing in studies of old people. *J. Geron.*, 1950, 5, 158-67.

23. HAVIGHURST, R. J., and SHANAS, E. Adjustment and retirement. *Social Soc. Rev.*, 1950, 34, 169-76.

24. JOFFEY, N. S. Dynamics of benefits among East European Jews. *Social Forces*, 1949, 3, 238-47.

25. JOHNSON, W. M. Adjustments to age. *Med. Ann. Dist. Columbia,* 1948, **17,** 614-701.
26. LAVERTY, R. Supportive geriatric casework. *J. Geron.,* 1949, **4,** 152-56.
27. ———. Nonresident aid—community versus institutional care for older people. *J. Geron.,* 1950, **5,** 370-74.
28. LAWTON, G. (ed.). *New goals for old age.* New York: Columbia University Press, 1943.
29. ———. *Aging successfully.* New York: Columbia University Press, 1946.
30. MARTIN, L. J. *A handbook for old age counsellors.* San Francisco, Calif.: Geertz Printing Co., 1944.
31. MAVES, P. B., and CEDARLEAF, J. L. Older people and the church. Nashville, Tenn.: Abingdon-Cokesbury Press, 1949.
32. MECHNIKOV, E. *The prolongation of life.* Translated by P. C. Mitchell. New York: G. P. Putnam's Sons, 1908.
33. MORGAN, C. M. *The attitudes and adjustments of recipients of old age assistance in upstate and metropolitan New York.* Arch. Psychol., N.Y., 1937, No. 214.
34. *Never too old.* State of New York, Joint Legislative Committee on Problems of Aging. Leg. Doc. No. 32, 1949.
35. NOYES, H. The use of leisure time in the adjustment of older people. *Geriatrics,* 1950, **5,** 104-7.
36. OGBURN, W. F., and NIMKOFF, M. F. *Sociology.* Boston: Houghton Mifflin Co., 1946.
37. *Old people.* Report of a survey committee on the problems of aging and the care of old people. Published for the trustees of the Nuffield Foundation. London: Oxford University Press, 1949.
38. OLES, E. Religion in old age; a study of the possible influence of religious adherence on adjustment. Master's thesis, Psychology Department, Bucknell University, 1949.
39. PAN, JU-SHU. A study of the influence of institutionalization on the social adjustment of old people. *J. Geron.,* 1948, **3,** 276-80.
40. ———. Personal adjustment of old people in church homes for the aged. *Geriatrics,* 1950, **5,** 166-70.
41. POLLAK, O. The criminality of old age. *J. crim. Psychopath.,* 1941, **3,** 213-35.
42. ———. A statistical investigation of the criminality of old age. *J. crim. Psychopath.,* 1944, **5,** 745-67.
43. ———. *Social adjustment in old age: a research planning project.* Soc. Sci. Res. Council Bull., 1948, No. 59.
44. POWELL, A. S. The family welfare agency community planning for the aged. *Geriatrics,* 1950, **5,** 288-91.
45. PRESSEY, S. L., and SIMCOE, E. Case study comparison of successful and problem old people. *J. Geron.,* 1950, **5,** 168-75.
46. *Proceedings of the National Conference of Social Work,* 1948. New York: Columbia University Press, 1949. Pp. 381-430.
47. RABINOWITZ, P. Living arrangements. In TIBBITTS, C. (ed.), *Living through the older years.* Ann Arbor, Mich.: University of Michigan Press, 1949.
48. RANDALL, O. A. The essential partnership of medicine and social work. *Geriatrics,* 1950, **5,** 46-50.
49. SCHULZE, O. *Recreation for the aged. J. Geron.,* 1949, **4,** 310-14.

50. SHANAS, E. The personal adjustment of recipients of old age assistance. *J. Geron.*, 1950, **5**, 249-53.

51. SHELDON, J. H. *The social medicine of old age.* Published for the trustees of the Nuffield Foundation, London: Oxford University Press, 1948.

52. SIMMONS, L. W. *The role of the aged in primitive society.* New Haven, Conn.: Yale University Press, 1945.

53. ——. Attitudes toward aging and the aged: primitive societies. *J. Geron.*, 1946, **1**, 72-95.

54. ——. Old age security in other societies. *Geriatrics*, 1948, **3**, 237-44.

55. STEAD, W. H. Trends of employment in relation to the problems of the aging. *J. Geron.*, 1949, **4**, 290-97.

56. STERN, K., WILLIAMS, G. M., and PRADOS, M. Grief reactions in later life. Paper delivered before the 2d International Gerontological Congress. Abstract in *J. Geron.*, 1951, **6**, 153.

57. STIEGLITZ, E. J. *The second forty years.* Philadelphia: J. B. Lippincott Co., 1946.

58. *Suggested standards for homes for the aged.* New York: Welfare Council of New York City, 1948.

59. VISCHER, A. L. *Old age: its compensations and rewards.* New York: The Macmillan Co., 1948.

60. *Young at any age.* Report by State of New York Joint Legislative Committee on Problems of Aging. Legislative Document No. 12, 1950. Albany, N.Y.: The Committee, 1952.

PART II

ABNORMAL LIFE CHANGES IN AGING

Chapter 6

COMMON DISABLING PHYSICAL CONDITIONS

General Considerations

Thus far we have discussed the normal changes in various areas of life which can be expected to occur in every individual who lives long enough. We purpose now to discuss those abnormal life changes which all too frequently occur in individuals during the aging process (12, 17, 35, 36, 37, 39, 43, 44, 51). This does not involve an intent to delve into the field of geriatric medicine, for this study is an extensive specialty far beyond the scope of this book, but rather the desire to deal briefly from a psychosomatic viewpoint with those conditions which most commonly disrupt the normal flow of the life stream in the latter part of its course.

We have seen that aging is a gradual process involving all the organs and tissues of the body. We have also seen that the rate of aging is differential both in regard to the individual as a whole and to the separate organs and tissues of the body. We shall see now that there is no sharp line of demarcation between normal and abnormal aging processes. The normal merges imperceptibly into the abnormal, so that at some points it is impossible to differentiate between the two. Also, abnormality in one area or system may result in accelerated aging in other areas or systems.

Generally speaking, physical disorders in the aged are not due to the factor of aging alone but to the insults suffered by the body over a period of years, resulting in decreased tolerance for stresses. Injuries to the body and diseases affecting various organs and systems throughout life all take their toll, so that the older, already weakened organism cannot readily withstand new stress. Most physical disorders can occur at any time of life, but some are more characteristic of the period of later maturity and old age than others and some are more likely to be disabling when they occur in later life than when they occur in youth. Their onset is more gradual and their course less stormy but more persistent, and recovery from them is slower. In other words, when diseases do occur in later life, they are complicated by the aging factor even though they may not be considered disorders due to aging alone (26). Their development is also dependent upon the basic personality makeup of the individual and the emotional trauma to which he has been subjected throughout life.

Self-discipline in living, which involves good mental and physical hygiene, will do much to avert disabling conditions in later life. As we have already seen, healthy living involves taking good care of the body and mind—proper diet, rest, exercise, and recreation, prompt medical attention when the need is indicated, and forward-looking, healthy mental attitudes.

Nevertheless, in spite of care, disabling physical conditions can and do occur. Chronic diseases are common in the latter half of life (see Table 1), and today large numbers of older persons suffering from chronic diseases fill our hospitals. These large numbers are due in part to the increasingly large numbers of older persons in our society and in part to the fact that chronic diseases usually have a slow onset. Because they are slow in developing, chronic diseases are slow in being detected, and often they are not discovered until the patient is stricken with an acute disease. Often an older person will call a physician for treatment of an acute respiratory or other disorder only to discover, after the physician's examination, that he has a chronic disorder of some sort. Sometimes he will have had no definite or acute symptoms at all, and sometimes he may only have felt tired or weak and considered the matter not serious enough to call for medical aid. Both the progress of disease and that of recovery are slower in the aged than in the young.

TABLE 1

INCIDENCE OF DISABLING PHYSICAL CONDITIONS IN OLD AGE AS A PERCENTAGE
OF TOTAL INCIDENCE *

Diagnosis	Total Annual Incidence per 1,000 Persons	Per Cent of Total Incidence in 65-and-Over Age Group
Degenerative diseases	90.6	29.7%
Respiratory diseases, excluding pneumonia	76.7	16.8%
Accidents	42.0	10.3%
Rheumatism	26.6	8.1%
Digestive diseases, excluding appendicitis	24.0	6.5%
Orthopedic impairments	17.4	5.5%
Nervous and mental diseases	14.7	3.6%
Pneumonia	12.7	3.2%
Cancer	7.2	2.4%
Communicable diseases	27.5	0.8%
All other diseases	82.6	13.1%

* Based on figures taken from Federal Security Agency, *Illness and Health Services in an Aging Population*, Public Health Service Publication No. 170 (Washington, D. C.: United States Government Printing Office, 1952).

Decreased Efficiency of the Homeostatic Mechanisms

We have already discussed the normal decline in operation of the stabilizing processes in the aging organism and shown how this accounts for the fact that it takes the older person a longer time to recover from the effects of undue strain, excessive exercise, injury, or disease. It follows obviously that when a person in later maturity suffers from an acute disorder, the prolongation of his convalescence may avoid much irreparable damage to his body. This, however, poses a neat problem of timing, for while we know that prolongation of convalescence may be a safeguard against damage, we know also that a too lengthy convalescent period may result in both psychological and physical damage to a patient of any age. This problem is important to consider in the aged, because of the feelings of uselessness and fears of discard which so frequently accompany illness in later years.

Early ambulation in convalescence is important psychologically so that the patient may quickly look forward to getting well, to being useful, and to resuming his usual place in society. Physically also early ambulation is often necessary as, for example, in order to avoid the development of pneumonia in certain types of bedridden elderly patients. Sometimes the conflict between the needs for early ambulation and for prolonged convalescence can be resolved by making the patient ambulatory as early as possible but making his periods of ambulation brief and interspersing them with much longer periods of rest. Giving him the means of helping himself and of being useful, even though it be in a small way, will also tend to offset the psychological dangers of a prolonged convalescence.

The development of a chronic illness or a disabling physical condition of any sort is psychologically traumatic to a person of any age, but to the older person the blow is probably greater, for it may presage uselessness, dependency, and even death. It may also mean a change of lifelong habits, and this is not easy. A chronic illness may necessitate an entire change in a person's way of living, and this change may not be acceptable to one who has grown old and inflexible. A change of residence to a place where the climate is more favorable but friends are lacking and a change from an active life to a life of retirement and perhaps complete inactivity may be necessary to preserve the life of a patient, but if these changes are not accepted by the patient himself, he will not get well. Habits of a lifetime cannot be changed abruptly; the changes must come about slowly, and the patient's receptivity must be helped along. If he has been a heavy smoker or drinker all his life, he cannot abruptly be told to cease indulging in these habits and be expected to accept the change gracefully and happily. Curtailment of certain activities may be necessary, but it is the patient himself who must be brought to see the need for this and to initiate the curtailment. This requires skill on the part of the one handling the patient, but if he can be helped to accept living within his limits, his recovery will be facilitated.

The Psychosomatic Approach to Disability in Older Persons

Psychosomatic unity is so inherent in the human organism that, when a disorder is present, components of both psychic disturbance and organic disorder often are found. In certain somatic conditions of older persons, emotional maladjustment may be overlooked even though it may be a definite factor in the aggravation of the disorder. Contrariwise, in the older neurotic patient who has for years voiced innumerable somatic complaints, a true somatic involvement may be overlooked. Emotional disturbances can produce symptoms which may appear to be purely somatic and vice versa, so that a dual approach is always necessary. It must be remembered that the aging process itself involves a threat to the body-image, the self-esteem, and the feelings of usefulness and power, and that with illness in this period this threat becomes magnified. It is for this reason that the emotional aspects of illness in later maturity must never be overlooked or minimized. Healthy emotional attitudes will not only help to retard the aging process in general but will also prove a potent ally to early recovery from illness.

Since health is relative rather than absolute, it can be improved, but both the medical and the psychological aspects of health and illness must be taken into consideration. As Ruesch and Bowman (36) have shown, chronic illnesses have important psychological aspects, and those who suffer from disorders of this sort have personality problems which need early recognition and treatment. For example, the most characteristic psychological symptoms of chronic patients are their poor adaptive behavior and their inadequate techniques in meeting social changes, and these are psychological maladjustments which often do respond to psychotherapeutic aid. Until recently the outlook, both medically and psychologically, in regard to the older patient was far too pessimistic. It was taken for granted that, because he could not be "cured," nothing could be done for him, and physicians and psychotherapists did not want to bother with him. Now, however, recognizing the relative nature of both physical and mental health, it is known that much can be done to improve the elderly patient both medically and psychologically. The psychologist has a definite place in working with the aged, but he must be careful not to overstep his bounds, and he must at all times be careful not to neglect the physical side of his patient. In this perhaps more than in any other type of case, it is essential that the psychologist work in collaboration with a physician.

In working with the older convalescent or chronic patient, it is first necessary to have a complete knowledge of the environmental situation, and this can be accomplished only by a thorough study of the patient and those with whom he lives. It must be remembered that aging itself is easier in a favorable environment and the recovery or adjustment to illness will be facilitated in an understanding, helpful environment. Conversely, illness and maladjustment will be aggravated by a hostile, unsympathetic environment or by dependency-producing surroundings. In evaluating the environmental situation, however, it is not possible to go by superficial appearances alone, for the verbal reports of both the patient and his relatives are likely to be distorted due to personal bias. This is particularly true in initial contacts, where both are wary and anxious to make a good impression. Later, when better rapport has been established, more pertinent material for evaluation will come out.

In addition to an understanding of the environmental situation, the therapist of the physically disabled oldster must have a knowledge of his inner mental processes and resources. The therapist must be optimistic, interested in the old person himself, and willing to listen for a long time. He must feel respect and let his patient know he feels respect for him, and he must treat him as a mature, capable person who can make his own decisions. He must be careful to avoid treating him as if he is in any way childish or deteriorated, even though he may be, and he must give him an incentive to live and to get well. He must teach him to live within the limits of his physical disorder and help him to accept his new limitations. If he has family difficulties, it may be necessary at first to side with him against his relatives until such time as he has sufficient confidence in the therapist to face the situation and his own problems and faults realistically. Also, the therapist must be most cautious about approaching any topics which may cause an emotional crisis for the sick oldster, for this may seriously retard his physical recovery as well as destroy his confidence in the therapist (19).

Choice Between Home and Institutional Care

How best to care for an elderly disabled patient presents a problem which is sometimes difficult to solve (5, 38). Will he be better off in his own home, in a convalescent or nursing home, or in a hospital? In reaching a decision in this matter, it is essential that the personality, attitudes, and wishes of both the old person and his family be considered, but particularly those of the patient. Serene and healthy mental attitudes contribute much both toward early recovery and toward acceptance of physical disability. These cannot be achieved if the patient feels too dissatisfied with his surroundings.

Usually, at least in the more acute stages of a disease, it is advisable, if possible, to have a nurse to look after the older person, and this nurse should ALWAYS be one who genuinely likes old people. Many older patients become cantankerous and difficult, and only the nurse who likes them will be able to tolerate their vagaries and be really successful in handling them. Even with the efficient and kindly care of a professional nurse, however, some of the aged feel also the need of loving care and attention from those belonging to them. They recover better in their own homes because they feel happier and more secure there in the love of their family. Many of these carry with them an early, deep-rooted fear of hospitals, so that the very thought of entering one presages death to them and spells neglect and rejection. They greatly prefer the inefficient ministrations of their loved ones and the opportunity to gossip a little and "keep a finger in the family pie" to the expert but cold efficiency of the best hospital. Of course, this desire must be watched too, for some, whose family relationships have been poor, may use their incapacitation as an opportunity to punish members of their family for earlier real or imagined neglect. Some also may seize upon it as a means of restoring lost power. With these persons, the motivation for remaining at home during their illness is not good, so that to accede to their wishes would be more likely to retard than to facilitate their recovery.

Other older patients worry about being cared for at home because they dislike being dependent upon their families and fear becoming a burden to them. They prefer the cool efficiency and routine of a hospital to the fussy attentions they might receive at home. Many feel too that they prefer to pay for care they receive rather than have it given to them through a sense of duty. Deciding then to have care outside the home, the question still remains whether to go to a hospital or to a nursing or convalescent home. The latter vary considerably in size, type, and care offered. If this is to be the choice, one should be chosen which will best meet the peculiar needs of the patient in the light of his background, temperament, and physical condition.

With these general considerations in mind, we shall now proceed to a study of some of the specific disabling physical conditions which are most commonly found among the aging population. The conditions studied by no means constitute a complete or all-inclusive list for, as mentioned earlier, any disease or disabling condition can occur in later maturity or in any other period of life. Rather, it is intended merely as a discussion of some of the more commonly occurring, disabling physical conditions of later life, with particular attention to the psychosomatic aspects of these conditions.

Fractures

Fractures are not at all unusual in older persons, especially fractures of the neck of the femur (thigh bone) (2, 4, 41). This is probably the most common type of fracture encountered in the elderly, although fractures of the spine are also not infrequent. This susceptibility to fracture is due to the fact that, as one grows older, one's bones become more fragile and less elastic. There is a loss of unit strength and a loss in the thickness of the bony wall. Frequently also there are senescent changes in the bone resulting from arteriosclerosis of the vessels of the bone and degeneration of the bone cells. When these conditions are present in sufficient degree, they may retard or even prevent repair. There is evidence too for the belief that unconscious motives and emotional factors may play a large part in those accidents which result in fractures, as well as in the retardation of healing of those fractures. These may include a deep resentment against those with whom the old person lives and an unconscious desire to get even with them by forcing them to take care of him. Feelings of guilt and a consequent need of self-punishment for his rebellious, hostile feelings may also be a part of the picture. Likewise, a general dissatisfaction with life and preoccupation with death may be important predisposing emotional factors. Obviously, it is essential always to deal with these emotional concomitants (1, 14).

Fractures may occur while the older person is in excellent health, merely from falling on an icy street, tripping over a frayed rug, or stumbling over a break in the sidewalk. On the other hand, they frequently occur while the patient is recovering from another illness or injury and is trying to get around when he is still weak. Obviously then, the treatment must be considered not only from the point of view of the fracture itself but also from the point of view of the general physical and mental condition of the patient. The usual tendency now, when the physical condition of the patient warrants it, is to fix the broken bone by means of pins, screws, or nails in fractures of the neck of the femur, in preference to cast immobilization or long bed rest. The stress seems to be on early ambulation in order to avoid hypostatic complications and thrombosis, and it appears that advanced age is no obstacle to this type of treatment, as it has proved successful even with patients in the nineties. Simple compression fractures of the spine resulting from minor injuries can generally be controlled by means of a light back brace and physical therapy. In simple spinal fractures, recumbency is usually not necessary; in femur fractures, the patient is frequently able to get around on crutches in one or two weeks.

In spite of this stress on early ambulation, however, there is a longer period of convalescence during which the patient must avoid weight-bearing and during which he cannot yet resume his full activities and customary routine. This relatively long period of convalescence may bring with it exacerbation of the original emotional disturbance, which may have been somewhat relieved by the initial accident, and many additional fears. There is sometimes pain and with it the fear of further pain, fear of falling, fear of another injury, and fear of never walking again. Sometimes also there is a fear of death and other vague, more nebulous fears, such as the fear of dependency and future uselessness and a sort of generalized fear or anxiety. Diet, rest, and elimination are important factors to control in fracture patients, and attention to physical therapy is essential. According to Dinken (13), after the age of fifty account must be taken of age changes, such as delayed healing, skin changes, intolerance to heat, cold, and irradiation, muscular weakness, tendency to contracture, etc., in giving physical therapy. Nevertheless, he recommends early activity and the avoidance of long, debilitating inertia.

Perhaps even more important than these physical measures, however, are the emotional attitudes of those with whom the fracture patient comes in contact, particularly the emotional attitude of the immediate family, relatives, and close friends. There should prevail an attitude of optimism regarding the patient's early recovery and return to usefulness, a calm acceptance of the fact that he will soon be well again. He needs understanding of his basic emotional difficulties and sympathy, but not an overprotective, excessive sympathy which stifles his desire to get well and provides him with so many secondary gains in his illness that his incentive for improvement is counterbalanced. The patient should be encouraged to do things for himself and for others, his interest should be kept alive, and every effort should be made to avoid the development of dependency. He should be encouraged to get up and around as soon as his physician considers it safe for him to do so. Often this can be accomplished by making the patient feel that he is not only wanted but needed.

When amputation is necessary, it is often extremely difficult for an older person to get accustomed to the use of prosthetic devices. As the weight of these devices seems to be one of the major complicating difficulties, Raagaard (33) has recommended the use of a pasteboard leg for lower-limb amputees. Because it is light and inexpensive and can be made by a physician or craftsman, he recommends its use especially with elderly amputees. However, with all these conditions, the need and use of prosthetic devices, etc., it is the acceptance of the handicap and the will to live happily and effectively with it and in spite of it that determine what kind of adjustment the patient will make.

Joint Diseases

It has been said that few individuals reach later maturity without evidence of disorder in some of their joints and that with time, this evidence increases and becomes more widespread (2, 25, 29, 47). Joint diseases are often painful and cause restriction of activities, and both of these developments may be disturbing to the patient. Experiments in the treatment of arthritis with ACTH and gold have recently proved successful from a medical standpoint, but the emotional aspects must also be considered. In the etiology of joint diseases, it appears that there are common emotional factors, usually dating back to early childhood. The patient, because of early restrictive, overprotective parental influences, develops a chronic state of rebellious hostility. In his earlier life this is expressed through sports and outdoor activities, but in his later years it is expressed through a combination of serving and controlling the environment (1). When this pattern is interrupted, there is an increase of muscle tonus, and arthritis may result. Understanding and treating these basic emotional factors will facilitate the effects of medical treatment. Accepting the disease and the limitations it imposes and conforming to the prescribed treatment are necessary, but these attitudes are often very difficult for the older person. Treatment is frequently monotonous and progress slow, so that the patient becomes discouraged and depressed and is in need of help with his emotional outlook as well as his physical condition. Although there are different kinds of joint diseases, each of which has its own etiology, symptoms, and treatment, we may from a psychological viewpoint loosely group these diseases under the term "arthritis."

Arthritis is a disease which is accompanied by pain, wasting, and debility, and consequently it usually brings fear with it. The pain and consequent reluctance of the patient to use the afflicted parts often results in further deformation and crippling, which is generally followed by increased pessimism. Although some of the new drugs and therapies, especially cortisone, seem to offer a somewhat better outlook for relief in certain cases of arthritis, the bases for treatment are still bed rest and exercise. Weeks of bed rest may sometimes be required, and during this period it is often most difficult to keep up the spirits of the patient. Bed rest with a suitable routine of quiet, isolation, and exercise can best be regulated in a hospital, but the cost is often prohibitive, and the patient becomes so lonesome and depressed away from his family and friends that his condition is aggravated instead of relieved. Emotions play such an important part both in the acceptance of and in the recovery from arthritis that they must not be overlooked. Patients experience more pain when they are emotionally upset and some have noted an increase in pain in direct proportion to the intensity of anger or other emotional upset. Therefore the patient with arthritis should always be treated in a setting most suited to his temperament and one where he will experience the least emotional stress and tension. He must be helped to face his problems realistically and to solve them in the best possible manner. As cooperation is essential, the arthritic must be helped to an intellectual understanding of the need for modification of harmful habits and to an emotional acceptance of change and the possibility of finding other satisfactions in life.

Exercise should be carried out under medical direction and should become habitual. Those who are working with the older arthritic patient must furnish him with some incentive to continue these exercises and try to give him a feeling of optimism regarding his recovery. The ingenious may devise varying ways of stimulating his interest, relieving the monotony, and making him feel that he is playing an important part in his own treatment, all of which will speed his recovery. Analgesics, heat, and gentle massage may be applied under competent direction. Diet should be kept normal, with particular attention to adequate vitamin, protein, and fluid intake, and excesses of all sorts should be avoided.

In addition to the importance of emotional factors in the recovery from arthritis, the part played by emotional factors in the etiology of the disease has also been noted. It is felt by some that emotional conflicts or other psychogenic factors may precipitate or otherwise bring to the surface organic symptoms which ordinarily pass unnoticed. It has also been observed that patients with arthritis and Parkinson's disease differ in temperament and emotional makeup from persons who develop hypertension (7). Those who develop arthritis tend to be dominated by an urge for individualistic independent action, and they respond with aggression when provoked by obstacles. Perhaps, as some have postulated, the functioning of the body even in disease reflects the basic personality structure.

Heart and Circulatory Disorders

Heart and circulatory disorders constitute the most prevalent group of all disorders of older persons (6, 11, 18, 20, 30, 40, 42,

45, 52). They probably disable more than any other disorder in later maturity and are responsible for about half the deaths of older persons. They also complicate the picture in many other diseases of the aged.

There are many kinds of heart and circulatory disorders, and, contrary to popular opinion, they are not necessarily fatal. Age, however, is a complicating factor, and more old than young persons die of disorders of this sort. Emotions also play a very important part (particularly in heart disorders), since there is often a psychogenic basis for many symptoms which seem to be organic in nature, but this should never be taken for granted when symptoms of cardiac disorder appear. Regardless of emotional symptoms or involvement, an extremely careful physical examination is essential in all conditions with symptoms of heart disorder as well as in cases of circulatory disorder where cardiac symptoms are not present.

Heart Failure.—Heart failure (42) or cardiac decompensation seems to be the heart condition most feared by the majority of persons who have somatic concern. This is probably because to many persons "heart failure" signifies sudden death. Fortunately, this view is erroneous, since actually heart failure means that the heart is no longer able to maintain a normal circulation, although it does maintain a circulation of some sort by compensatory hypertrophy of the heart muscle to offset the injury or defect elsewhere in the organ. It may do this so effectively that the heart may remain competent for all normal activities but not for excessive demands. It may do it less effectively, so that varying degrees of limitation of activities will be necessary, or it may be so ineffective that distress will be present even while at physical rest in bed.

There are many causes of heart disorder and also many complications of heart and other diseases, but of these hypertension and coronary disease predominate among older persons.

The symptoms of heart trouble vary. They include irregularities of pulse, breathlessness after normal or less than normal activity or in excess of the demands of the activity, a persistent cough in the absence of bronchitis or a chest cold, edema, and pain which may vary in severity and type. Of course, these symptoms may have causes other than heart disorder, but when they are present, it is most advisable to have a thorough physical examination with special emphasis on examination of the heart.

In addition to certain drugs and even surgery, which may be prescribed by the physician, elimination of all focal infections is essential. Following this, rest, exercise, and diet should be considered. The patient with heart disease must have sufficient rest and must be careful to avoid overtaxing himself. On the other hand, unless his condition is so severe as to require complete immobilization, he also needs to put his body to some use, to have some activity and some exercise. The amount of rest he must take and the amount of exercise he can stand will, of course, depend upon his heart condition, and this can only be determined by his physician after careful physical examination. Diet also is most important, as obesity adds to the load the heart must carry and must therefore be controlled. Glucose is needed by the heart, but fats and caloric intake should be reduced.

All these things mean that the patient must learn to live with his heart disorder, and in this the emotions play a large part. The physician prescribes, but the patient must accept, emotionally as well as intellectually. Individuals who are not well adjusted or accustomed to facing their problems realistically may react in ways injurious to their welfare. For example, one person may refuse to accept the verdict of heart disease and continue with increased vigor his excessive activities and his usual deleterious diet, with the result that his days are numbered. Another may accept it in part only and reduce either his diet or his activities but not both, with the result that he may soon do further damage to his heart. Still another may go to the opposite extreme and become so paralyzed with fear that he almost starves himself and refuses all activity and semblance of a normal life. This last reaction may be quite as harmful as the first two, for the resultant worry and lack of interest in anything except the self and the heart disorder create an emotional upset and tension which will aggravate the cardiac symptoms and nullify any attempts at therapy. The emotionally healthy person who faces his condition realistically, accepts the limitations imposed upon him by it, and then proceeds to live as normally as possible with his handicap has the best chance of recovery, or at least of optimal repair of his heart damage.

Emotional factors play an important part in the etiology, the symptomatology, and the therapy of heart conditions and cannot be overlooked. Cardiac symptoms, particularly palpitation accompanied by feelings of suffocation and dyspnea, are common in psychoneurotics, who may have no organic basis for their complaints. Obviously, the basis of treatment of patients of this sort is psychotherapy. However, studies show the efficacy of a psychosomatic approach to the problem even when the basis of the difficulty is not psychogenic, for there are usually if not always emotional factors involved. For example, Duncan and Stevenson (15) made a complete study of twenty-six patients showing paroxysmal arrhythmias, thirteen of whom had structural heart disease and thirteen of whom did not. His study of individual patients extended over a period of time lasting from several weeks to eighteen months. He found that the role of stress in the life situations of the individuals of both of these groups played an important part in their symptoms, and that all could be helped by psychotherapy. Although each person had his own individuality, certain emotional or personality factors stood out in the group: chronic anxiety, hostility which was usually repressed in greater or less degree, some compulsive behavior, and depression.

Kaufmann and Poliakoff (24) have likewise pointed out the importance of psychosomatic treatment of heart disease and the need of considering both the patient's ideas and his family customs and environment in helping him to plan his routine. The patient must be helped to accept a flexible routine and the maximum of activity, facing his disease realistically and regulating his ambition, income, work, rest, exercise, and recreation accordingly. Acceptance of the condition can often be helped by hobbies of a sedentary nature. As fear and anxiety decrease cardiac efficiency, it is important to the patient's recovery that he develop an optimistic outlook regarding his disease. Actually, this is warranted in view of the increasing longevity following the onset of heart failure.

Coronary Disease.—One of the most common sources of heart injury in older persons is coronary disease. The coronary vessels lie within the heart wall and supply oxygen and nourishment to the muscles of the heart. When, because of arteriosclerosis or other interference, these vessels cannot carry the normal blood supply to the heart muscle, damage to the heart results. The basic causes for the development of arteriosclerotic conditions are not fully understood, although some (30) are of the opinion that disturbances in cholesterol and lipid (i.e., fat) metabolism may be etiologic factors in the development of coronary arteriosclerosis and aortic atherosclerosis, two of these conditions. Diabetes and hypothyroidism favor the development of both coronary arteriosclerosis and high blood pressure, and a high percentage of women develop coronary disorders on the basis of diabetes and hypertension. However, coronary disease occurs four or five times as often in men as in women, except for cases in which diabetes is involved.

The personality of the individual seems also to be an important factor in the development of the disease. According to Mittelmann (28) and Dunbar (14), the person who develops coronary disease is likely to be perfectionistic, ambitious, and driving. He usually does well in school, holds onto his job, and makes few or no impulsive changes in his life situation. Resentment over failure or rejection, hostility, fear, and guilt feelings are frequent emotional components of the disorder.

Damage may occur in different parts of the heart because of a spasm, extreme narrowing of the vessels from arteriosclerosis, or a thrombosis or clot formation in one of the coronary arteries. The clinical picture of the sufferer from coronary disease differs according to the type and extent of the damage (32).

Recovery will, of course, depend upon the general condition of all the coronary blood vessels and upon the extent and severity of the damage suffered. Stieglitz (45) reports that about 35 per cent of victims of coronary occlusion (closure) die instantly, but that the average survival period is almost four years, and some patients survive more than ten years after the initial attack. No doubt coronary disease is the basic cause of many of the cardiac irregularities and myocardial insufficiencies (weaknesses of cardiac muscular tissue) in later life.

Since emotional disturbances as well as undue physical exertion will precipitate coronary disorders, it is important that the older person practice good physical and mental hygiene. If he is aware of any coronary disorder, he must accept the limitations imposed by his disease, try to develop a more placid and optimistic outlook on life, and above all do his best to avoid fear and anger. The fear of a "coronary" is great in many individuals, and yet it is extremely important emotionally to eliminate this fear. Much reassurance and help in developing other satisfactions in life and a forward-looking attitude are often needed.

Hypertensive Heart Disease

Hypertensive heart disease (20, 32, 42, 45) is the major cause of heart failure in the aged. This differs from the usual hypertension of advancing years where customarily there is found a rise only in the systolic blood pressure (pressure on contraction) and perhaps no abnormal cardiovascular (heart and blood vessel) changes of significance. In the usual hypertension of the aged, there may actually be a fall in the diastolic blood pressure (pressure on dilatation). In hypertensive heart disease, on the contrary, there is a pathological diastolic hypertension which causes the characteristic picture. Arteriosclerosis actually is a separate pathological condition, but both often occur in the same patient. Hypertensive heart disease may be found in younger as well as in older persons, but when it is found in an older person age is a complicating factor. According to Kaufmann and Poliakoff, it is just "one manifestation of a systolic disease picture with cardiac, vascular, cerebral, emotional, renal, and other aspects" (24). Renal (kidney) involvement is especially common, as can be seen by the fact that cardiovascular-renal disease predominates among the disabling diseases of later life.

The cause of hypertensive heart disease is rather uncertain, and there seem to be several factors of importance. First, there apparently is a hereditary vulnerability to the disease. Much of it seems to be on a constitutional basis and associated with the nervous, overanxious type of personality which reacts to emotional stress with a rise in blood pressure. In addition to the constitutional basis for the disease, there is also the matter of structural changes and damage induced by the continued hyperactivity of the arterioles (minute arterial branches) and the persistent spasms to consider.

Treatment for these patients centers around the personality and the emotional problems as well as around the strictly medical approach (40). Diet is helpful, particularly for the purpose of weight-reduction, since fat places an extra load on the heart. Some have had success with a low sodium diet and some advocate using a rice diet. Drugs also are occasionally used, mostly for sedation, but emotional adjustment and physical and mental relaxation are the most important aspects of treatment. Complete cooperation of the patient is essential. One who would deal successfully with a person with hypertensive heart disease must be willing to take the time to review the whole life situation of the patient and his family. A reorientation of the patient to his environment and a recognition and acceptance of his own limitations is essential. The patient must both understand and accept his condition and learn moderation in all things if he wants to lead a healthy life. He may have moderate exercise but no overexertion, and he must avoid both mental and physical strain.

Since the person who develops hypertension is in general likely to be an aggressive, energetic, ambitious, explosive, active worrier, this is not always easy. He is used to responsibility, scoffs at inactivity, has many anxieties, and cannot relax. Nevertheless, he must learn to relax, mentally as well as physically, and he must learn to play and to rest. He must take vacations and learn how to enjoy life, instead of working all the time and driving to get ahead. Hobbies of not too violent nature will be helpful. He must accept the fact that he will have a less stormy life, but at the same time he must also see that he can still have a useful as well as an enjoyable life. In dealing with the patient with hypertensive heart disease, it is most important to have a sympathetic and hopeful attitude, an attitude of understanding and optimism. Every effort should be made to relieve the patient's fears and worries and to keep his interest alive and directed toward things other than himself and his illness.

Essential Hypertension.—A common condition of advancing years, essential hypertension ordinarily involves a rise in the systolic blood pressure only. It results from a widespread constriction of the arterioles throughout the vascular system. The diastolic pressure may remain constant or even fall, and there may be no significant cardiovascular changes. However, as high blood pressure favors the development of other disabling physical conditions, particularly coronary arteriosclerosis and heart disease, it is important for the health as well as the comfort of the individual to control the rise of the systolic blood pressure.

High blood pressure is more common and occurs at earlier ages in women than it does in men. Similarly, it is more frequently found in American Negroes than among members of the white race. Coronary arteriosclerosis, on the other hand, is more infrequent among the Negroes. Evidence also points to the psychogenic nature of essential hypertension. In addition to the hereditary aspects, the focal infections, the chemical injuries, diseases such as influenza, and endocrine disturbances in the etiology of the disorder, it would appear that there are certain types of personalities that are prone to develop high blood pressure.

It has long been recognized that extreme anger and other violent emotions can cause a rise in blood pressure, but recent research tends to show also that unconscious as well as conscious chronic hostility, aggression, and anxiety can both cause and sustain a rise in blood pressure. The studies of Dunbar (14), Weiss (48), Houston (22), Mittelmann (28), Alexander (1), and others all indicate the importance of aggression in hypertensive individuals. This aggression, which is often repressed and basic to anxiety, may result from hurt to self-esteem or position, sexual unsureness or injury, rebellion against parents, or other emotional causes arising from early experiences. Often the hypertensive personality is socially shy and inclined to be perfectionistic. He strives to keep from getting angry and is troubled by fears of failure. He has hostile, competitive tendencies which conflict with dependency longings and result in anxiety and inferiority feelings. According to Mittelmann (28), the hypertensive individual is apt to be either an active, aggressive person who fights for everything or an ostensibly calm, submissive person who submits to rules but carries much repressed hostility in his makeup. This hostility creates fear, a dependent attitude, and inferiority feelings, with consequent conflict, according to Alexander (1). Booth (7), in studying a group of hypertensives, found these individuals to be dependent in their relationships through identification with their social environment. He reported that their actions seemed to be determined by material needs and social standards.

Obviously, a psychosomatic approach to the treatment of essential hypertension is necessary. Diet is important, and adequate vitamin intake, protein and fluid intake, and elimination of condiments are occasionally recommended.

Perhaps even more important than the medical treatment of this disorder is the treatment of the emotionally disturbing elements and the personality of the individual. In general, a less tension-producing environment and pace combined with psychotherapy of supportive type will help to alleviate the symptoms, but real psychosomatic treatment of the disorder can be undertaken only after a thorough investigation into the emotional history and the life situation of the individual. The patient must be helped to accept his aggression and hostility and to understand the reasons underlying his reactions. He must also gain insight into his basic fears, anxieties, and emotional needs and be willing to do something about them. Only if he can understand and accept the relationship between his emotional problems and his physical disorder will he be able (in most instances, at least) to work toward a more effective emotional adjustment rather than continue to clamor for more medicine. This, however, will take time. All psychotherapy with older persons takes time and patience, and this is especially true when a physical disorder, which the patient is convinced is of purely organic origin, is involved.

Cerebral Hemorrhage and Cerebral Thrombosis

Cerebral hemorrhage and cerebral thrombosis are often loosely and indiscriminately termed "stroke" or "shock," although actually the causes of these conditions differ (10, 27, 49). A cerebral hemorrhage occurs when a weakened blood vessel wall is ruptured, usually by high blood pressure or by a sudden rise in blood pressure, such as may occur under activity or sudden strain. It is more common between the ages of forty-five and sixty than it is among older persons. It is usually accompanied by a period of unconsciousness of varying duration and followed by a hemiplegia which may or may not clear up entirely or partially with time. The blood pressure in these patients must be lowered, and stimulants, excitement, and emotional upset should be avoided. Bed rest, a calm routine, drugs, and diet are used in treatment.

Cerebral thrombosis results from arteriosclerotic changes and is the cause of the majority of "apoplectic strokes" in persons over sixty-five years of age. In contrast to cerebral hemorrhage, this condition is usually brought about by a lowering of the blood pressure and obstruction of the blood flow through the arteries to the point where the normal function of the parts cannot be maintained. It may come on suddenly, or slowly after a long period of bed rest. Because the brain area affected is generally less than that in a cerebral hemorrhage, there is usually no loss of consciousness, although there may be paralyses or aphasias. If the normal blood flow is re-established within a short time, however, complete restoration of function may occur. Nevertheless, there may be recurrences of thromboses or further brain involvement, so that the patient must be watched carefully. Iodide and stimulants, such as whiskey, strychnine, and caffeine, may be used in the treatment and, unlike cases of hemorrhage, these patients do not ordinarily need bed rest or avoidance of moderate excitement. The blood pressure should not be reduced. Both emotional and intellectual changes, the latter most noticeable in the memory area, may result from any cerebral lesion.

In both these kinds of cases, physical therapy may be helpful if paralyses are present, but this should always be undertaken only under the supervision of someone who fully understands the condition, since the patient with cerebral thrombosis can stand excitement and stimulation which the patient with a cerebral hemorrhage must be careful to avoid.

Emotionally, the factor of crippling due to paralyses complicates the adjustment difficulties. Crippling is hard to adjust to at any period of life, but it is probably especially difficult for sensitive persons in later maturity, since it often brings with it feelings of hopelessness, helplessness, and uselessness. The patient may envision himself as a chronic invalid, fear and resent his enforced dependency, and feel that his days are numbered. It is most important therefore that he be helped to view his condition with optimism and hope and try to help himself toward recovery. Some can and do learn to accept their condition and to live a reasonably normal and active life in spite of a permanent handicap. The following case is illustrative of this type of person:

E.J. suffered a cerebral hemorrhage at the age of fifty-six. She had been an energetic, alert, bright woman who tended to dominate those around her and to let nothing stand in the way of what she wished to accomplish. As the result of her hemorrhage, her entire right side was paralyzed and her speech partially affected, although the latter cleared up fairly well with time. Distressed by her partial invalidism, this woman sought all kinds of medical treatment until convinced of the impossibility of complete recovery. As she gradually came to accept her condition, she decided that she would not remain incapacitated and useless because of it. Thereupon, she set out to train herself and to use her left hand, doing all those things with this hand which she had customarily done with her right hand. She learned to write fairly well left-handed and also developed a rather amazing strength in this hand which enabled her to lift without help heavy roasts and pans of food in the preparation of meals for her family. She continued to live a relatively happy and useful life for about eight years until her death from another cerebral hemorrhage.

Cancer

A cancer is a malignant tumor or mass of spreading cells whose growth extends rapidly and in disorderly fashion until, if not checked, it destroys the organism (2, 42). As the cells multiply they tend to revert to primitive or undifferentiated form, so that they soon come to differ markedly from the tissue from which they are derived. There are as many different kinds of cancer as there are different kinds of cells in the body, but the two general classifications made are carcinoma, in which the cancer arises from the epithelial cells covering the skin and mucous membranes, and sarcoma, in which the cancer arises from supporting tissues, such as muscle, bone, or connective tissue. While not all tumors are malignant, there is always the possibility that those which are benign may at some time become malignant. It is for this reason that prompt treatment of all tumors is of the utmost importance. One of the major points of differentiation of benign from malignant tumors is that the former tend to be more localized than the latter.

Cancer is essentially a disease of later maturity. Although it sometimes does occur early in life, there is a marked increase in its incidence after the age of forty. The most commonly affected areas are the stomach, rectum, uterus, breast, skin, prostate, kidney, and mouth. While cancer does not account for the chronic disability of as many older persons as some other diseases do, it does account for about one eighth of the deaths. Because its progress is likely to be slower in very advanced years and pain is sometimes a late development, death often results in cases where treatment might have been effective if begun early enough. In most cases, however, permanent disability and death are not inevitable, regardless of age. The extent of disability and the probability of death will, of course, depend more upon the severity and location of the cancerous growth than upon the age of the individual, in spite of the fact that age is always a complicating factor.

In the etiology of cancer, heredity is an important predisposing factor, even to the area affected, although it cannot be said that the disease as such is inherited. Rather, it is that certain irritations may induce the development of cancer in vulnerable individuals. These irritations may be traumatic in character, such as continued blows or mechanical irritations to specific areas, or they may be due to excessive exposure to strong sun, X rays, or radium. Certain chemical agents such as tar, soot, pitch, arsenic, etc., likewise are conducive to the development of cancer. The part played by the hormones is probably also very important, particularly in later maturity, but knowledge of this area is as yet incomplete.

The two principal methods by which physicians treat cancer are destruction of the growth by radiation (X rays or radium) and surgical removal of the tumor and the regional lymph glands. There is also considerable research being carried on concerning the efficacy of different drugs and hormones. While the results are as yet inconclusive, the outlook appears far from hopeless. In addition to the alleviation of pain and discomfort by means of drugs, certain hormones have been found effective in retarding the development of some kinds of cancer. For example, as already mentioned in Chapter 2, cancer of the breast and cervix may be indirectly prevented by proper and careful administration of female sex hormone. Obviously, though, much further research needs to be done along these lines.

In regard to the psychogenic factors in the etiology of cancer, knowledge is inadequate. Certainly, however, it would seem that psychosomatic techniques in the treatment of the disease can be effective only in the early stages when the mind might have some chance of being helped to keep or to regain control of the body, for after the cells have started to run wild, medical and surgical techniques only are effective (14). Nevertheless, in the course of cancer there are emotional problems with which the patient can be helped, and this, in turn, may accelerate recovery or at least help the patient to gain peace of mind and a greater acceptance of his condition. Fear of cancer is common, particularly among persons in later maturity, and fear is detrimental to recovery from any disease. In cancer patients there is a fear of prolonged pain and suffering and a feeling of hopelessness in regard to a cure. Therefore, re-education and reassurance are necessary in helping the patient to attain a more optimistic view concerning the possibilities of his recovery and avoidance of excessive pain. Development of interests and activities and a religious or philosophical ideal are most helpful with cancer patients.

Benign Prostatic Hypertrophy

Enlargement of the prostate gland or a benign new growth in one or more parts of the prostate gland is a common occurrence in men in later maturity, particularly in those past sixty years of age (31). Although the onset of the condition may be earlier, the majority of those who come for operative procedures fall between the ages of sixty and eighty years (3). The cause of prostatic hypertrophy is unknown. It is a troublesome malady, mostly because it so often leads to obstruction of the urethra and difficulty in urination. The symptoms usually begin with the need for frequent urination at night and difficulty in passing the urine. This condition may increase until there is complete retention of the urine and even a chronic distention of the bladder and kidneys. This latter condition may be accompanied by loss of weight and strength, constipation, dry mouth, and fever. Although research is being carried on concerning the efficacy of hormone treatment of prostatic hypertrophy, present knowledge seems to indicate that operative procedures for the removal of all or part of the prostate gland are usually necessary even in those of advanced age. One reason for this seems to be because of the possibility that the now benign growth may suddenly become malignant.

The psychogenic aspects of this malady must also be considered. From the standpoint of symptoms alone, there seem to be more psychogenic cases than there are cases of true prostatic hypertrophy. Increased frequency of nocturnal urination is rather common from the mid-forties onward, and of itself it need not be of particular significance. For the body-conscious person who is overly concerned about himself, however, this may be a serious symptom and indicative of prostatic hypertrophy. Thereupon he becomes very conscious of and overly concerned about his urination, until before long he develops all the symptoms of prostatic involvement, although actually there may be no hypertrophy present. In some cases there seems to be a connection between this condition and sex difficulties. Obviously these individuals are in need of psychotherapy rather than treatment for prostatic hypertrophy. Reassurance and optimism in regard to recovery from the disorder will also help to alleviate the fears and worries of those who actually do suffer from it.

Diabetes Mellitus

Diabetes mellitus is a rather common disease in the latter half of life (8, 9). Considering all ages, diabetes ranks seventh in causes of death and fifth in chronic invalidism. Although the actual number of initial incidences of the disorder decreases after reaching a peak in the fifties, there is an increasing number of persons over sixty years of age who develop it. Diabetes mellitus is a metabolic disorder which manifests itself by an excessive amount of sugar in the blood; there may or may not be sugar in the urine. It generally occurs in obese persons who are accustomed to consuming excessive quantities of sweets, and about one third of those who develop the disease have a family history of diabetes mellitus. It is a result of the failure of the islets of the pancreas to secrete enough insulin to check a rise in blood sugar occurring through release of glycogen stores in the liver or absorption of glucose ingested; in other words, there is insufficient insulin to maintain a proper sugar balance. Sometimes there are no marked symptoms at the onset of the disease, so that its presence may remain unknown until detected during a routine physical examination which reveals glycosuria in the urinalysis. In other cases, the patient seeks medical advice because of loss of weight, weakness, and perhaps pains in the joints, trouble with vision, or a burning sensation on urinating, which seems to be necessary more often than normally. The presence of diabetes will be confirmed or negated by the glucose tolerance test, which will also give an idea of the severity of the disease and consequent treatment needs. Because there is a normally expected rise in blood sugar after fifty years of age and a temporary rise may occur in connection with certain other diseases, a complete life history of the patient and frequent checks on the blood sugar are necessary.

Treatment of diabetes may include administration of insulin in varying amounts, regulation of diet, or a combination of insulin intake and diet restriction. Proper elimination through bowels and kidneys, exercise, and rest are also important.

When considering the diet of the older diabetic, the fact that diabetes may be a predisposing or at least a complicating factor in coronary arteriosclerosis and high blood pressure must not be overlooked. Sudden, abrupt, and radical changes in long-established habits of eating, drinking, and smoking are probably inadvisable, in spite of the fact that diet control is desirable and the use of alcohol deleterious.

In order to avoid some of the complications of diabetes, particular attention should be paid to the care of the skin and the circulation in the lower extremities since, without this care, conditions sometimes develop which require the amputation of part of the lower extremities, and this is often dangerous physically in elderly diabetics, as well as emotionally traumatic.

It seems to be fairly well established that emotional factors will influence the course of diabetes mellitus, and it is also possible that psychogenic factors may be important in the etiology of the disease. Given a certain physiological makeup (apparently a congenital matter) excessive emotional upset or stress may induce hyperglycemia. Fear and rage, for example, have long been known to cause at least a temporary rise in blood sugar. Dunbar (14) also finds certain personality patterns apparent among those patients who develop diabetes mellitus. She finds many of them to be infantile, dependent individuals who have been "spoiled" children, dominated by and tied to the mother, seeking always to be babied, passive, sexually maladjusted, submissive (at least on the surface), and sometimes resentful because of frustrated infantile demands. Alexander (1) reports from psychoanalytic studies that the diabetic patient seems to have some basic conflict in regard to food and that this is expressed in exaggerated oral incorporative tendencies. The result may be an excessive desire for food and receiving gratification in relationships with others or an exaggerated identification with the mother, with consequent impaired psychosexual development. The fact that obesity is present in about 75 per cent of diabetics suggests also the importance of psychogenic factors in the etiology of the disease, for it is well known that obesity is frequently the result of a basic emotional maladjustment. The obese person gains his satisfaction from eating because of his failure to achieve emotional satisfaction from other areas of life.

Considering then the emotional factors involved in diabetes mellitus, it is obvious that with many cases a psychosomatic approach to the disorder will be more effective than medical treatment alone. As Dunbar (14) has pointed out, no amount of emotional stability will restore the diabetic's pancreas to its former level of efficiency in producing insulin, but it will affect the course of the disease by reducing the fatigue, debility, and irritability and helping the patient to adjust better to his diet and even at times to increase his diet while eliminating the need for insulin. Even in those cases where it is not feasible to go too deeply into the basic emotional problems, supportive therapy and reassurance can do much to help the patient to effect a more satisfactory adjustment. The emotional distress, of course, is aggravated when paralyses are involved. In all cases, however, it is important to help the older diabetic to face his limitations and to imbue him with the determination to lead a normally useful and happy life in spite of his limitations and handicaps.

The efficacy of supportive therapy carried on by a general practitioner in a rural area can be seen in the case of N.B., a woman in her fifties who has become almost blind and has lost two toes as a result of diabetes. By nature a sweet, dependent, submissive woman, she quickly reached a state of complete helplessness and despondency on learning of her condition and the not too favorable prognosis. With the cooperation of her family who were instructed to indicate their NEED for her, her physician spent considerable time with her on each visit, letting her talk about herself, her problems, and her illness and giving her much needed reassurance and support. After some time he was able to help her achieve a more optimistic outlook on her disease and the belief that she could be happy and continue with most of her normal activities. Today she does most of her own housework, visits her friends and relatives, and lives a normally busy, cheerful life.

Respiratory Disorders

Tuberculosis.—Among the respiratory disorders (2, 34), tuberculosis is probably the most important, since it ranks fourth among the chronic disabling physical conditions. Tuberculosis usually occurs before middle life, but it may not be detected until then, when another acute disorder may bring it to the physician's attention. Artificial pneumothorax (collapsing and immobilizing of the disabled lung) and some of the newer drugs are proving effective medical therapy in tuberculosis, but rest and healthy, happy emotional attitudes are still indispensable to recovery. Although rest is most important to recovery, many older persons who have been leading active, useful lives find it difficult to adjust to inactivity.

The psychogenic factors in the etiology of tuberculosis are imperfectly understood, but their importance in the course of the disease are well recognized. There seems to be a hereditary vulnerability to the disease, and excessive physical strain and unfavorable living conditions are contributing factors in its development. Unhappiness and emotional stress also seem to play a part, although their part in retarding recovery is better understood. Regardless of the extent of lesions (within limits, of course), the patient who is happy and has a real incentive to get well recovers fast. Cases have been reported of younger persons with severe lesions who showed remarkable recovery even under unfavorable environmental conditions, whereas others with relatively slight lesions died in spite of all that could be done to save them; the former seemed to have an inner contentment and happiness, whereas the latter could not achieve emotional ease. Obviously, helping the older person, who may feel that there is little in life left for him, to achieve this inner peace of mind is no mean task, and yet, without this, an acceptance of his disease and the limitations it imposes upon him, and an optimistic outlook toward recovery, he will probably not get well.

Recurrent Bronchitis.—Recurrent bronchitis is rather common among persons of very advanced years. Many have prolonged attacks during the colder half of the year and seem to get little relief so long as they remain in the cold climate. It is advisable for these persons to spend the cold months in a warmer climate, but it is not always easy to get them to do so. With some it is a very real question of money, but with others it is the emotional difficulty of uprooting themselves and resettling in a strange place. This is an important factor to consider, for if the old person is not happy in his new surroundings, his moving will have done him more harm than good. He may not have his recurrent attacks of bronchitis, but the chances are that he will develop some new ailment which will be just as troublesome. We can never consider the body alone; we must always consider the emotions as well.

Pneumonia.—Only a relatively short time ago, pneumonia was considered inevitably fatal in older persons, and it is still a serious disease. With the newer drugs now in use, however, the number of deaths from pneumonia has dropped markedly. Nevertheless, the incidence and death rate are still high, especially after the age of seventy years, when the rate is from 80 to 100 per cent. Pneumonia may occur in the aged as a primary disease or as the terminal stage of some other acute or chronic illness. There are different forms of pneumonia, but in general the disease is caused by a mixture of the bacteria normally found in the respiratory tract. The disease may follow essentially the same course in older persons as in younger persons, but more often it is less stormy and has fewer abnormal physical signs. Many cases of pneumonia can be avoided by maintaining good general health and, in so far as this is possible, preventing colds and other diseases predisposing to pneumonia. Prompt treatment also is essential. In addition to good medical and nursing care, the patient should have as much activity as is consistent with his general condition, since inactivity favors the development of hypostasis (settling of blood in the lungs) and the invasion of bacteria. If it is necessary for the patient to be in bed, his position should be changed frequently and he should take deep-breathing exercises at regular intervals in order to prevent hypostasis. He should sit up as soon as his temperature is normal and should return gradually to activity. Heart, blood pressure, pulse, and elimination should be watched carefully. Frequent rest periods should alternate with activity. Diet, with particular reference to vitamin intake, is also important Surroundings should be cheerful, warm, light, and well ventilated, and those who care for the pneumonia patient should reflect cheerful optimism regarding his recovery and be ready to give him emotional support and reassurance as he needs it. Encouragement toward an early return to activity is important, since many old persons may be fearful of this and thus retard their own recovery.

Digestive Disturbances

The digestive system is such a favorite seat for the development of psychogenic disorders that, whenever a disturbance is found in this area, a careful investigation into all factors is essential (1, 14, 16, 42, 49). Because of the prevalence of psychogenic digestive disturbances, a real somatic basis for the difficulty may sometimes be overlooked. On the other hand, even where organic involvement is evident, emotional factors are usually present also. For this reason, a study of the older person's personality makeup, his life situation, and his emotional adjustment is important for the facilitation of an improvement in his digestive condition. As it is well known that the functioning of the digestive system is affected by such emotional disturbances as fear, worry over family or business affairs, quarreling, etc., care should be taken to avoid the occasion for these destructive emotions in so far as it is possible.

Some real organic changes in the functioning of the digestive system, resulting in part at least from the aging factor, may be basic to a digestive disturbance in an older patient. These include the diminution of output of saliva, gastric juice, and pepsin in the gastric juice, which result, among other things, in a decrease in the amount of starch digested in the mouth and stomach. Still more common is the lack of secretion of hydrochloric acid by the stomach. Increasing numbers of persons after the age of forty suffer from this defect, which causes digestive difficulties and may lead to more serious conditions.

Nutritional difficulties may also be the cause of digestive disturbances. These may be due to poor teeth, with consequent inadequate diet, although actually this is often a reciprocal process. The poor diet was in large part responsible for the early loss of teeth, and now the poor teeth make an adequate diet impossible. Usually, in these cases, the diet is protein-deficient and overloaded with fats and starches, so that obesity results. Avitaminosis, especially the lack of various forms of vitamin B, is common and closely allied to nutritional difficulties. One of the greatest problems in treating nutritional difficulties in older persons, however, is to convince them of the need to change their diet. It is hard to break the dietary habits of a lifetime, and many old persons are stubbornly resistive to this. Some will take medicines without protest, or even eagerly, but they refuse to change their eating habits or to recognize the necessity for doing so. Often much tact and understanding are needed to persuade the old person to cooperate in the dietary routine which will give him the greatest relief. Sometimes vitamins given in pill form and a generally improved emotional adjustment will help considerably.

Anorexia.—Loss of appetite or anorexia is more frequently found among the very old than among the middle-aged and those approaching senescence. The middle-aged person is prone to overeat and become obese, but it is seldom if ever that a very old person is obese; the obese person generally dies before he reaches a very old age. Whereas the middle-aged person may gain by overeating the satisfactions he lacks in other areas, the very old may no longer gain any satisfaction in this area either.

This may be due to a general decline of interest in all areas, to nutritional difficulties which may result from factors just discussed or from lack of money to provide an adequate diet, or to other organic factors, such as the continuous diminishing of the taste buds of the tongue and the resulting inability to enjoy food. In these cases the onset is usually gradual; the causes must be determined and removed. An adequate and interesting diet should be provided, and efforts must be made to stimulate greater interest in life and living. This is sometimes difficult, as the general will to live diminishes together with what is called *joie de vivre*. Sometimes certain drugs will help to stimulate the appetite.

In other cases of anorexia in later maturity, and these are usually before a very old age has been reached, there may also be organic factors involved, but the emotional factors are more subtle and potent than a mere decline of interest (1). The anorexia patient carries much envy and jealousy in his personality makeup, but these traits are inhibited by his conscience. Spite is also frequent, but all these traits are rejected by the conscious mind and give rise to guilt feelings. Oral aggressive and receptive tendencies are usual and may be eroticized by these patients. The individual who develops anorexia may have a need to punish himself and to destroy himself. It is unwise to force persons with this difficulty to eat, for this may result in violent reactions and an exacerbation of self-destructive tendencies; even suicide may sometimes occur. While drugs may offer temporary relief to these patients, some emotional adjustment must be made before any permanent improvement can be effected. With older persons, this should begin by a careful investigation into the present life situation and disturbing emotional factors in the environment. Since it takes so much longer and is so much harder for old persons to change than for young persons, environmental manipulation is most important in dealing with the aged. Pressures should be eased, irritations removed, and relatives helped to understand the patient's emotional needs. In addition to aiding the old person's emotional adjustment, these preliminary measures give him confidence in his physician or therapist, who can then deal more effectively with his basic personality or emotional difficulties.

Peptic Ulcer.—A peptic ulcer (1, 2, 14, 16, 23) is an open sore in the mucous membrane of the stomach or duodenum. It occurs in those regions which are subjected to the digestive action of acid gastric juice. No one single cause of peptic ulcer can be given, but it is known that reduction in the vitality of the mucous membrane will render these tissues more susceptible to ulceration from the corrosive effect of the gastric juice. Fatigue, poor diet, allergy, endocrine disorder, spasm or embolism of the arteries, infection, or trauma—any one or a combination of several may be a factor in the etiology and continuance of peptic ulcer, but most investigators agree also that emotional factors are of paramount importance and that medical treatment can at best give only temporary relief unless the basic emotional disturbance is cleared up.

The connection with the emotions can readily be understood when we recall that the vagus nerve carries impulses through the midbrain to the intestinal tract. This part of the brain is believed to regulate the automatic functions of the body and emotional expression in the involuntary nervous system. Thus, when there is emotional disturbance, an unduly large number of impulses may be transmitted along these nerve fibers to the intestinal tract. This affects the secretion of gastric juice, causes tension in the smooth muscles, and may result in irritation and lowered vitality of the mucous membrane. The soil is then ready for the development of an ulcer when scratchy or irritating food comes in contact with the already weakened mucous membrane.

Peptic ulcer occurs more frequently in men than in women, although the discrepancy in numbers is rapidly decreasing, possibly because of the increasing number of women entering into the competition of the business world, and may exist for some years before the individual finally seeks treatment. The primary symptom is a gnawing, generally localized pain and hungry feeling which appears from one to three hours after meals. It is a persistent pain, but, after reaching a peak, it usually disappears before the next meal. Sometimes there is nausea and occasionally vomiting of blood. Medical treatment is directed toward inhibiting the disintegrating and digestive properties of the gastric juice, and this may be accomplished by small feedings every hour and antiacid medication on the half-hour throughout the day. Generally, especially at first, only soft, neutralizing foods are permitted. Alcoholic beverages and highly seasoned, fibrous or coarse foods are avoided. If the ulcer is far advanced, surgery may be necessary to remove it. Vagotomy, which involves a severing of the vagus nerves to the stomach, has also proved effective in many cases, but it is well recognized that no surgical procedure will remove the basic emotional conflict which induced the disorder and that so long as this emotional conflict exists, there may be either a recurrence of the ulcer or disturbances elsewhere.

The ulcer patient usually has a personality with deep-seated neurotic conflicts. Generally, he is of asthenic type, intelligent, ambitious, striving, and most rejecting of his unconscious feminine tendencies. He reacts to his basic insecurity and unconscious feelings of hostility and aggression. The typical conflict situation is one in which the wish for infantile dependency is in conflict with pride and aspirations for independence, accomplishment, and self-sufficiency; the dependency desires are then frustrated and the trouble starts. The ulcer patient has usually been attached to his mother and torn by his impulses to lean and his need to assert his independence. He suspects that he is inferior, and in an attempt to escape this suspicion and to hide his desire for dependency, he rejects his weaker impulses, refuses help, and displays much ambition and activity. Many of these individuals were feeding problems in earlier life, and one cannot but wonder whether they may not have an inherited weakness or vulnerability of the digestive system. These patients generally enjoy talking about themselves and frequently recognize an emotional basis for their pain, although they cannot always see or admit the real emotional conflict. Once started, an ulcer will be aggravated by fear, worry, anger, resentment, and hostility.

With most older persons, the ulcer must first be cleared up by medication, diet, or surgery as indicated. Then the life situation must be investigated carefully, and, in so far as it is possible, all irritants and conditions conducive to destructive and harmful emotions eliminated or at least lessened. Then, depending upon the general condition of the patient, his receptivity, and his desire for help, an attempt can be made to uncover the basic emotional conflicts and help him to rebuild a more adequate personality.

Colitis.—The colitis patient (14, 21) has a personality makeup similar to that of the peptic ulcer patient, save that he is even more infantile. He too is intelligent, tied to his mother, fearful and passive in his life attitudes, egocentric, sensitive, and greatly in need of love and sympathy. There is a conflict between his wish for affection and material tokens of this affection and his unconscious desire to make up for his dependency wishes by taking on new duties and responsibilities. According to Dunbar (14), these patients have a generally self-destructive drive so that, when an operation is necessary, it must be timed with an upswing from this drive, for if their attention is focused on dying, they will die regardless of treatment.

Allergies.—Allergies not infrequently develop in old persons, although the reason why they develop so late in life is not clearly known. There are hypersensitivities to certain stimuli, such as pollen, dust, food, animal fur, etc., which show up as reactions in the skin, nasal tissues, bronchial tissues, stomach, or other parts of the body. The most common forms of allergy are hay fever, asthma, and skin rashes, and of these skin rashes seem to be the most common in later maturity. There seems to be a hereditary vulnerability to the development of allergies, even to the specific kinds of allergy, but in many it appears that an emotionally disturbing stimulus is necessary to induce the allergic reaction. In others the reaction may be initiated during a low period of poor general health, infection, or other depressed physiological state and continued and aggravated by emotional disturbance.

The importance of psychogenic factors in the allergies of elderly persons is often more obvious than in infants and young children, although even in these cases the possibility that metabolism, tissue, or other physiological changes connected with aging may be precipitating factors must not be overlooked. Usually a psychosomatic approach to the problem proves the most effective. Certain drugs are helpful and may afford some relief to the sufferer, but their effects are often transitory. Help with disturbing life situations and emotional conflicts may prove more permanently effective. Skin allergies, such as hives and eczema, are often precipitated by the personal loss of someone dear to the patient. The sufferers may differ in personality, but their outstanding feature is their emotional conflict between the desire for affection and the fear of being hurt if they seek it. They are often lonely, self-conscious, retiring, and conventional in their attitudes. They tend to repress their annoyance and frustration, but the result is the eruption of the skin. Their scratching of the itchy rash may be symbolic of their repressed hostility. The following case shows rather clearly the relationship between emotional disturbance and skin allergy:

A.H. had his first eruption of hives at the age of sixty-eight, about a year after the death of his wife, to whom he was much attached in spite of her domineering ways. Following the death of his wife, he had taken his son and the son's family to live with him. Having strong family feelings, he expected a close bond of affection and companionship with these members of his family, but he soon found that his hopes were in vain. He sensed his daughter-in-law's lack of real feeling for him and began to feel unloved and unwanted in his home. He disapproved of the way the children were being raised, of the quarrels in the family, and of the carelessness and destructiveness of his son's family. He experienced special annoyance when he observed things precious to him carelessly destroyed. However, believing it the better policy to hide his feelings and keep peace, he said nothing. His feelings were not vocalized, but they were expressed through his skin eruptions. He was found to be allergic to animal fur and house dust and received transitory relief from drugs. Drugs, however, were ineffective when he was very disturbed emotionally. Contrariwise, during those periods when he had happiness and peace of mind, his hives disappeared without the aid of medicine and even when he fondled the cat and dog around the house.

Summary

The common disabling physical conditions of later maturity have their bases in the aging factors within the organism, the insults offered to the body throughout life which render it less able to withstand stress, and the specifics connected with the actual disease. Psychogenic factors are also important in the etiology of most diseases, as well as in their continuance, so that a psychosomatic approach is usually the most effective in therapy.

It is psychologically important for the older person not to have his convalescence prolonged more than is absolutely necessary for his physical welfare. Early ambulation and careful attention to the life situation and emotional disturbances are important.

Whether to care for an elderly, disabled patient in his own home, in a convalescent or nursing home, or in a hospital will depend upon the personality and wishes of the old person himself as well as upon the existing facilities and finances. He will make his quickest recovery in the place where he is happiest.

Fractures of the neck of the femur are common among the aged, and the outlook for early ambulation and complete recovery is good at this time. There is evidence that emotional factors may be predisposing to the accidents which result in fractures and also important in the retardation of recovery. These and the fears which frequently arise during the convalescent period must be considered in any recovery program.

Arthritis is a term often used loosely to cover some common forms of joint disease. Heat, massage, rest, exercise, diet (particularly in the matter of vitamin intake), and certain medications are helpful in the treatment of these diseases, but the concomitant emotional factors must also be considered and treated.

Among the heart and circulatory disorders, heart failure (cardiac decompensation), coronary disease, hypertensive heart disease, cardiovascular-renal disease, essential hypertension, cerebral hemorrhage, and cerebral thrombosis predominate. In all these conditions, medication, diet, rest, exercise, acceptance of the condition and the limitations it imposes, a determination to live a normal healthy life within the limits of the disease, and an optimistic outlook toward recovery are important.

Emotional factors are usually evident in the etiology and course of heart and circulatory disorders, and these must be given consideration in the treatment of the patient.

Cancer is essentially a disease of later maturity, since there is a marked increase in its incidence after the age of forty. The most commonly affected areas are the stomach, rectum, uterus, breast, skin, prostate, kidney, and mouth. Treatment is usually by surgery or radiation or both, although research is being done in the efficacy of certain drugs and hormones in some types of cases. Knowledge of psychogenic factors in the etiology of the disease is inadequate, and it would seem that psychosomatic treatment might be effective only in the very early stages of cancer. However, during the course of the disease supportive therapy, reassurance, re-education, and optimism may help the patient, particularly with his fears.

Benign prostatic hypertrophy is common in men past sixty years of age. Surgery is the most effective treatment of the disease and is usually successful. However, care must be taken to differentiate between true prostatic hypertrophy and those psychogenic cases which have all the symptoms of the disorder but no real hypertrophy. In these latter cases psychotherapy is the only effective treatment.

Diabetes mellitus, although among the most common of the chronic disorders, can usually be fairly well controlled if treatment is instituted early enough. The usual treatment is diet, insulin, or both. Emotional factors seem to be important in both the etiology and the course of the disease, excessive emotional stress or upset often aggravating the already present hyperglycemia.

Among the respiratory disorders, tuberculosis, recurrent bronchitis, and pneumonia are most common. Tuberculosis usually has its onset before middle life, but it often goes undetected until then. In addition to the modern medical treatments, rest and healthy, happy emotional attitudes are essential to recovery. Emotional disturbance will accelerate the destructive course of this disease.

Pneumonia may occur as a primary disease in the aged but more often it occurs as the terminal stage of another acute disease. Reassurance, encouragement, cheerfulness, diet, and early return to activity with frequent rest periods are important. Avoidance of remaining too long in bed may avert the development of hypostatic pneumonia during other illnesses.

Digestive disturbances very frequently found in the aged include nutritional difficulties, anorexia, peptic ulcer, colitis, and allergies. Basic to the development of some of these conditions may be poor teeth, inadequate diet, lack of hydrochloric acid in the stomach, and age changes in the tissues, but in most cases there are fundamental personality patterns and emotional factors which are more important.

The anorexia patient is often envious, jealous, and spiteful but represses these tendencies, with the result that he has guilt feelings and the need of punishing himself as well as others. He may have strong self-destructive tendencies.

Peptic ulcer has been treated by diet, surgical removal of the ulcer, and section of the vagus nerve, but these measures are usually only temporary unless the basic emotional maladjustment is also treated. Once started, an ulcer will be aggravated by destructive emotions.

The colitis patient has a personality makeup similar to that of the ulcer patient, except that he is more infantile and may have a stronger self-destructive drive.

Allergy in any form may be found among older persons, but hives and other skin eruptions are most commonly found. They are often precipitated by the loss of someone dear. The outstanding feature of allergy sufferers is their emotional conflict between their desire for affection and fear of being hurt if they seek it.

As a general summary of this chapter, we might say that man is essentially a psychosomatic being, so that either normal or pathological aging in one area will in turn affect normal or pathological aging in other areas. Since aging is a natural phenomenon of life and must occur in all living organisms, drugs cannot forever stop aging, but drugs and other therapeutic measures can alleviate suffering, help to retard pathological aging, relax the patient, and sometimes help him to develop a happier outlook on life. Likewise, good mental and physical hygiene will not prevent normal aging, but they can retard pathological aging and make prolonged life worth living. Those who handle the physically disabled older person must make him feel that they expect his early recovery, they both like and respect him (his ability or judgment, for example), and they consider him an important individual. They should be optimistic with him and use suggestion, persuasion, support, and reassurance as indicated. They should encourage his gradual and early return to activity and usefulness. He should not have too much activity too early, but care should be taken that he does not remain too long dependent. Wherever possible, his life situation should be investigated and the environmental pressures eased. Those who are working with the older patient should try to help him to accept a decrease in his activities when this is necessary and to find less strenuous activities which are both useful and interesting, since useful and interesting activities are essential to happiness and well-being. They should also encourage him to keep well groomed, since this does much to keep up morale. In this connection, an occasional compliment will prove helpful.

REFERENCES

1. ALEXANDER, F. *Psychosomatic medicine: its principles and applications.* New York: W. W. Norton & Co., Inc., 1950.
2. BARKER, L. F. Ageing from the clinical point of view. In COWDRY, E. V. (ed.), *Problems of ageing.* Baltimore: The Williams & Wilkins Co., 1939.
3. BEATTY, R. P. Surgical treatment of prostatism. *Geriatrics,* 1950, **5,** 196-202.
4. BICK, E. M., and COPEL, J. W. Fractures of the vertebrae in the aged. *Geriatrics,* 1950, 5, 74-81.
5. BLUESTONE, E. M. Medical care of the aged. *J. Geron.,* 1949, **4,** 305-9.
6. BOAS, E. P. Cardiovascular problems after age 70. *Geriatrics,* 1950, **5,** 85-89.
7. BOOTH, G. Organ function and form perception; use of the Rorschach method with cases of chronic arthritis, Parkinsonism, and arterial hypertension. *Psychosom. Med.,* 1946, **8,** 367-85.
8. BORTZ, E. L. Diabetes mellitus. In STIEGLITZ, E. J. (ed.), *Geriatric medicine.* Philadelphia: W. B. Saunders Co., 1949.
9. BURNSTEIN, N. Supplementary treatment of diabetes mellitus with steroid hormones. *Geriatrics,* 1950, **5,** 93-98.
10. CAMP, C. D. Organic diseases of the brain, spinal cord, and peripheral nerves. In STIEGLITZ, E. J. (ed.), *Geriatric medicine.* Philadelphia: W. B. Saunders Co., 1949.
11. COHN, A. Old age and aging from the point of view of the cardiovascular system. Discussion by E. P. BOAS. *Amer. J. Orthopsychiat.,* 1940, **10,** 43-55.
12. CRAMPTON, C. W. The essentials of the geriatric examination at 50. *Geriatrics,* 1950, **5,** 1-14.
13. DINKEN, H. Physical medicine in disabilities of the aged. *Arch. phys. Med.,* 1949, **30,** 78-81.
14. DUNBAR, F. *Mind and body: psychosomatic medicine.* New York: Random House, Inc., 1947.
15. DUNCAN, C. H., and STEVENSON, J. P. Paroxysmal arrhythmias: a psychosomatic study. *Geriatrics,* 1950, **5,** 259-67.
16. EYERLY, J. B., and BREUHAUS, H. C. Diseases of the esophagus and stomach. In STIEGLITZ, E. J. (ed.), *Geriatric medicine.* Philadelphia: W. B. Saunders Co., 1949.
17. FLEETWOOD, J. F. Problems of old age in general practice. *J.M.A. of Erie,* Jan., 1950.
18. GAVEY, C. J. The cardiology of old age. *Lancet,* 1949, **257,** 725-35.
19. GINZBERG, R. Psychology in everyday geriatrics. *Geriatrics,* 1950, **5,** 36-43.
20. GRECO, G. F. Hypertensive heart disease in older patients. *Geriatrics,* 1950, 5, 15-25.
21. GROEN, J. Psychogenesis and psychotherapy of ulcerative colitis. *Psychosom. Med.,* 1947, **9,** 151-74.
22. HOUSTON, A. B. Psychogenic aspects of hypertension. *Manitoba med. Rev.,* 1947, **27,** 567-69.

23. Ivy, A. C. Digestive system. In Cowdry, E. V. (ed.), *Problems of ageing*. Baltimore: The Williams & Wilkins Co., 1939.

24. Kaufmann, P., and Poliakoff, H. Studies of the aging heart. *Geriatrics*, 1950, **5**, 177-87.

25. Kelly, M. Somatic and psychic factors in the causation of fibrositis. *Rheumatism*, 1946, **3**, 40-42.

26. Ludwig, A. C. Some psychosocial factors in cases of severe medical disease. *Appl. Anthrop.*, 1948, **7**, 1-5.

27. Marks, E. S. Small unrecognized strokes. *N.C. med. J.*, 1947, 8, 88-90.

28. Mittelmann, B. Psychosomatic medicine and the older patient. In Kaplan, O. (ed.), *Mental disorders in later life*. Stanford, Calif.: Stanford University Press, 1945.

29. Monroe, R. T. Diseases of the joints. In Stieglitz, E. J. (ed.), *Geriatric medicine*. Philadelphia: W. B. Saunders Co., 1949.

30. Morrison, L. M., and Gonzales, W. F. The effect of blood cholesterol disorders on the coronary arteries and aorta. *Geriatrics*, 1950, **5**, 188-95.

31. Pelouze, P. S. Diseases of the prostate. In Stieglitz, E. J. (ed.), *Geriatric medicine*. Philadelphia: W. B. Saunders Co., 1949.

32. Priest, W. S. Angina pectoris, myocardial infarction, and acute coronary failure. In Stieglitz, E. J. (ed.), *Geriatric medicine*. Philadelphia: W. B. Saunders Co., 1949.

33. Raagaard, O. V. A pasteboard leg prosthesis for elderly patients. *J. Geron.*, 1950, **5**, 245-48.

34. Reimann, H. A. Acute diseases of the lungs and pleura. In Stieglitz, E. J. (ed.), *Geriatric medicine*. Philadelphia: W. B. Saunders Co., 1949.

35. Rockwell, F. V. Psychotherapy in the older individual. In Kaplan, O. (ed.), *Mental disorders in later life*. Stanford, Calif.: Stanford University Press, 1945.

36. Ruesch, J., and Bowman, K. M. Personality and chronic illness. *J. Amer. med. Ass.*, 1948, **186**, 851-55.

37. Ruesch, J., Harris, R. E., Christiansen, C., Heller, S. H., Loeb, M. B., Dewees, S., and Jacobson, A. *Chronic disease and psychological invalidism: a psychosomatic study*. Psychosom. Med. Monogr., 1946, No. 9.

38. Rusk, H. A. America's number one problem: chronic disease and an aging population. *Amer. J. Psychiat.*, 1949, **106**, 270-77.

39. Shock, N. W. Physiological aspects of mental disorders in later life. In Kaplan, O. (ed.), *Mental disorders in later life*. Stanford, Calif.: Stanford University Press, 1945.

40. Simon, A. The role of the psychiatrist in cardiovascular disorders. *Calif. Med.*, 1948, **69**, 185-89.

41. Steindler, A. Diseases of the bones. In Stieglitz, E. J. (ed.), *Geriatric medicine*. Philadelphia: W. B. Saunders Co., 1949.

42. Stieglitz, E. J. *The second forty years*. Philadelphia: J. B. Lippincott Co., 1946.

43. ———. Foundations of geriatric medicine. In Stieglitz, E. J. (ed.), *Geriatric medicine*. Philadelphia: W. B. Saunders Co., 1949.

44. ———. Principles of geriatric medicine. In Stieglitz, E. J. (ed), *Geriatric medicine*. Philadelphia: W. B. Saunders Co., 1949.

45. ——. Hypertensive arterial disease and hypotension. In STIEGLITZ, E. J. (ed.), *Geriatric medicine*. Philadelphia: W. B. Saunders Co., 1949.

46. TALBOT, J. H. Gout. In STIEGLITZ, E. J. (ed.), *Geriatric medicine*. Philadelphia: W. B. Saunders Co., 1949.

47. WATKINS, A. L. Clinical application of physical medicine in older patients. *Med. Annals, D. of C.*, 1950, **19**, 242-48.

48. WEISS, E. Psychosomatic aspects of arterial hypertension. *Amer. Pract.*, 1947, **2**, 19-24.

49. WEISS, E., and ENGLISH, O. S. *Psychosomatic medicine*. Philadelphia: W. B. Saunders Co., 1949.

50. ZANGWILL, O. L. Some qualitative observations on verbal memory in cases of cerebral lesion. *Brit. J. Psychol.*, 1946, **37**, 8-19.

51. ZEMAN, F. D. Physical illnesses and mental attitudes of old people. In Family Welfare Association of America, *Mental hygiene in old age*. New York: The Association, 1937.

52. ZIEGLER, L. H. *Cardiovascular diseases*. New York: Grune & Stratton, Inc., 1949.

Chapter 7

PSYCHONEUROSES

A psychoneurosis is a minor, functional mental disorder. It is a disturbance of psychic life which carries with it both physical and affective symptoms, although there are no apparent physical causes to account for the disturbance. The disturbance is of those complex functions of the nervous system which are concerned especially with the adjustment of the individual to his environment. The individual, in his failure to effect a satisfactory adjustment to his environment through emotional or ideational causes, develops somatic symptoms and associated psychic disturbances. His behavior is not necessarily queer or abnormal, but the symptoms he shows serve for him some useful role, obscure though this role may sometimes be.

The basis for psychoneurotic reactions lies in the unconscious, where, according to Freud, conflicts between the id, the ego, and the superego are usually fought out. There may be strong drives or desires which are unacceptable to one's concept of self or one's self-ideal, or they may be such that, if given expression, would come into conflict with the established mores of society. A struggle then ensues until some sort of compromise is reached. If a normal, rational solution is not effected, substitutive reactions may be forthcoming in the form of psychoneurotic symptoms. These symptoms may be disguised gratifications of the unacceptable drives or desires or they may serve as a defense against these desires. For example, the man who, after many years in a mediocre job, is suddenly promoted to a responsible position for which he feels himself totally unfit and unworthy may be unable to admit, even to himself, that his feelings of inadequacy, sense of guilt, and fears of failure are so strong that he does not want to take the new job. Thereupon he develops a paralysis or blindness which makes it impossible for him to take the position he consciously so much desires; his unconscious desires are gratified. Similarly, unconscious sex drives may be so unacceptable that the individual feels a constant compulsion to wash. This is a symbolic cleaning or washing away of the "unclean" thoughts, a defense against letting the unwelcome impulses seep into consciousness.

The symptoms may appear to be unpleasant afflictions, but actually they serve some useful role in the life of the psychoneurotic. As we have just seen, they may provide disguised gratification or enjoyment, or they may protect the individual from unwelcome knowledge about himself. They result from the excessive and unhealthy use of unconscious mental mechanisms—mechanisms which prevent one from seeing the truth or recognizing the reality of one's less desirable self.

Characteristic Features of Psychoneuroses

As mentioned above, psychoneuroses embody both psychic and physical symptoms although the disorder is psychogenic in origin. The symptoms may take a variety of forms and may differ in intensity, but it is characteristic that both the psychic and the physical symptoms occur in the same individual alternately or even at the same time.

Psychic Symptoms.—Symptoms of a psychoneurotic disturbance include painful emotions of all sorts, particularly fear, anxiety, and apprehension. The individual may have vague, uncomfortable feelings of anxiety or apprehension, or he may become tense and even panicky without knowing why. On the other hand, he may develop definite and abnormal fears, such as claustrophobia (fear of enclosed spaces) or agoraphobia (fear of wide open spaces). He may become afraid to ride the subway or go to the top of a high building, or he may develop a fear of harming someone dear to him.

Sometimes the psychic symptoms are displayed in the form of intellectual rather than purely emotional disturbances, and the individual develops disturbances in the thinking or memory area. He may become obsessed with an idea which he knows to be ridiculous but which he cannot banish, or he may develop partial or complete amnesia. Thus, persons have been known to disappear completely from their accustomed surroundings only to reappear in a distant city with a new name and a new occupation and without any recall of the earlier period of life.

Physical Symptoms.—Symptoms of a physical nature may include disturbances in any area and of any type. There may be sensory, motor or vasomotor, respiratory, cardiac, gastro-intestinal, or genitourinary disorders, and they may cause mild or acute distress.

Sensory disturbances may include deafness, blindness, and loss of or increase of sensitivity to cutaneous stimuli. Although there is no real organic basis for the disorder, the individual actually may be unable to hear, to see, or to feel because of his emotional disturbance which leads him to try to cut out certain unpleasant factors from his hearing, his sight, or his touch.

Vasomotor symptoms in the form of sweating, flushing, or fainting are rather common. A normal amount of these reactions can be seen in everyday life, but with the psychoneurotic the reactions are excessive. Without apparent cause he may break out in a sweat, accompanied by feelings of fear and perhaps other psychosomatic symptoms. Or he may faint readily under stress. Likewise, he may develop motor symptoms, such as convulsions, aphonia, or paralyses, without organic cause. For example, many soldiers who during wartime have marked fear of combat but are unable to admit their fear to themselves, may develop paralyses which prevent their entrance into combat duty. This is a disguised and convenient way of getting what one desires and still "saving face," both with one's comrades and with one's self.

Respiratory and cardiac symptoms frequently appear in the same individual. There may be shortness of breath, palpitation of the heart, and sometimes pain around the heart; these symptoms are usually accompanied by feelings of anxiety, fear, and at times even acute panic. The role these symptoms play in the life of the patient is often obscure and can be uncovered only by the prolonged efforts of an expert therapist.

The gastrointestinal region is another favorite area of complaint of the psychoneurotic. Gastrointestinal symptoms include nausea, excessive gas, vomiting, etc. It will be recalled that in the last chapter some of the physiological reasons why the gastrointestinal system is so readily affected by emotional disturbances were discussed. Even popular speech recognizes this connection, for we often hear, in expressing annoyance or disgust with a person, "He makes me sick" or "I can't stomach her."

Mental Mechanisms

Many mental mechanisms are used normally throughout life, and in some periods of life some are used more frequently than others. For this reason, we shall merely mention briefly a few of those mental mechanisms which are most frequently used in an unhealthy manner by the maladjusted person in later maturity.

Aggression is one of the mechanisms which is accentuated in old age. The frustration and deprivation attendant on old age may arouse aggressive impulses in addition to the aggressive mechanism resorted to in order to build up a threatened ego and body-image. The aggression of old age is either expressed overtly in the form of actual physical violence and abusive and insulting behavior, or it is repressed. When repressed, it may lead to a psychoneurotic, psychotic, or psychosomatic disturbance.

Projection is also accentuated in old age. The bodily and psychic changes which the individual refuses to admit are projected onto others, who are held responsible for whatever happens to the patient or his external world. Sensory impairment also leads to defective contact with reality, which in turn favors the use of projection.

Regression to earlier, usually inadequate modes of adjustment is another concomitant mechanism of old age deterioration. Infantile impulses and processes are often reactivated by the elderly person, who in the last stages of senile deterioration may even regress to incontinence.

Conversion, or the discharge of impulses through physical channels, is a primitive characteristic which may be revived by the aged. It is frequently seen in the hysterias.

Withdrawal from the objects, persons, and activities of everyday life is another characteristic mechanism of old age. As the withdrawn interest is usually concentrated on the person's own self and body, egocentrism and hypochondriasis result.

Repression is also frequently used in old age to avoid solving conflicts which should be brought to consciousness and faced realistically. Many pathological symptoms are produced by these unhealthy repressions, as the unpleasant things which have been repressed lurk in the unconscious and continue trying to thrust themselves into consciousness.

Psychoneuroses and Psychoses

Psychoneuroses have been termed "minor psychoses" by some to differentiate them from the major mental disorders or "major psychoses" (8). There are some basic and important differences between the two, and, contrary to popular opinion, the belief is held by many psychiatrists that the psychoneurotic does not and probably will not develop into a psychotic. It might be well at this point, therefore, to discuss some of the differences between the two disorders.

To begin with, the psychoneurotic is generally affected only in limited areas of the mind, so that his personality remains socially organized, whereas the psychotic is affected in greater areas, so that his personality becomes distorted and he may lose his capacity to adjust to ordinary society. Although he may be self-centered and socially difficult, the psychoneurotic does not lose his contact with and awareness of people, so that he does not generally give the impression of being queer. The psychotic, however, is quite likely to lose his awareness of people and his contact with reality and to give the impression of being queer, odd, or different.

The psychoneurotic individual maintains his grasp of social relations, remains well oriented, and recognizes the external world for what it is. He may have fantasies and daydreams, but he recognizes these for what they are and does not invest them with reality. The psychotic individual, on the other hand, tends to lose his capacity for discriminating between his fantasies and the reality of the external world. He may develop delusions or hallucinations, or he may lose his grasp of social relations or his orientation. Reality and environment become altered and distorted for the psychotic, whereas for the psychoneurotic they remain essentially intact. The psychoneurotic may overreact emotionally to certain elements in his environment which for him are surcharged with affective values, but he does not distort reality. He retains his interest in the outside world and does not withdraw into a little world of his own as the psychotic so frequently does.

The psychoneurotic does not develop true delusions and hallucinations, although these are commonly found among psychotics. This is probably because he maintains his contact with reality in a way the psychotic fails to do.

The psychoneurotic tends to maintain repression, whereas in the psychotic the capacity for repression has been markedly diminished. Thus, while the psychotic may say whatever he pleases regardless of time, place, or appropriateness, the psychoneurotic cannot verbalize the content of his unconscious, which has momentarily become conscious. His physical or emotional disturbances may be symbolic expressions of his unconscious conflicts, but his ego will not accept his impulses or fantasies and continues to attempt control of them. The ego of the psychotic, on the other hand, has become so weakened or broken down that it may tolerate all things uncritically.

Although the psychoneurotic as well as the psychotic may have an infantile, immature personality, the psychoneurotic does not regress to the infantile practices of wetting and soiling as the psychotic may. The psychotic may regress even to the extreme of assuming prenatal posture, but regression of this sort almost never occurs in the psychoneurotic.

Also, the psychoneurotic often has a keen awareness of his illness, suffers very much, and consciously is most anxious to get well. Unconsciously, of course, he may have some motives for not wanting to get well, but consciously he wants nothing in the world so much as to be sound and healthy again. He has an appreciation of his condition but cannot seem to do anything about it. He is often able to stand back and view himself with a certain amout of objectivity, see the undesirability of his reactions, and even recognize an emotional basis for them, but he is powerless to help himself. In contrast to this, the psychotic generally does not recognize that he is ill and has no desire for a change in his subjective status. Although some psychotics do realize that they are ill and do seek help, the majority have no real appreciation of being mentally ill and little or no real desire to effect a change within themselves. If they desire change, it is in some other person or thing onto which they have projected their own difficulties.

Psychoneuroses in the Aging

The psychoneuroses which occur in later life are essentially the same as those which appear in earlier life (1, 5, 7, 13, 16, 21). Both the causes and manifestations of, and the mechanisms involved in, the psychoneuroses are basically the same no matter at what period of life they occur, although in later maturity there may be some modification due to the factor of biological aging. Re-emphasizing the principle of psychosomatic unity, we can readily understand how the tissue and organ changes accompanying aging may affect social and economic life and create resultant emotional stress in the aging individual. As we have already seen, some real changes with advancing age are unavoidable; if they are not accepted and faced realistically, abnormal changes in one or another area may result.

It is doubtful, however, that the factor of aging alone is ever fully responsible for the development of a psychoneurosis. More often, the psychoneuroses found in later maturity are merely accentuations of earlier maladjustments. Sometimes the condition is a frank reoccurrence of an earlier psychoneurosis; at other times it is an exaggeration of symptoms which have been present in milder form for many years. The basic personality features and behavior reactions may have been evident for a lifetime, but the development of a true psychoneurosis was not necessary because the individual was able to control his environment and those around him fairly well and gratify most of his desires. With the advent of senescence, however, when the usual control of the environment has been weakened, efficiency and adequacy have declined, and gratification of desires is not so easy, the psychoneurosis may develop as the only, or at least the easiest, means of getting one's own way and satisfying one's wishes. It is a socially undesirable and a personally unhealthy and destructive mode of reaction, for, with continuance of the condition, the only result can be further unhappiness, increased rejection by society, and greater maladjustment.

Contrary to earlier views, which seemed to consider emotional disturbances of older persons hopeless signs of beginning decay and to look upon therapy as a waste of time, the older psychoneurotic patient can be helped to effect a better adjustment. Unless intellectual deterioration has advanced to an extreme degree, he can respond to essentially the same type of psychotherapy (with perhaps some modifications) as younger persons. As with those of other ages, the older patient, assuming he has normal intelligence, can change if he wants to badly enough. Also, proper preventive measures, and by this we mean good mental and physical hygiene and more favorable environmental conditions, may avert the development of many psychoneuroses of later maturity as well as decrease the severity and shorten the duration of those which do occur.

Distribution of Psychoneurotic Disturbance.—The incidence of psychoneuroses in later maturity is probably rather high, although no accurate figures are available because so many pass without being recognized for what they are. It is known that there are many more psychoneuroses in later life than there are deteriorative psychoses, that the incidence is higher in women than in men and in whites than in Negroes, and that the greatest numbers are found among the professional and managerial classes, the next greatest among farmers and farm workers, and the fewest among clerical and skilled workers, but the exact numbers or percentages are not known (8). The reason for the inaccuracy of the data is that many of the complaints for which patients consult the general practitioner are actually psychoneurotic disorders but are never diagnosed as such. Some physicians claim that the majority of the illnesses of their patients are psychogenic, but that they treat these patients with placebos and palliatives, since they would never accept referral for psychiatric treatment. Some patients, as is well known, trot from doctor to doctor and are treated for every disorder under the sun except a psychoneurotic one.

Etiology of Psychoneuroses

Much of the etiology of psychoneuroses among the aged is obscure. Nevertheless, the individual's reactions to the normal changes and stresses accompanying his advancing age must always be considered when evaluating etiological factors in the older psychoneurotic, for aging itself offers a threat to the body-image and the self-esteem.

Constitutional Factors.—The individual with a "neurotic constitution" or neurotic temperament has a hereditary makeup which is sensitive and high-strung, so that he cannot readily withstand the vicissitudes and stresses of life. He generally comes from nervous, unstable forebears who have been unable to provide him with an emotionally stable, healthy environment and teach him to face reality and accept responsibilities. This does not imply that psychoneuroses as such are inherited or that all nervous, sensitive, high-strung persons will develop psychoneuroses, but it does seem that unstable individuals are more likely to produce offspring who are less strong emotionally and more likely than others to break down under stress. They need care, training, and good mental hygiene, particularly in their formative years, and they should be helped early to develop good emotional habits and strength. Persons of neurotic temperament are often very interesting, sensitive to the niceties of life, and likely to achieve much if their assets rather than their liabilities are developed.

Physiological Decline.—Of course, it is not the actual physiological aging itself which is so important; rather, it is the individual's reaction to his physiological decline which is the precipitating factor in the development of the psychoneurotic condition. We have already seen that some decline of strength, vigor, endurance, and skill are the normal accompaniments of advancing age and that some genuine disability may result from irreversible organismic decline. These changes are destructive to the body-image and may be so completely unacceptable to the individual that his emotional reaction results in a psychoneurosis.

In addition to the general decline of strength and vigor, there are changes in the organs and tissues of the body which we have already discussed. For example, visceral changes may often be overreacted to, perhaps because of the close connection with the emotions. As emotional disturbance may result in visceral disorder, so visceral changes may result in untoward emotional reaction. Minor dysfunctions may be overemphasized and misinterpreted, often leading the individual to believe he has cancer or some other dread disease. This may then result in considerable anxiety and fear—fear of death and invalidism, fear of pain, and fear of dependency and rejection by society. When the psychoneurosis has fully developed, it is very difficult to determine the extent to which the symptoms are basically psychic in origin and the extent to which they are due to organismic decline.

Likewise, changes in the blood vessels and heart and the decreased efficiency of the homeostatic mechanisms may produce symptoms which focus the attention of the individual upon himself. If he is already an anxious and not too well-adjusted person, he may begin to watch every bodily change and symptom, overemphasizing and worrying about each. Shortness of breath after exertion may be interpreted as indicative of imminent heart failure, and the need of more frequent rest periods as the beginning of decline and early death. This anxiety over and excessive attention to bodily symptoms, which actually may be the entirely normal accompaniments of advancing age, may, in turn, result in an exacerbation of these symptoms until an abnormal organic condition develops. We have then the components of a psychoneurosis—organic symptoms and fear, anxiety, and depression. It remains only to determine, for treatment, which is basic—organismic change or emotional conflict.

Contrary to popular notion, brain damage as such does not cause psychoneuroses. There is, in fact, very little evidence for the belief that there is any direct relationship between the extent of brain damage and the severity of abnormal symptoms displayed, in spite of the role of organic brain damage in certain psychotic disorders. However, changes in the brain and nervous system may have an indirect bearing upon the development of a psychoneurosis, for with brain changes will come a decreased efficiency of mental functioning. This may render the individual less able to cope both with the ordinary problems of everyday living and with the special inner and environmental stresses to which he, as an aging person, is subject. Also, cerebrovascular disease may produce focal neurological signs which may result in anxiety, fears, depression, or other destructive emotional reactions.

Sensory impairment, particularly the impairment of vision and hearing, may likewise be an important physiological factor in the etiology of a psychoneurosis in later maturity. Inability to see or to hear tends to lead to the development of suspicion, and this attitude may be even more evident in the partially than in the totally impaired. Sensory impairment creates a partial isolation from the environment at any age. In later maturity, when acceptance is often far from complete anyway, it may lead to increased feelings of rejection. Things incompletely seen or heard are often misunderstood or misinterpreted according to the fears or other emotional bias of the individual. Being unable to enter into full communication with those around him or to participate fully in the activities of the environment, the old person with sensory impairment may live with his suspicions unexpressed or uncorrected, so that they build up to major proportions and intensify those fears, anxieties, and other disturbing emotions which are already present. He sees slights where none may be intended, and he imperfectly hears remarks which he misinterprets as disparaging allusions to himself. These suspicions, of course, lead to further rejection and loss of friends, resulting in even greater anxiety and discouragement on the part of the older person. A situation of this sort is one which requires much patience, tact, and understanding.

Cameron, however, reports that sometimes sensory impairment may reduce instead of increase the severity of old neurotic reactions, particularly when the individual has been oversensitive to light and sound (5).

Decline of sexual potency and decrease in attractiveness to the opposite sex are perhaps among the most important physiological factors in the etiology of psychoneuroses in later maturity. Again, however, it is the individual's reactions to these changes which are gradually occurring in his aging body that will determine what influence they will have upon his adjustment. It frequently happens that the sexual and other bodily changes merely serve to intensify those psychoneurotic reactions which have already been present for a long time.

In Chapter 2 we discussed in some detail the sexual and psychosexual changes which occur as part of the normal aging process. Abnormal reactions to these changes are largely an exaggeration of the normal emotional stress experienced at the climacteric. With the loss of reproductive function, the most common emotional symptoms are anxiety, fear, depression, and feelings of inadequacy, uselessness, and rejection. The general view of society that sex is something shameful which should be eschewed by those in later maturity tends to increase these frustrations and destructive emotional reactions. Often it seems that the storm and stress of puberty are re-enacted in old age.

Some individuals react with aggressive denial to their loss of sexual potency and attractiveness. They try in every way to enhance their attractiveness and to look young, and they may engage in diverse unsuitable love affairs, often with disastrous results, in their efforts to prove themselves adequate and desirable. Others may show their aggression by active resentment toward any manifestation of sexual interest or activity by others. They may practice a pious prudery or become scandalous gossip-mongers as a protest against their own loss of sexual power and appeal, a projection of their own unadmitted impulses. Still others may show their aggression in the business or professional area or, in more disguised form, by a neurotic domination of the family through illness and the consequent need of care and attention.

Individuals of different temperament may react to sexual frustration and decline by a retreat into fantasy. Erotic fantasy life may come to occupy the major portion of their time and serve to give them the sexual gratification they crave. Sometimes, though, instead of giving satisfaction, these fantasies cause tension in the individual which he cannot relieve in the normal way. He may then resort to autoerotic and pregenital measures which, if they bring him the gratification he needs, may become more or less fixed modes of response. Masturbation in these individuals is common, and increased interest in excretory functions and in oral drives may readily be observed. Unfortunately, these regressive gratifications frequently give rise to the conflicts attendant upon them in earlier periods of life, so that considerable anxiety may be induced. The aging individual who engages in sexual fantasy and autoerotic practices may experience strong feelings of guilt, unworthiness, and inadequacy which intensify his general maladjustment and emotional disturbance. The whole picture then favors the development of psychoneurotic reactions such as anxiety states, reactive depressions, compulsions, hypochondriacal symptoms, and chronic fatigue states.

Environmental Factors.—Environmental factors arising from social stress loom large in the etiology of the psychoneuroses in any period of life, but perhaps they are even more important in the later years of life. While there are constitutional factors basic to the development of most mental disorders major or minor, there must also be unfavorable environmental factors in order to bring the disorder to full flower. Despite the presence of constitutional factors favorable to the development of a mental disorder, the view is commonly held that suitable environment may avert the maturation of the disorder. With most aging persons, however, environmental influences seem to be stressful rather than conducive to the development of good mental health.

Economic stress, for example, is especially difficult for the older person because it generally carries with it a rather hopeless outlook. A young person who experiences economic reversals may not find it as difficult because he has his whole future before him and can look forward to a change and recouping his losses. For the old person who has no money, the picture is not as bright, for he has little future to look forward to and few prospects of building anew his economic independence. Loss of economic independence means loss of prestige and social status; it means social dependence. The man who has been a power in his household and in his business, who has held the purse strings and doled out the money, must now come to his offspring or other sources for his needs. He may have to change his abode and manner of living, and an uprooting with separation from old friends is not easy for an aging and perhaps rigid personality. The result may be exaggerated tension, anxiety, and depression.

Even in the absence of real economic stress, the mere matter of retirement is a stress-producing situation for the older person. He may have a reduced income to which he must accommodate, but, even more important than this, he may have nothing left to keep him busy. With retirement his prestige goes and his usefulness as a wage-earner departs, so that little may remain of the importance of his previous role in life. If he has not prepared beforehand for this period of life or is not basically a well-adjusted person, he is likely to become in a short time an unhappy, discontented, lonely person. With nothing else to think about, his attention may become focused upon his bodily symptoms; the soil is thus prepared for the development of a psychoneurosis.

Economic stress and retirement often result in dependence on offspring, which may be traumatic for the oldster. He is no longer the head of the family he produced; his offspring no longer need him, nor are they willing to listen to his injunctions; he must take a back seat. This role is so difficult for many old persons that they will not relinquish their hold on the family without a desperate struggle—a struggle in which they will use every known or imaginable means of continuing their domination. They may be open or subtle about it, demand their rights or seek sympathy, or perhaps resort to physical illness. It is not easy to be a "wallflower" at any age, and it is probably especially difficult after a lifetime in the limelight. This situation, difficult in itself, may be worsened by the reaction of the offspring to the aged dependent parent. There is a reversal of the parent-child role, and the offspring who has not resolved his own conflicts in regard to his feelings toward his parents may take advantage of this reversal to get his revenge for earlier "mistreatment." He may show his hostility and aggression toward his parent by dominating him, restricting his freedom, and generally making life miserable for him in a dozen different ways. This stressful situation, of course, paves the way for the development of a psychoneurosis in an already emotionally maladjusted person.

It has been pointed out that both the biological and the sociological change in status may bring about neurotic maladjustments in senescence which are similar in character to those found in adolescence. Both show a tendency toward a vague, uneasy, perplexed sense of personal disorientation. This may be due to the endocrinological changes which are taking place, to the reduction in the repressive strength of the ego, and to the change from a position of relative security to one of insecurity. Maladjustments in both periods of life tend to induce feelings of inferiority, inadequacy, unattractiveness, and rejection. When the change in status is abrupt and sudden, it is, of course, more difficult to accept than when it is gradual. The person who has always been passive and dependent may experience no real change or threat to his security, whereas the one who has been dominating, powerful, and important may find neurotic manifestations his only solution to his loss of status. These help him to maintain some semblance of the control and power to which he has been accustomed.

In general, we might say that the social attitudes toward the aged contribute much of the environmental stress experienced by those in later maturity. There is the tendency to discard them economically to make way for younger workers, regardless of their fitness to continue at their chosen work. There is no place for them economically or socially, no reward, and nothing to look forward to. Sex life is frowned upon, and few gratifications of any worth are open to them. Society views their lives as finished and expects them to vegetate gracefully and without protest. This is impossible for many, and those who are less strong may find their outlet through psychoneurotic or other abnormal emotional disturbance. Certainly if psychoneuroses in later life are to be avoided or at least decreased in number, society must pay more attention to the human needs and values of this period.

Emotional Factors.—Emotional factors constitute the major component of all psychoneuroses, but some assume greater importance than others in the etiology of these conditions, particularly in later life. Of course, the important immediate causes for the development of psychoneuroses are always emotional dissatisfaction and affect-laden ideas. However, it is doubtful that many psychoneurotic conditions appear for the first time in senescence without previous indications of maladjustment. Usually similar patterns of unsuccessful and inadequate attempts at adaptation to personal difficulties have been evident in earlier years, although perhaps to a lesser degree, because the old have had more years in their lives to build up and to crystallize their bad patterns. If their life histories are investigated, it will usually be found that in childhood these psychoneurotics experienced certain psychic and physical reactions which might have indicated the possible future development of a psychoneurosis. Many were enuretic until an advanced age; many were sleepwalkers or suffered from night terrors; others were abnormally fearful or shy; and some were given to temper tantrums. According to Watters (21), when the conflicts and problems of childhood are unsettled, there remains a potential nucleus or source of trouble which, with provocation, may erupt in senescence. Maladjustments tend to increase with age, so that the neurotic need of satisfaction and also of punishment may become pronounced in later years.

Sometimes, even those psychoneuroses which appear to be newly developed in later maturity have, in reality, been developing over a long period of time. They did not come forth in full bloom merely because there was not a need for them. The earlier attempts at domination, control of the environment, and being the center of attention were successful, so that a frank psychoneurosis was unnecessary. However, at the approach of senescence, with its changed biological and social status, the maintenance of power became impossible, and the reaction was one of disappointment and frustration—a blind, childish, striking out against the environment. A similar reaction against the environment might have been evident in childhood and the infantile demands for gratification of other needs in evidence throughout the whole course of life, but only in senescence when success broke down did the full psychoneurosis develop.

In addition to the life pattern, however, there is in later maturity the emotional reaction of the individual to his own aging to be considered. Important changes occur in the lives of everyone —bodily changes, social changes, and the like—but the important thing is how the individual takes these changes. For example, the climacteric constitutes a psychic trauma for the individual, male or female, and the menopause offers narcissistic injury to the female, but not everyone who experiences these changes becomes so disturbed emotionally that he develops a psychoneurosis. Rather, it is the individual who cannot accept these changes in himself or herself who develops the psychoneurosis. Likewise, in the tense, rigid repression of drives which may be entirely normal but unacceptable to the particular individual, we find substitute gratifications that constitute the psychoneurotic syndrome. However, we must not consider these repressed internal factors to be the sole emotional basis for psychoneurotic reactions, for sometimes external situations involving emotional stress seem to be more important contributing causes. This is particularly true in the case of the aged, who, as we have seen, are frequently subject to considerable environmental stress.

Given then the constitutional basis, the biological changes accompanying the aging process, and the environmental stress attendant upon growing old, the results are unhealthy emotional reactions to one's own aging and an intensification of already existing, unhealthy patterns of emotional reaction. Aggressive reactions, for example, are common in aging individuals, and in elderly psychoneurotics these aggressions are aggravated. They may take a variety of forms, since the older psychoneurotic has lived longer and therefore usually knows the more potent weapons to use. It may vary from quiet, passive, sullen resistance to open attack, vituperation, accusations, and temper outbursts. The most popular forms with the aged, though, are those having to do with health and depression. These are potent weapons and means of gaining and maintaining control over adult offspring. They are aggressive ways of punishing and of gaining power and attention. They gain sympathy and arouse feelings of guilt and anxiety in the offspring, thus paving the way for domination. The greater the success of the domination and the infliction of suffering upon others, the longer the aggressive reaction, whatever its form may be, will continue.

Instead of responding with aggression, the more passive individual may show his emotional response to his own aging by withdrawing and gaining his satisfactions from his fantasy life. He may feel rejected, inadequate, and useless in his present life, and these feelings may be intensified by his recognition of his waning abilities in all areas. He may then give up the struggle and live in the more satisfying world of his own fantasy. Finding it increasingly difficult to remember recent events, he dwells on his past achievements, enhancing and enlarging upon his successes and triumphs. Sometimes he develops routines which simplify his environment and serve as protective devices to eliminate sources of tension. These serve as a defense against competition and consequent anxiety, and they must be rigidly adhered to. When used to excess, these routines become true compulsions, and when they are interfered with, anxiety develops.

Erotic fantasies are the frequent component of withdrawal reactions. Rather than being basically abnormal, these fantasies may merely be the result of loneliness, rejection, and a craving for love and attention. They do, of course, offer some temporary gratification, but in the long run they are not satisfying. Also, the fantasies may lead to increased anxiety and emotional disturbance. For example, the erotic fantasies may lead to feelings of guilt, inferiority, and anxiety; the reminiscences may cause the individual to remember past pains, sins, failures, and the like and result in feelings of guilt, self-accusation, and anxiety; and the withdrawal from the environment and increase of self-interest may lead to preoccupation with bodily symptoms and consequent feelings of anxiety and guilt.

Types of Psychoneuroses in Later Life

It is difficult to make a clear-cut classification of the psychoneurotic disorders of the senium because many patients show symptoms of several different disorders. Also, as previously mentioned, large numbers of psychoneurotic individuals are being treated by general practitioners for all sorts of disorders other than the psychoneurosis which is the basis of the difficulty. Some physicians estimate that anywhere from 40 to 75 per cent of their consultations for routine ailments are, in reality, psychoneurotic conditions. In addition, the picture in later maturity is complicated by the actual organic changes which may have taken place. Nevertheless, the following psychoneurotic disorders are frequently encountered in the elderly (4, 8, 9, 12, 14, 17, 20).

Hypochondriasis usually occurs as a part of other psychoneurotic states, and often even of psychotic states, but occasionally we find individuals in whom the hypochondriacal symptoms constitute the major portion of the disorder. Their whole attention and interest in life are centered around the viscera, and they can talk for many hours a day about their ailments and the state of their bowels.

Preoccupations with bodily functions are fairly common as one grows older, has fewer interests and less participation in the major things of life, and comes more in contact with illness. When emotional privations are actually extreme, or are seemingly so to an unstable personality, this normal tendency to think more about one's body may become aggravated. At times, this attention to the body or a particular organ may become so excessive as to initiate a real functional change in the organ. Bodily functioning actually becomes less efficient with advancing years. Whereas this usually passes unnoticed or is accepted casually by the normal person, the emotionally unstable, deprived individual may overemphasize this normal decline and read all sorts of dire threats to himself in it. The social and bodily threats attendant upon aging tend to accentuate his narcissism, and he concentrates all his attention on the functioning of his body and magnifies every minor symptom or even awareness of organ functioning he might have. It becomes a fascinating subject for him, and he will regale anyone who will listen with endless tales of his somatic complaints. He soon sees, too, the advantages his illness brings him. He gets the attention and care he craves, and his illness proves a powerful weapon to wield over those around him. It provides a means of dominating and controlling the offspring or marital partner. It gives also a way of getting revenge and expressing hostility and aggression in disguised form.

Hypochondriasis may take any form, but usually attention is centered on the viscera. The symptoms are multiple and varied, and the more contact the individual has had with illnesses and operations, the more varied his symptoms are likely to be. It is so easy for the suggestible person to develop the symptoms of diseases he knows all about! Organs are imagined to be diseased and not functioning properly, and the individual may travel from doctor to doctor and from clinic to clinic in his efforts to find one doctor who will agree with him that he has the diseases he knows he has. He expresses his desire to be rid of his ailments and may have the air of accepting his troublesome or painful ills with resigned fortitude and patience. Although he may seem depressed, there actually is no true depression present; rather, the picture is one of constant gloom.

Gastrointestinal symptoms are the most common in hypochondriasis, and several reasons have been advanced to account for the possible cause of this. Poor diet and lack of enough interests and participation in life play a part, of course, as does also the fact that digestion is easily affected by emotion. The overconcern with eating and evacuation which these individuals show has been interpreted by some as a return to infantile levels of libidinal gratification, although the evidence for this is inconclusive. Others believe that gastrointestinal symptoms are a displacement upward from genital symptoms, but again, this view is largely theoretical and not supported by conclusive evidence.

With the decline of reproductive function, genital symptoms are also common. These are probably tied up largely with the threat which the decline of sexual potency offers to the aging individual. Cardiovascular and respiratory symptoms likewise are frequent, and so is the belief that one has cancer, as in the following case:

S.H., aged sixty-one, ate too much, sat too much, and was too fat. She had twelve children, but as the older ones reached an age where they could help, she never considered herself well enough to assume the responsibility for her babies. Menopause was complete by the age of fifty-two, and although she complained endlessly of her symptoms, actually she welcomed the end of her reproductive period. By this time, however, most of her children had grown up, married, and left the home, so that she had few active interests left. She began to concentrate more and more on her bodily complaints, visited everyone she heard of who was ill or hospitalized for any reason, spent long periods in telling them of all the people she knew who died of the illness from which they suffered, listened avidly to the patient's symptoms, and in a few days found similar symptoms in herself. She developed "heartburn," stomach pains, excessive gas, shortness of breath, and heart trouble. For eight or ten years until her death, she was convinced that she had cancer—which traveled from one area of the body to another but in the end always returned to the stomach! She visited innumerable doctors and had many X rays in an effort to vindicate her diagnosis, but to no avail. One physician informed her family that she was suffering from hypochondriasis of long standing but as she would not accept this or consent to psychiatric treatment, she was permitted to continue her gloomy search for a doctor who would agree that she had cancer and treat her for this ailment. She finally died in a railway accident.

Anxiety states are frequent among the psychoneuroses at any age, and later maturity is no exception to this rule. Usually these states do not appear for the first time in later maturity but have been evident in greater or less degree in other periods of life. In anxiety states we find increased tension, restlessness, difficulty in concentrating and in sleeping, fears, and a sense of impending doom (2). Sometimes the fears are vague, nebulous worries, and sometimes they are definite phobias such as fear of dying, fear of subways. These psychic symptoms are accompanied by physical symptoms referable to various parts of the body. Cardiac and respiratory symptoms are common: the individual gets palpitation of the heart and dyspnea, which further increase his fears. He may also perspire heavily, get headaches and tremors, and show gastrointestinal symptoms. He feels he is in danger of dying or having something awful happen to him, and he cannot dispel these fears. He experiences a morbid anxiety which is not based on external danger but is rather a reaction to an inner unconscious and unrecognized danger to the personality.

Those anxiety states which include phobias are sometimes known as anxiety hysterias. In these individuals the same psychic and physical symptoms are present as in those anxiety states which do not include phobias, but abnormal fears of specific things are also present. The reasons why the individual is abnormally afraid of high places, of enclosed places, of wide open spaces, and the like are often so obscure that they can be uncovered only by prolonged and skilful psychotherapy. The basis of them lies in the unconscious, usually in instinctual drives that have been repressed because they are unacceptable and feared. The phobia is symbolic of the other repressed fear which the person dare not admit into consciousness. Frequently this repressed, instinctual impulse or fear is of a sexual nature. The individual who suffers from a phobia knows that his fear is abnormal, that it does not arise from any real danger from the environment, and that it comes from within himself, but he is powerless to control it or to understand, without help, the real reason for his fear.

The etiology of anxiety states is generally conceded to lie in emotional factors arising from external or internal stress. Frustrations, threats to security, social and economic discard, and lack of love are factors which tend to induce anxiety states in certain types of older persons. Often these occur in tense, basically insecure, unstable individuals who have had prolonged situational difficulties which they may have tried to overlook for a long time but for which they can find no adequate compensation. Often too, anxiety states with accompanying panic reactions may result from guilt feelings over sexual fantasies, urges, or practices or from hostile, aggressive impulses for revenge against supposedly dear ones who have emotionally traumatized the individual in some way. These fantasies and impulses cause conflict which results in the anxiety state. Often the conflict lies deeply buried in the unconscious.

Although anxiety states are conceded to be generally of psychic origin, a few studies indicate the possibility that sometimes they may arise from somatic disorder. For example, Ferraro (10) has shown how disturbances of the autonomic nervous system and other somatic factors may induce anxiety neuroses. Likewise, Ziegler (22) reported that one of his patients had an anxiety state which cleared up after the healing of his peptic ulcer; he concluded that the anxiety state was induced by the physical symptoms. Certainly, in older persons with anxiety states the possibility of an organic basis for the disorder, or at least organic involvement, must not be overlooked. We must remember that with an aging individual there normally are progressive bodily changes and there may also be abnormal changes, both of which may operate to produce emotional distress. In psychosomatic disorders we must remember the somatic as well as the psychic factors, for there is a reciprocal interaction between the two.

Psychotherapy with older persons suffering from anxiety states can often prove helpful in uncovering and resolving the basic emotional conflicts and in helping the individual to effect a more satisfactory adjustment. In working with the older patient, the conditions of living must be improved as well as the personal relations, and to do this it is sometimes necessary to work also with those with whom the older patient lives. The patient must be helped to accept himself as he is, to recognize his decreased potentialities, and to develop greater tolerance for himself. The two following cases illustrate chronic anxiety states in aging persons. The second case involves marked hypochondriacal symptoms and phobias.

A.B., male, aged fifty-nine, consulted a psychiatrist because of extreme tension, marked inability to concentrate, restlessness, palpitation of the heart, and excessive sweating. He also complained of fatigue and headaches, which he had had intermittently since boyhood. He had consulted psychiatrists previous to this, and had also been seen at the Mayo Clinic, where a diagnosis of "psychoneurosis" was made. He reported two earlier "breakdowns," one at the age of twenty-eight and another at the age of thirty-one. On both occasions he experienced symptoms similar to those from which he was suffering at this time. His tension, anxiety, inability to concentrate, and physical symptoms made it impossible for him to keep his job, and on this occasion he was also in danger of being unable to continue his work.

The case history of this man revealed that he had shown anxiety and other psychoneurotic symptoms from an early age, due possibly to an unfavorable environment superimposed on a constitutionally unstable individual. His father had an alcoholic psychosis and was always difficult around the house. His mother died when he was a year and a half old, and his father then married the mother's sister. He was always an insecure, irritable, fearful child, a nail-biter, and a sufferer from headaches.

This man always reacted to stress, frustration, and challenge with anxiety symptoms: he became panicky as a child when he had to go to school; he developed typical anxiety symptoms when he planned to marry and when an examination for promotion to a better job came up; and he developed these same symptoms in later maturity when faced with the possibility of retirement at the age of sixty.

M.F., female, aged fifty-eight, married, sought psychiatric help because of fears of dying, palpitation of the heart, dyspnea, and a "complete nervous breakdown." She gave a long history of maladjustment and emotional disturbance, beginning from early childhood and continuing until the present with remissions and reoccurrences. Her father was emotionally unstable and alcoholic. He died when she was a child, and her first symptoms began shortly after this. She became very fearful and "nervous," expressing particularly her fear of dying. She also became very tense and voiced many somatic complaints. Periodically these symptoms disappeared, only to reappear under stress. On the occasions of the birth of her children, the death of her favorite uncle, her husband's excessive drinking, her son's broken marriage, and her daughter's engagement to be married, she became tense, anxious, and fearful, experienced palpitation and pains around the heart, and complained of innumerable somatic disorders. Her most powerful recurring phobias were her fear of dying and her fear of subways. At the time of this visit she had not ridden on a subway for years.

She came irregularly for psychotherapy over a period of eight months. During this time she showed improvement, but a short while after discontinuing treatment there was a full return of symptoms, the most outstanding of which were her fear of going out, of the dark, and of staying alone, her hypochondriacal complaints, and her marked tension and anxiety. Her husband's drinking was one of the precipitating factors in both of her psychoneurotic episodes in later maturity.

Both of these cases illustrate anxiety states which have existed intermittently over a period of many years. Both responded to the ordinary stresses of life with a psychoneurotic anxiety pattern. Both were constitutionally unstable and subjected to unstable early influences in life which they were not emotionally strong enough to withstand.

Obsessive-compulsive disorders are those in which the individual is bothered by recurring thoughts (obsessions) of which he cannot rid himself or feels an irresistible urge to perform certain acts (compulsions), even though he may consciously not wish to do so. Although it need not necessarily be the case in every instance, obsessions and compulsions usually occur together in the same individual. They may develop in conjunction with psychotic disorders, with anxiety states, or alone, although anxiety is usually present in some form as, for example, when the compulsive acts of the individual are interfered with or prevented.

The development of obsessive-compulsive states is usually gradual, so that they seldom appear full-blown for the first time in later maturity. Generally, trends of this sort have been present for a long time, and often there have been earlier episodes of obsessive-compulsive disorder. The person who develops this kind of disorder is likely to be one who feels insecure, inadequate, and inferior and tends to be perfectionistic, meticulous, and overconscientious. Often he is given to doubts and cannot make up his mind; he tends to dwell too long on happenings and hurts; and he is inclined to be overly concerned about details and rituals. Also, despite a sometimes different surface impression, he is basically aggressive, wilful, obstinate, dominating, and full of hate and jealousy. He may appear to be mild, meek, and docile, but underneath the exterior he is quite the opposite.

Obsessive-compulsive disorders stem from impulses or drives that are warded off. They may be protective devices against hostile, erotic, or vengeful impulses which arouse guilt and anxiety or appear as a potential danger or threat to the personality. Essentially, they result from a conflict between these aggressive, hostile desires and a fear of consequences; they represent a fear of one's self and of one's impulses. In the aging, the threat of declining abilities and power to keep up with a changing environment offers additional insecurity. Physical and mental decline, waning of sexual potency, rejection, deprivation of love, social discard, retirement, or unemployment, with consequent feelings of uselessness, may serve to release the repressed emotions, which in turn induce further anxiety. As a defense against this anxiety, the individual may revert to earlier patterns of obsessive thinking or compulsive behavior, or he may resort to rituals and stereotyped ways of reacting in an ineffectual attempt to simplify the environment and keep it familiar and within the limits of his declining potentialities.

Obsessive-compulsive states in late maturity show essentially the same symptoms as those occurring earlier in life. An unwelcome, powerful, and disturbing thought may keep popping into the mind and refuse to be banished, foolish or shocking though it may be. Perhaps it is a sacrilegious thought or a thought of harming someone close and supposedly dear, but in any case it is a thought which is vehemently rejected by the conscious mind. On the other hand, it may be a compulsion to wash or clean constantly, to count or touch things, to check a certain number of times on locking the door or putting out the light, or to do or not to do some other irrational thing. The patient does not know why he does these things, although he sometimes offers some weak reason, but he feels compelled to perform certain acts and may become extremely anxious and disturbed if for any reason he is not able to do so. The following case illustrates this condition:

M.M., female, aged sixty-four, unmarried, sought psychiatric help because of scruples, an obsession about dirt, and a compulsion to spend all her time cleaning the house. She was obsessed with the idea of germs everywhere, so that she felt compelled to sterilize everything. She enjoyed playing bridge but would play only with her own cards, which were washable, and was loath to play with strangers who might contaminate the cards. She spent most of her day washing herself and cleaning her house, and she had complicated rituals for these functions. She had four washcloths for herself: one for her face and neck, one for her arms and the upper part of her body, one for the lower parts of her body, and one for her legs and feet. She regularly used the same number of towels to dry herself. She also had certain dustcloths which she could use only for certain pieces of furniture, and she became upset and had to destroy them all if anyone varied their uses. She was also obsessed with the idea of sin and read it into every thought and action; she felt compelled to make the sign of the Cross frequently in order to ward off the dangers of her sin.

Miss M. stated that she had been troubled by these symptoms for about a year, but further investigation revealed that she had experienced similar symptoms at other periods of her life and had always been an overly conscientious, religious, meticulous, perfectionistic person who was constantly tormented by doubts as to whether she was doing the right thing. In childhood she used to invent "growing pains" to escape things, and at the age of fourteen she became very scrupulous. She was bothered by thoughts of sin and thought her menstruation was a punishment for her sins. At the age of twenty-six she became interested in a man, but, as the time for marriage approached, she had a "nervous breakdown" and broke the engagement. She felt she was unworthy to marry and would harm the young man. She felt compelled to pray for him three times a day and for a period of two years went through an elaborate ritual of washing. She went through the menopause at about forty-nine with no outward physical symptoms but was tense and anxious and experienced psychic symptoms similar to those described above.

Miss M.'s symptoms rapidly became worse. She was given a series of electric shock treatments and psychotherapy and showed some improvement, but it was felt that her pattern of psychoneurotic behavior was of such long duration that little more than a reduction of anxiety and some amelioration in symptoms could be expected. Cooperation of the family in minimizing tension also helped her to effect a better adjustment.

Obsessive-compulsive disorders are difficult to treat at any period of life, and this is especially true in older patients, where they are generally of long duration and may be the patient's last defense against anxiety. The patient's environment and whole pattern of living, his needs and frustrations, his anxieties, his hostilities, and his wishes must be investigated and evaluated. As with the above patient, the most that can generally be expected is a reduction of anxiety and some amelioration of symptoms. The goal must be to make the patient more comfortable and happier in his environment.

Hysterical disorders represent the failure of an individual to adapt to the demands of life. They provide the dependent, helpless person with an escape from the fear and frustration of an intolerable situation. Whereas the obsessive-compulsive individual is basically aggressive and ready to attack, the hysterical patient is weak and dependent and is seeking sympathy, help, and flight from danger. In conversion hysteria there is an exaggerated loss of function in the absence of any physiological basis for the disability. The disability is a cry for sympathy and a retreat from the demands of life. Since the patient cannot tolerate in himself any idea of fear, forbidden impulses, or escape from life situations, his emotional conflict becomes transformed into physical symptoms and there is no longer any need for his unacceptable emotions. The physical disability makes it impossible for him to do what he fears, and it is probably for this reason that he is able to seem so emotionally controlled, so well adjusted, and so indifferent to his physical symptoms. If the emotions were not repressed and converted into physical symptoms, the patient would develop an anxiety hysteria and be tormented by terrors and apprehensions.

True beginning conversion hysteria is not common in later maturity, but carry-overs of earlier hysterical phenomena are not unusual. Not infrequent are quasi-hysterical conditions in which the individual exaggerates a partial defect, such as a sensory defect or lameness, in order to elicit sympathy, love, and attention, to gain security or prestige, or perhaps even to punish and arouse guilt in others for their alleged neglect. If the individual is successful in his attempts, his pattern of response may become fixed. It must be remembered, though, that this is an unconscious reaction and not to be confused with malingering, which is a conscious use of physical disability in order to gain a desired end, such as, for example, compensation. The following case is an illustration of conversion hysteria.

S.B., male, aged fifty-two, was referred for psychiatric study because of increasingly frequent spells of unconsciousness, usually of several minutes' duration. He had been given thorough physical, and neurological examinations and an electroencephalogram had been taken. All were negative for epilepsy or other organic basis for the spells. This patient stated that six months previously he had experienced drawing, burning pains in both legs, "like a burning furnace." The pains disappeared after a while, although he received no treatment for them, but they soon came back again. The pains appeared first in his left leg, then in his right leg, and then spread to his abdomen. He said, "My legs go dead and I drop in a heap; I'm in agony all the time; both legs feel dead. I have burning feelings going up my spine." He also complained of pains around his heart and appendectomy scar, and of headaches. Spells of unconsciousness began shortly after the second onset of the pains in the legs.

This man was a sociable, outgoing person who enjoyed friends and the company of others, but he had always been unstable and had difficulty in adjusting to the responsibilities of life. He was inadequate in his job and had been threatened with discharge. He had many family troubles and felt that his wife was most unsympathetic and would never let him hear the end of it if he lost his job.

Actually, S.B. would have liked to quit his job, which he hated, and to leave his wife with whom he was incompatible, but he could not tolerate in himself any idea of shirking his responsibilities or of not loving his wife. Hence he developed physical symptoms which would soon make it impossible for him to keep his job, no matter how much he consciously wished to do so, and which should elicit sympathy from his family.

Neurotic depressions (6, 19) are perhaps the most common of the psychoneurotic disorders of later maturity. They are much less intense and of shorter duration than psychotic depressions. Many are relatively so mild and shallow that they pass unrecognized and undiagnosed as neurotic depressions. Patients with conditions of this sort often consult a physician for a somatic complaint and are told to "go away for a rest" or to "take a two-week vacation in Florida." They show some hypochondriacal symptoms, tend to withdraw and complain of lack of interest in anything, and may be inclined to ready tears, but the condition is mild and may be no more than a brief episode which responds to the stimulus of change and improved physical condition.

Real neurotic depressions which occur in the aging are often precipitated by factors having to do with the aging process itself. Changes in biological, social, and economic status engender feelings of rejection, inadequacy, and uselessness, and the individual begins to feel pessimistic about the future. He internalizes the origin of his feelings and feels his unfortunate state is the result of his own unworthiness, inferiority, and decline. Seeing nothing ahead of him but further decline and rejection, he loses hope and interest and gives up the struggle. He becomes discouraged and self-centered, bewails his fate, regrets his past, and voices numerous somatic complaints. His melancholy attitude, irritability, and complaints make him less acceptable in every field, so that rejection is increased, and this in turn perpetuates the condition. Sometimes phobias or obsessive-compulsive ideas may accompany neurotic depressions. Often the patient is unable to sleep at night and complains of always feeling tired and worn out.

Treatment of neurotic depressions is important, especially to avert something more serious. Some have found electric shock treatment effective (11), although others apparently would reserve this type of treatment for the psychotic depressive patient. Benzedrine and allied compounds are often helpful in stimulating the patient and making him feel less tired, and sedatives are frequently used to help him sleep at night. Adjustment of deleterious environmental influences and psychotherapy are also helpful. A case of endogenous neurotic depression is described below:

E.Z., male, aged sixty-three, sought psychiatric help because he felt depressed and easily annoyed and was having difficulty in sleeping. He complained that for two months he had been bothered by pains in the head, itching in the rectum, double vision (eye examination showed vision to be normal), irritability, and sleeplessness. He had many self-derogatory thoughts and frequently dreamed of a cemetery and undertaker, although there were no real suicidal trends. He had cut off his contacts with his friends.

E.Z. had been fearful since childhood and was always a conscientious, worrisome, meticulous individual. He had long shown mild hypochondriacal trends and paid frequent visits to doctors. Eight years prior to this visit, his wife had become sick, and four years later she had died; his son died two years later. He was depressed and sorrowful after his wife's death but got over this and showed no unusual symptoms for about three years. His present depression was relatively mild in character but troublesome to him.

This patient was given sedation at night to insure sleep and benzedrine in the morning to stimulate him, although this was discontinued after he began to show improvement. He made frequent visits for psychotherapy at first, and then his visits were gradually spaced. Encouragement, reassurance, and suggestion were used freely. He was encouraged to return to his business, which he had given up, and gradually to develop new interests and to re-establish his contacts and friends. He made a fairly rapid recovery.

Therapy of Psychoneuroses in Aging Patients

For many years, therapy of the psychoneuroses of later life was considered largely a useless waste of time. Lately, however, the outlook has been more hopeful and optimistic, and considerable work is being done in this field (5, 9, 12, 17). In general, the first things to consider are whether the older patient is biologically capable of rebuilding and of making over his old habits, and what the extent of his capabilities is. If he is capable of changing only with greater effort and lessened gratification, which in the long run may result in irritability, resentment, depression, and feelings of inadequacy, his treatment will obviously be different from that if he is fully capable. If he is incapable of change, it will be foolish to spend much time in therapy, but it may be worth while to help those with whom he lives to develop greater tolerance and understanding.

Considerations of Health.—The health of the older patient is the first thing to be considered, for there are few in later maturity whose health cannot be improved. When seemingly hysterical or hypochondriacal complaints are voiced, it is always advisable first to determine whether there is any possible organic basis for the complaints. Any organic ailments found during a thorough physical examination should be treated at once. This is a good approach to the elderly patient and serves to establish rapport and confidence. Suggestions should be made for improvement of the general health and comfort of the patient as these are indicated. Vitamins and improvement of diet and a proper routine of rest, exercise, work, and recreation are usually helpful. The older patient should also be encouraged to keep up his general appearance, to visit a barber or a beautician, to develop and maintain good posture and gait, to plan a program in accordance with his abilities and interests, and to maintain a suitable level of activity.

The Patient's Environment.—Living conditions of the older patient should be investigated and modified as the need is indicated. If they are a source of distress, his abode may be changed or alterations made within the framework of his usual environment. His family should be interviewed and helped to gain insight into his condition and needs and to develop greater tolerance for him. He should be given the opportunity for the privacy and independence of action he needs.

The social life of the older patient should especially be investigated, for often this is a source of distress to him. The opportunities for gainful employment and avocational activities suited to his needs, interests, and abilities should be considered. Clubs with social activities, hobbies, recreational outlets, and occupational therapy are good, for the older patient is especially in need of association with his contemporaries. However, it must be remembered that suggestions for activities along these lines may be met with considerable resistance at first and accepted only after the patient has developed full confidence in the therapist.

Acceptance of Aging and Reality Factors.—The personal attitudes of the patient are also extremely important to consider. Acceptance of aging is necessary, but resignation is not good, for resignation leads to nothing but hopelessness, passivity, and decline. Acceptance, on the other hand, involves recognition of the aging process but at the same time a continuance of participation in life and the search for new values and potentialities.

In considering what and how much therapy to use with the older patient, it is necessary to evaluate his abilities and potentialities in every area. His life patterns, habits of adaptation and maladjustments, and the degree of modification which can be expected must be evaluated carefully in considering his ability to establish a workable therapeutic relationship.

Reality factors must also be taken into consideration—the patient's age, health, flexibility, desire for change, finances, and general environmental situation. Only by taking all these things into consideration can it be decided whether the elderly psychoneurotic would best benefit by a prolonged psychoanalysis, a brief analysis or psychotherapy, or merely a supportive therapy.

Medical Procedures.—Medical procedures, as mentioned earlier, are helpful with some older psychoneurotics, not only for amelioration of general health and correction of defects but also for specific treatment of the condition. Sedatives, for example, may help those patients who suffer from sleeplessness, and benzedrine and allied compounds may act as stimulants to many depressed patients. Care must be taken, however, that benzedrine is not used with those patients who suffer from coronary disorders. Insulin shock therapy has been tried successfully with some anxiety patients (15), and electric shock therapy with some depressives (11).

Psychotherapy.—On an individual interview basis, psychotherapy can be successful with many older patients if their general mental ability and emotional outlook show no gross aging (18). When organic brain damage is involved, therapy will be of limited value and usefulness; then the problem will be largely one of rearranging living in such a way as to insure the patient's greatest comfort. Care must be taken, especially when actual organic conditions are involved, in the approach to topics likely to cause emotional crises, hostility, and other disturbed reactions. In some cases, it may be advisable to warn the patient beforehand that certain topics about to be discussed may prove painful and result in the appearance of physical symptoms. Sometimes too, with older patients it may be advisable to be noncommittal and tentative in interpretations and to indicate a willingness to change the interpretations if necessary.

Group therapy either on an interview basis or with combined activity-interview sessions may also be an approach of value in the treatment of the older psychoneurotic patient. Having the opportunity for open discussion and evaluation of difficulties and using activities as ego-builders can prove helpful to many.

Rockwell (18) suggests that the therapist must assume obligation for the twenty-four-hour day of the patient. He must analyze the patient's complaints and the situational factors and utilize suggestion and other therapeutic measures. All factors involved must be analyzed, starting with the original complaint, and taking into consideration psychodynamic and somatic features, the constitutional makeup of the patient, and his general environmental conditions. Each interview should be terminated with a constructive formulation, synthesizing the material covered. Therapy should be distributed along the lines suggested by the history and the subjective needs of the patient as indicated during the course of treatment. Free association seems to be of less value in older than in younger patients, but the other usual psychotherapeutic techniques—rapport, dream analysis and interpretation, support, suggestion, hypnosis, and others—can be used successfully as the need is indicated.

Summary

A psychoneurosis is a minor functional disorder which presents both physical and psychic symptoms.

Although the symptoms may appear to be unpleasant afflictions, they actually serve some useful role in the life of the psychoneurotic. They result from the excessive use of unconscious mental mechanisms.

The mental mechanisms most commonly used by older maladjusted persons are aggression, withdrawal, projection, repression, conversion, and regression.

Psychic symptoms may include fear, anxiety, apprehension, obsessions, compulsions, and amnesia.

Physical symptoms may include sensory, motor, vasomotor, respiratory, cardiac, gastrointestinal, or genitourinary disorders.

It is difficult to make a clear differentiation between the psychoneuroses and the psychoses, but in general we might say that the psychoneurotic is affected in more limited areas, so that his personality remains better organized; he maintains his awareness of people and his grasp of social relations, remains well oriented, and recognizes the external world for what it is; he does not develop true delusions and hallucinations; he maintains repressions and does not regress to the degree that the psychotic does; he recognizes his illness and consciously wants to get well, even though he may have unconscious motives for not wanting to get well.

Psychoneuroses in later maturity are generally merely accentuations of maladjustments found in earlier periods, although the factor of biological aging is undoubtedly important. The incidence is rather high and may be even higher than is generally known, since many psychoneurotics are treated for everything except the psychoneurosis.

The etiology of psychoneuroses includes a multiplicity of factors, among which are constitutional factors, physiological decline and impairment (including organ and tissue changes, sensory impairment, and decline of sexual potency and attractiveness), environmental factors such as economic stress, retirement, dependence, and biological and sociological change in status, and emotional factors which include the life pattern of reacting and the present emotional response to aging and stress.

The most commonly found psychoneuroses of the senium include the following:

1. Hypochondriasis is a disorder that usually occurs in conjunction with other states but may occur alone. In hypochondriasis the increased preoccupation with bodily function which is the frequent accompaniment of aging becomes exaggerated and intensified until it is the major interest of the patient. Unconsciously it may be used to get attention, care, and affection or as a means of dominating and controlling others, or a way of getting revenge and expressing hostility and aggression. Attention may be centered on any bodily function.

2. Anxiety states carry with them fear, apprehension, tension, restlessness, sleeplessness, difficulty in concentrating, and a sense of impending doom. Phobias are common in those anxiety states known as anxiety hysterias. Accompanying physical symptoms are referable to various parts of the body, but the most common are cardiac, respiratory and vasomotor symptoms. Anxiety states may result from frustration, insecurity in various areas, lack of love, guilt feelings over sexual fantasies, drives, or practices, or conflict over hostile, aggressive impulses for revenge. Somatic disorder may also play a part.

3. Obsessive-compulsive disorders are those in which the individual is tormented by recurring thoughts (obsessions) of which he cannot rid himself or feels an irresistible urge to perform certain acts (compulsion), even though he may consciously not want to do so. They result from impulses or drives that are warded off and may serve as protective devices against hostile, erotic, or vengeful impulses which arouse guilt and anxiety or appear as a threat or danger to the personality. In the aging the threat of declining abilities and power to keep up with a changing environment offers additional insecurity. Often they are an

exaggeration of already existing obsessive-compulsive trends, or they may be a recurrence of previous similar episodes.

4. Hysterical disorders represent the failure of an individual to adapt to the demands of life; they are the dependent person's escape from an intolerable situation. In conversion hysteria the escape is in the form of an exaggerated loss of function in the absence of any physiological basis for the disability. They are not frequently found for the first time in later maturity but may be carry-overs from earlier states or a quasi-hysterical condition in which the individual exaggerates a partial defect in order to elicit sympathy, love, and attention, to gain security or prestige, or to punish others.

5. Neurotic depressions are the most common psychoneurotic disorders found in later maturity. They are milder, less intense, and of shorter duration than psychotic depressions. Neurotic depressions are often precipitated by factors having to do with the aging process itself. Withdrawal, disinterest, unhappiness, pessimism, feelings of unworthiness, and somatic complaints are common. Phobias or obsessive-compulsive ideas are sometimes present.

Therapy with older psychoneurotics can be successful if the patient is biologically capable of change. It involves investigation into the health, living conditions, social life, and personal attitudes of the patient and an evaluation of his ability to enter into a workable therapeutic relationship. Medical procedures include sedatives for sleeplessness, benzedrine and allied compounds for stimulation, and sometimes shock therapy. Insulin shock therapy has been used successfully with anxiety patients and electric shock with depressives. Psychotherapy is important, but the type, extent, and depth will depend upon the capabilities of the patient and other realities of the environmental situation.

REFERENCES

1. AFFLECK, J. W. Personality factors in the mental disorders of old age. *Med. Press,* 1949, **5765**, 422-24.
2. BENNETT, E. A. The anxiety state. *Postgrad. med. J.,* 1946, **22**, 375-78.

3. BERGLER, E. Elderly neurotics. *Dis. nerv. Sys.,* 1947, **8**, 35-36.

4. CAMERON, N. A study of thinking in senile deterioration and schizophrenic disorganization. *Amer. J. Psychol.,* 1938, **51**, 650-65.

5. ——. Neuroses of later maturity. In KAPLAN, O. (ed.), *Mental disorders in later life.* Stanford, Calif.: Stanford University Press, 1945.

6. CLOW, H. E., and ALLEN, E. B. A study of depressive states in the aging. *Geriatrics,* 1949, **4**, 11-17.

7. DEUTSCH, H. *Psychology of women.* Vol. II, *Motherhood.* New York: Grune & Stratton, Inc., 1945.

8. DORCUS, R. M. The psychoses and the psychoneuroses. In PENNINGTON, L. A., and BERG, I. A., *An introduction to clinical psychology.* New York: The Ronald Press Co., 1948.

9. FENICHEL, O. *The psychoanalytic theory of neurosis.* New York: W. W. Norton & Co., Inc., 1945.

10. FERRARO, A. Somato-psychic factors in anxiety neurosis. *J. nerv. ment. Dis.,* 1948, **107**, 228-42.

11. GALLINEK, A. Electric convulsive therapy in geriatrics. *N.Y. St. J. Med.,* 1947, **47**, 1233-41.

12. HADFIELD, J. A. *Psychology and mental health.* London: George Allen & Unwin, Ltd., 1950.

13. HAMILTON, G. V. Changes in personality and psychosexual phenomena with age. In COWDRY, E. V. (ed.), *Problems of ageing.* Baltimore: The Williams & Wilkins Co., 1939.

14. KAUFMAN, M. R. Old age and aging: the psychoanalytic point of view. Discussion by S. Atkin. *Amer. J. Orthopsychiat.,* 1940, **10**, 72-84.

15. KELLEY, D. McG., and THOMPSON, L. J. Insulin as an adjunct in the treatment of anxiety states. *N.C. med. J.,* 1947, **8**, 762-67.

16. LAWTON, G. Old age and aging: concluding remarks. *Amer. J. Orthopsychiat.,* 1940, **10**, 85-87.

17. MALAMUD, W. The psychoneuroses. In HUNT, J. McV. (ed.), *Personality and the behavior disorders.* New York: The Ronald Press Co., 1944.

18. ROCKWELL, F. V. Psychotherapy in the older individual. In KAPLAN, O. (ed.), *Mental disorders in later maturity.* Stanford, Calif.: Stanford University Press, 1945.

19. STERN, K., and MANZER, D. The mechanism of reactivation in depression of the old age group. *Psychiat. Quart.,* 1946, **20**, 56-73.

20. STRECKER, E. A. *Fundamentals of psychiatry.* Philadelphia: J. B. Lippincott Co., 1945.

21. WATTERS, T. A. The neurotic struggle in senescence. *Geriatrics,* 1948, **3**, 301-5.

22. ZIEGLER, D. K. Amelioration of anxiety symptoms accompanying the healing of a peptic ulcer: a case report. *J. nerv. ment. Dis.,* 1948, **107**, 276-78.

Chapter 8

PSYCHOSES

A psychosis is a major menal disorder which alters the feeling, thinking, and behavior of an individual. It is a reaction of failure in the never ending struggle to cope with the realities of life. Reviewing from the last chapter a few points of differentiation between the psychoses and the psychoneuroses, we might recall that in the psychotic the whole personality is usually involved, so that the individual may be socially disorganized. The psychotic may lose his capacity to differentiate between fantasy and reality, so that delusions and hallucinations are common. He tends to lose his capacity for effective repression, and his ego may become so weak that it will tolerate all things uncritically. Although some psychotics are aware of being ill, the majority have no real appreciation of being ill and little desire for change within themselves. Many give the impression of being "odd" or "queer." The legal concept of a psychosis, which carries with it the question of one's awareness of one's acts and of the difference between right and wrong, is obviously not applicable to the scientific or psychological concept of mental disorder.

Incidence of Mental Disorder

It has been said that one out of every twelve persons born in this country each year will spend some time in a mental hospital and one out of every sixteen of the present population has mental or personality difficulties.[1] Malzberg (29) in making a statistical analysis of 46,633 first admissions to New York State mental

[1] *Facts and figures about mental illness and other personality disturbances.* New York: National Association for Mental Health, Inc., 1952.

hospitals, found the average age of admission to be 48.5 years, with the rate of incidence increasing with advancing years. With a population which is growing older, we have an increase in the number of mental disorders in later life, and this is marked after the age of sixty years. According to Malzberg, the rate of incidence of first admissions of older persons to state mental hospitals is higher in urban than in rural districts, among the foreign-born than among the native-born, among the uneducated and lower economic classes than among the educated and wealthier groups, and among Negroes than among the whites.

TABLE 2

INCIDENCE OF PSYCHOSES IN RELATION TO AGE AT FIRST ADMISSION TO STATE HOSPITALS FOR MENTAL DISEASE, UNITED STATES, 1949 *

Age in Years	First Admissions			Percentage Distribution of Total First Admissions
	Total	Male	Female	
All ages	104,365	57,586	46,779	100.0%
Under 15	903	554	349	0.9
15 to 19	3,589	2,086	1,503	3.7
20 to 24	6,481	3,692	2,789	6.6
25 to 29	7,828	3,980	3,848	8.0
30 to 34	8,685	4,330	4,355	8.9
35 to 39	9,282	5,114	4,168	9.5
40 to 44	8,958	5,168	3,790	9.2
45 to 49	8,056	4,587	3,469	8.2
50 to 54	6,752	3,775	2,977	6.9
55 to 59	6,125	3,554	2,571	6.3
60 to 64	6,035	3,537	2,498	6.2
65 to 69	6,141	3,538	2,603	6.3
70 and over	18,836	9,933	8,903	19.3
Not reported †	6,694	3,738	2,956	——
Median age	46.9	47.2	46.6	

* From Federal Security Agency, *Mental Health Statistics*, National Institute of Mental Health, Series IMH-B52, No. 1 (Bethesda, Md.: Federal Security Agency, 1951).

† "Not reported" includes (a) first admissions shown on age and diagnosis schedules, but by age and not by diagnosis; (b) first admissions on movement schedules of hospitals not submitting schedules of first admissions by age and diagnosis; (c) first admissions with diagnosis, but with unknown age.

Pollack (37) relates those mental disorders that develop after the age of fifteen to successive age groups, placing dementia praecox and manic-depressive psychoses in the third, fourth, and fifth decades of life, general paralysis and alcoholic and involutional psychoses in the fourth, fifth, and sixth decades, and the senile and arteriosclerotic psychoses in the sixth, seventh, and eighth decades. Others, however, would confine the last group to the seventh and eighth decades.

Other studies from different areas of the country concerning the incidence of mental disorder in later life tend to confirm those from the New York area described above. Some believe that the relatively high incidence of mental disorder among the aged is associated with general factors of aging, arteriosclerosis, and the large number of chronic and debilitating physical disorders among those in later life.

Etiology

The etiology of psychoses in later maturity is generally to be found in a multiplicity of factors. Psychoses are not believed to develop from the mere fact of aging itself, although the individual's reaction to his own aging is always an important factor, nor are they generally the result of organic disease. Many of the psychoses of later maturity are recurrences of earlier psychotic episodes, and many are exacerbations of already existing maladaptive patterns, the exacerbation being the result of the stresses attendant upon the aging process.

Constitutional Factors.—Constitutional factors are undoubtedly predisposing to the development of a psychosis. This does not imply that psychoses as such are inherited, for this does not seem to be the case, but it does mean that the individual with a hereditary makeup which is unstable and weak may be less able to withstand the hardships and strains of life. Perhaps for everyone there may be a point beyond which stress can no longer be endured; for the individual who develops a psychosis, this breaking point is relatively low.

Although it does not follow that the mentally ill individual will necessarily produce offspring who are psychotic or who will develop psychoses, the family histories of psychotic patients generally show a larger than average percentage of mental or nervous instabilities or abnormalities in the forebears or collaterals. Nevertheless, it usually is the case that even in those individuals who are constitutionally unstable, environmental factors, either in the form of psychological stress or organic disorder, are necessary to precipitate the full development of a psychosis.

Reaction to Bodily Changes.—Physiological decline or illness may serve as a predisposing or precipitating factor in the development of a psychosis in later maturity. We have already seen how, in the psychoneuroses, the individual's reaction to his own bodily changes may induce emotional distress, largely in the form of fear, anxiety, or depression. The same reactions may operate in intensified form in those individuals who develop psychoses. Sensory impairment seems to be particularly important in this respect, for it is very easy for the maladjusted aging person who cannot see or hear clearly to become suspicious of those around him, and this suspicion may eventually lead to paranoid reactions. This is particularly noticeable in those individuals with hearing defects.

In addition to the individual's reaction to his own normal age changes, we must also consider the possible effect of the exaggeration of physiological age changes, particularly changes in the homeostatic mechanisms, which may occur within the body without known cause. As Shock (43, 44) has pointed out, interference with the normal supply of oxygen or glucose to the brain will result in impairment of mental functioning. Likewise, any interference in brain metabolism caused by disturbance of carbohydrate metabolism or enzyme systems may result in symptoms of mental disorder, which often disappear with the administration of suitable vitamins. Some recent studies tend to show the importance of constricted capillaries in the etiology of dementia praecox, and this may also prove to be an important factor in the psychoses of later maturity, since with age the number of capillaries may be diminished, cellular function impaired, and the flow of blood through the capillaries less adequate. This may result in an interference with the diffusion of oxygen in the brain and consequent mental disturbance. Arteriosclerosis, which is probably connected with these changes, may also be influential in producing mental symptoms. In connection with possible organic brain changes in the etiology of mental disorders of later maturity, it should also be mentioned that electroencephalographic studies show increasing abnormalities with advancing age, particularly in older psychotic individuals (16). Another factor of importance, as indicated by recent psychobiological research, may be found in hormone imbalance, which, as we know, is not infrequent in the aging, particularly in regard to the sex hormones. Infections, toxic conditions, and exhaustion may also play a part.

General weakening of the organism, particularly through organic disease, may also be an important factor in the development of a psychosis in later maturity. Because of the psychosomatic unity inherent in the human organism, an organic illness may induce or be accompanied by mental symptoms. We have already seen how emotional disturbance may induce somatic symptoms, and we must remember that the reverse may also obtain.

Tensions Induced by Environment.—Environmental stress, particularly that stress which is attendant upon the aging process and induces insecurity, probably plays an important part in the development of all psychoses of later maturity. Those environmental factors already discussed in connection with the development of psychoneuroses in later maturity might be mentioned briefly again, since they are probably even more important in the psychoses because the psychotic individual's reaction to them is intensified. Economic inadequacy and retirement, which may result in dependence on unwilling and perhaps spiteful offspring, may be a very stressful situation for many aging persons. Social and emotional deprivations likewise tend to induce feelings of inferiority, inadequacy, and rejection, and the individual, in accordance with his basic personality makeup, will react to these feelings and his treatment by others with hostility, aggression, depression, or withdrawal.

As with the psychoneuroses, psychoses seldom appear full-blown for the first time in later maturity without previous signs of maladjustment. As mentioned above, the psychosis may be an intensification, due to tension of some sort, of already existing maladaptive patterns or a recurrence of earlier psychotic episodes. It may also be a reactivation of an emotional disorder which occurred in adolescence. Even in those cases where the disorder is precipitated by an organic illness which is known to have a damaging effect on the brain, there appears on autopsy to be relatively little relationship between the actual amount of brain damage and the severity of the psychotic symptoms displayed.

Characteristic Changes in the Psychoses

Changes in the thinking, feeling, and behavior of the psychotic individual are so closely allied that it is difficult, if not impossible, to differentiate clearly between them. They usually occur together in varying degrees in the same individual, and disorder in one area influences the development of disorder in another area.

Intellectual Functioning.—Some of the common changes characteristic of the psychotic individual include thought disorganization and inefficiency of mental functioning. Ideas may become clouded or distorted and thoughts slowed, confused, fragmentary, or flighty. Impairment of mental functioning may occur in any area, although often it is most evident in the attention, learning, memory, and motor faculties. There may be ideas of reference or paranoid ideas. Delusions may be of somatic, grandiose, or persecutory nature. Perceptual disturbances may be seen in the form of illusions and hallucinations. Hallucinations may be present in any sensory field, although they occur most frequently in the auditory and visual areas. Emotional aberrations may include states of euphoria and elation, depression, overwhelming anxiety, tension, or apathy. Mannerisms and oddities of thought, speech, or action may be present; motor activity may be slowed or accelerated and consciousness and orientation may be disturbed. Social disarticulation may result to such a degree that the psychotic individual is unable to continue normal social intercourse. This, however, is not always the case, as can be seen from the fact that many paranoid individuals are able to maintain themselves in society for years without being hospitalized or even sent anywhere for treatment.

Scientific studies of the changes in the intellectual functioning of aged psychotics have been well summarized by Granick (15), who emphasizes the fact that relatively little work has been done in this field. Nevertheless, tests comparing aged psychotics with aged nonpsychotics and with various younger groups indicate intellectual deterioration in the psychotic so severe that the average performances of senile patients suffering from arteriosclerotic psychosis, senile dementia, and long standing schizophrenia are little better than those of young children. Impairment is evident in memory, language, and abstract thinking functions.

Emotional and Personality Changes.—Emotional and personality changes and alterations of behavior among older psychotics are similar to those found in psychotic patients of other ages, although in general it might be said that the older psychotic tends toward either paranoid or depressive types of reaction (42). These reactions are used as a defense against the tension and discomfort arising from frustrated drives and are a means of expressing aggression, in depression the aggression being turned inward toward the self, and in paranoid states outward toward others. Depressive states are associated with feelings of loss, deprivation, inadequacy, and rejection; and are often precipitated by the death of someone close, social rejection, retirement, economic strain, or other stressful situations. Paranoid conditions are not uncommon in later life but are often so mild that they pass for oversensitiveness and irritability. Other more severe paranoid states may occur in connection with involutional psychoses or psychoses with organic brain injury.

In speaking of types of psychoses, however, we must note that it is very difficult to make a satisfactory classification of psychoses in general, and this is particularly true of the psychoses in later life. Human beings, normal or abnormal, cannot well be categorized, and in psychotic conditions we frequently find considerable overlapping. Patients may show symptoms supposedly characteristic of psychoses of more than one type, so that it is difficult to make a clearcut diagnosis. In older persons there is the additional complicating factor of possible organic involvement. Nevertheless, we shall discuss those psychoses most frequently encountered in later maturity.

Functional Psychoses

Actually, it is not common for a functional psychosis to occur for the first time in later maturity or old age, although occasionally this does occur. More often, however, the functional psychosis found in later years is a recurrence of episodes experienced earlier in life. Sometimes also it may be a display of symptoms that are in accordance with the basic personality but are superimposed on an organic or degenerative psychosis.

Manic-Depressive Disorders.—Manic-depressive psychoses (18, 23, 47) constitute from 10 to 15 per cent of all psychoses and are more common in women than in men. Symptoms may vary from extreme elation to deepest depression. Some have referred to the manic-depressive psychoses as "alternating psychoses" because of the frequency with which some patients experience marked mood swings between the manic and the depressive states. Usually the patient has manic or depressive periods from which he recovers, seeming normal for a while, but then there is a tendency for a recurrence of the disorder.

In states of mania the patient becomes, in varying degrees, elated, overactive, euphoric, witty, self-confident, uninhibited in speech and behavior, gay, and perhaps aggressive. He may have difficulty in sleeping, become constipated, and lose weight. If his manic condition becomes very acute, he may grow extremely excitable, restless, highly distractible, and impatient and talk incessantly and often irrelevantly, with ideas shifting so quickly from one to another as to lose coherency. He may become angry and abusive with little provocation, show a complete lack of inhibition in his clownishness and obscenity, and indulge in unbridled criticism of others, although he himself may be very sensitive. At the height of a manic attack, the patient may become disoriented, uncontrollable, and even dangerous, so that segregation from others is essential. He may have delusions, usually of a grandiose nature but sometimes also of a persecutory nature. In very severe states, the patient may hallucinate frequently, but in most manic states hallucinations tend to be transitory and not too important.

In contrast to this picture of elation, excitement, and overactivity, the depressed patient becomes, in varying degrees, sad, dejected, underactive, and lacking in initiative. He may experience difficulty in thinking, show psychomotor retardation, and become self-accusatory and self-disparaging. He may lack self-confidence, feel hopeless, have no appetite, and be unable to sleep. He seems to expect and to feel that he merits punishment, and he may have hypochondriacal complaints. Suicidal trends are so common among depressed patients that they must be watched carefully in order to avert any attempt at suicide. In some retarded depressives, the depression may become so deep that the patient goes into a stupor. In other depressive states the patient, instead of becoming retarded, becomes agitated. He may grow restless, anxious, overactive and overtalkative, moan, wring his hands, express many hypochondriacal complaints, utter phrases of despair, and voice his ideas of his own sin, worthlessness, and expected punishment.

General hygiene, with particular attention to diet and elimination, is important in both manic and depressive states, Also, whereas the retarded depressive may need measures to stimulate him, the manic and the agitated depressive will need measures to quiet and soothe—sedation, baths, soothing hot packs, and the like. Other therapies which have proved helpful in these disorders include different kinds of shock treatment but especially electroshock, narcosis (induction of prolonged sleep) particularly in states of excitement, endocrine treatment (especially with the female hormone called estrone), prefrontal lobotomy (severing fibers in the prefrontal lobe of the frontal brain so as to separate it from adjacent areas), lobectomy (removing the entire frontal lobe) and topectomy (excising certain areas). Psychotherapy during the convalescent period may prove helpful.

A case of manic-depressive psychosis is described below:

M.S., male, aged sixty-two, started his mental illness with a depressive state following the death of his wife, the serious illness of his daughter, and his own operation. He felt very sad, dejected, and unworthy, blamed himself for the misfortunes which were happening to him, and expressed the idea that he was being punished for his failure as a husband and father. After two years of this depression, for which he was not hospitalized, he went to Florida "for a vacation and a new outlook." While he was there his depression improved considerably, and he remained apparently well until several months later when, following a disagreement with his son, his mood swung to one of elation. He became excitable, overactive, flighty, and grandiose in his ideas. Although he had always been rather dignified and reserved, he now began to go around slapping people on the back with exaggerated friendliness. He spent money freely and with poor judgment and wanted to remarry, selecting a woman much younger than himself and most unsuitable from every point of view.

M.S. had always been a moody, worrisome type of person who was overly concerned about details and reacted severely to the stresses and strains of life. Although his mother was said to have been quick-tempered and emotionally unstable, there was no definite history of mental illness in his family. As far as could be determined, this was his first psychotic episode, even though he had always shown a tendency to become unduly upset over things.

M.S. was admitted to a mental hospital with a diagnosis of manic-depressive psychosis, manic stage. He was observed for a period of time and given superficial psychotherapy, but shock treatment was withheld because of his poor general physical condition and the belief that his psychosis might clear up without it. This proved to be the case within a relatively short time, and he was discharged from the hospital. A year later he was still well.

This case illustrates a relatively mild manic-depressive psychosis occurring for the first time in the senescent period. As mentioned above, it is rather unusual for a manic-depressive psychosis to appear for the first time in this period, but it will be noted that this man, as is the case with most others who develop psychoses, had long shown signs of emotional instability and inability to withstand the stresses of life. Also, his psychosis was not severe, and he did recover rapidly. However, it would not be at all surprising to see a recurrence of his psychosis should life's stresses again prove too much for him.

Schizophrenia.—Schizophrenia or dementia praecox (18, 23, 47) is the most common of the early psychoses, constituting 20 to 30 per cent of state hospital admissions. It may appear at any age but occurs more often in adolescence and young adulthood than in other periods of life. It generally develops in the withdrawn, tense, egocentric personality who tends to blame others for his own inadequacies. Characteristically, there are disturbances of thought, behavior, and emotion. The schizophrenic shows a disharmony of thought and mood, seems queer, does bizarre things, appears to live in a world of his own, and is given to inappropriate behavior. He seems indifferent and unaware of what is going on around him and tends to disregard the realities of life. He often has ideas of reference, believing that even chance remarks heard on the street pertain to him, and he may have delusions and hallucinations. Delusions are frequently of persecutory nature, although sometimes somatic delusions and delusions of grandeur are also present, and hallucinations are most likely to be in the auditory field, although visual hallucinations and hallucinations in other sensory areas also occur not infrequently.

The four main types of schizophrenic disorder show considerable overlapping of symptoms, and one type seldom appears in a clear-cut fashion, without any of the symptoms of any of the other groups. Nevertheless, the differentiation is generally made when the symptoms of one group predominate.

1. *Simple schizophrenia* shows a gradual withdrawal, loss of interest, and deterioration. The disorder may go unrecognized for a long time because of the lack of striking symptoms: the individual merely seems apathetic, unconcerned, without ambition, and not interested in advancing himself. Thus, although it is not the usual thing, some of these simple schizophrenics may be so diagnosed for the first time in later maturity. Actually, the disorder may have been of many years' standing but unrecognized because the individual was able and content to maintain himself at a low level. It is possible too that some cases may never be diagnosed as schizophrenic, although even to family and friends their history and behavior are strongly suggestive of mental disorder or deterioration.

An example of simple schizophrenia, known to the writer, is the case of a college graduate and a certified public accountant, who spent thirty-five years of his life taking care of the lawns and doing other simple manual work in an institution. He was married, owned his own home, and performed his work satisfactorily, but he had no friends or social outlets, seldom engaged in conversation with anyone (including his wife), and had absolutely no interests of any kind. His entire existence was one of working, eating, and sleeping, all of which he seemed to do in a little world of his own. He died of pneumonia at sixty-two.

2. The *hebephrenic schizophrenic* is characterized principally by his silliness and the incongruity of his manner and

behavior. His affect is inappropriate, and he shows incoherence and foolishness in his speech and conduct; he may decorate himself with all sorts of things, show an abnormal interest in his urine or feces, indulge in grimaces, and use odd symbolic gestures and speech. He may have fantastic hallucinations and delusions and may show aggressive, retaliatory behavior against those he thinks are concocting weird plots against him. If the condition is not treated at an early stage, deterioration may be rapid. This type of schizophrenia, when found in later maturity, is generally an old, chronic case, usually one that has been hospitalized for a long time or cared for by his family with the understanding that he is suffering from a mental disorder. Note also the circumstances in the following case:

Oddly enough, the writer had, at one time, brief contact with a married, childless couple, presumably in the fifties, both of whom apparently were suffering from a hebephrenic type of schizophrenia. They came into a business office, both dressed rather oddly and decorated with all sorts of buttons. The woman did not participate actively in the conversation but stood aside with a silly smile and occasionally interjected the remark "God's will" at most inappropriate points. The man marched into the office and demanded to know why the person in charge of the firm had sent him a plague of mosquitoes. Although he said this in a belligerent manner, he smiled afterward so that the owner thought he was joking and made a facetious remark, whereupon he became excitable, grimaced horribly, and made most fantastic accusations. He became so aggressive and threatening that it was necessary to call a policeman and have him removed.

Later, on questioning the owner of the business, the writer learned that the couple lived on a small, isolated farm in the country, the man (whom the owner described as an "odd duck") having purchased the place five years previously because he thought it would help his wife whom he knew to be "crazy"!

3. *Catatonic schizophrenia* is characterized by extreme negativism and muscular rigidity, although there are often also periods of excitement and violence. Stereotyped behavior, pos-

turing, and grimacing are common; odd and uncomfortable postures are sometimes maintained for hours or days. Sometimes these schizophrenics become mute, incontinent, and resistive, refuse food, and have to be tube-fed. The disorder rarely occurs for the first time in later maturity, but it may be seen there as a recurrence of an earlier episode or as a continuance of a long-existing mental illness. Usually cases of this sort must be hospitalized permanently.

4. The *paranoid schizophrenic* may be diagnosed for the first time in later maturity more often than some of the other types of schizophrenics because he has been able to maintain himself for a long period of time despite his psychosis. The disorder is a delusional state which develops gradually in a suspicious although often highly intelligent personality. Delusions are generally of persecutory or grandiose nature, although somatic delusions are frequently present also. The delusions build up gradually, and ideas which at first seemed rational become irrational and distorted. The more intelligent and better-preserved personality may keep these ideas under control or unexpressed for a long time, so that he is able to maintain himself in society for many years, but with others the delusions may more rapidly come to include all the environment and to dominate the thoughts and behavior so that hospitalization becomes necessary for the protection of society. Hallucinations may or may not be present. The greater the amount of mental disorganization, the quicker the disorder is detected. A case of paranoid schizophrenia, recurrent in nature, is described below:

D.W., female, aged sixty-three years, had a postpartum schizophrenic reaction at the age of twenty-six which was, at the time, called a "hysterical spell." The condition cleared up rather quickly without treatment and did not recur until five years later, following the birth of her second child. At that time she showed symptoms similar to those she displayed in lesser degree five years before: she became seclusive, withdrawn, and suspicious, accused her husband of infidelities, and heard voices which tormented, accused, and persecuted her. This episode cleared up in about two months, but after that time the "spells" recurred every few years. The symptoms followed a more or less set pattern: withdrawal, apathy, oddness, suspicion, auditory hallucinations, and accusations of infidelity against the husband. The episodes were always of relatively brief duration, usually lasting from two weeks to two months, and she had never been hospitalized because she remained fairly manageable and did not become loud or boisterous. Between her psychotic episodes, she was said to remain fairly well except for being extremely sensitive and given to quick anger and suspicion. However, for a few years the spells had been recurring with greater frequency and had been of longer duration. At the time of this contact, her current psychotic episode was already of three or four months' duration and as yet showed no signs of abating. For this reason, hospitalization and insulin shock treatment were recommended. She showed rapid improvement and seemed entirely normal at the time of her discharge less than two months later.

This case illustrates how some chronic schizophrenics, particularly those of paranoid type, may manage to maintain themselves more or less adequately for years and never be hospitalized until later maturity, when they have a psychotic episode during which the symptoms become more acute and of longer duration.

General Paralysis (Paresis)

General paralysis is a psychosis which used to be found not uncommonly in later maturity, but fortunately, because of new drugs and therapies, it is rapidly disappearing. It is caused by syphilis which has attacked the brain tissue, and it has been known to occur years after the patient thought he was cured of syphilis. Of late years, however, the treatment of syphilis has been so much more effective that it is now rather rare to see a case of paresis. Also, the new drugs and fever therapies have improved tremendously the prognosis in this once hopeless disorder. However, age may be a complicating factor in the course of the disease. The paretic patient shows both physical and psychic symptoms. He may suffer from headaches, dizzy spells, tremors, and difficulties of gait and speech. His pupils are small and often unequal, and they fail to react to light, although they do react in accommodation for seeing at different distances. Sometimes he has convulsions. He may be elated and euphoric, have grandiose delusions, and spend his money recklessly and with poor judgment; or he may be despondent and inclined toward suicide. In considering the symptoms shown by the paretic, Wooley (48) has pointed out that paretic patients respond to their brain damage in accordance with their pre-psychotic personality, the introvert tending to react with schizoid symptoms and the extrovert with manic or depressive tendencies. According to this theory, the depressive reactions will occur if the brain damage has been sufficient to interfere with judgment, whereas the manic reactions will occur when judgment has been impaired and inhibition lost.

Alcoholic Psychoses

Alcoholic psychoses (23, 47) are not essentially mental disorders of later maturity, but they may occur then as well as in any other period of adult life. Of course, not all alcoholics become psychotic. Those who do usually have first a rather prolonged period of alcoholism, so that most are well into adulthood and some have reached the years of later maturity by the time the psychosis develops. Also, although emotional maladjustment is evident in all alcoholics, it is more pronounced in those who develop psychoses than in those who do not. Basic to the alcoholism itself are probably both physical and psychological causes. Vitamin deficiency, for example, has been advanced as one of the possible physical causes of alcoholism, and there are probably also other, as yet unknown, physical factors involved. Psychologically, it may serve as an escape from reality, a defense against a repressed homosexuality, or a regression to infantilism, or it may be the reaction of a basically inferior personality.

Delirium tremens is an alcoholic psychosis which generally occurs after a severe alcoholic spree, although it may develop in a chronic alcoholic after an illness or injury. It seldom occurs before the age of thirty years and may occur during the years of later maturity. The symptoms may vary in intensity and duration, but they usually last from three to six days. The disorder is characterized by restlessness, excitability, sleeplessness, and fear. The patient may become disoriented and hallucinate actively. He may feel things crawling over him, see frightening creatures, or hear horrible, accusatory voices. When he does manage to get to sleep, he is quickly awakened by terrifying nightmares. He may start at the slightest sound and perspire profusely. Medical and nursing care are important, and the patient should be observed carefully at all times. Rest, hot packs, and diet, especially vitamin intake, are important therapeutic procedures, and psychotherapy may help in the convalescent period.

In addition to the fact that delerium tremens may occur in later maturity, age itself may be a complicating factor in the psychosis. Any one of the diseases common to the period of later maturity may be the precipitating element in the development of the psychosis; when the psychosis has already developed, one of these disorders may have a deleterious effect upon recovery. Nephritis, cardiac decompensation, or exhaustion resulting from the decreased efficiency of the homeostatic mechanisms, for example, may retard the recovery or even be responsible for the death of a patient. Elderly patients also must be watched carefully for fractures during their periods of extreme restlessness and fear when they are trying so desperately to escape from their horrors.

Korsakow's psychosis is another mental disorder which may result from prolonged alcoholism or other toxic conditions, often being associated with a polyneuritis, although this is not always the case. It seldom occurs before the age of fifty and is more prevalent among women than among men. It is characterized by a severe memory defect (particularly for recent events), disorientation of time and place, mental confusion, and a marked tendency to confabulate. Fabrication of fantastic stories may result from the patient's need to try to fill in the gaps arising from this memory defect. Although this is basically an organic psychosis, the work of Lindberg (26) and that of Davidson (8) both show the importance of psychogenic factors and of affectivity in the disorder, particularly with respect to memory defects and confabulation. On free association tests these patients showed a delayed response to emotionally charged words, and under sodium amytal they became spontaneously productive and ceased confabulating. Because of the changed affectivity and the productions secured under sodium amytal, it was felt that this drug could be helpful in the treatment as well as the prevention of the disorder.

Involutional Psychoses

The involutional psychoses are mental disorders of middle and late maturity. They occur more frequently in women than in men, and often they are closely associated with the menopause. They used to be called "involutional melancholia" by some and were classified by others under the manic-depressive psychoses. Now they are generally recognized as a separate group containing, in the main, two types of patients, the depressed and the paranoid, although there are some individuals who present features of both types. For the most part, it is considered that for the depressed involutional psychotic the prognosis for recovery is essentially good, for the paranoid type poor, and for the mixed group doubtful.

Although it is usually said that the involutional psychoses are those that occur for the first time in the middle or later years of life without previous history of mental illness or organic intellectual defect, studies tend to show that those individuals who become psychotic at this time have a basically unstable personality makeup or have shown signs of emotional maladjustment prior to the onset of their illness. This was brought out by Stern and Prados (46) in regard to the depressions of menopausal women and by Greenhill (17) in regard to the psychoneuroses of women in this period. Often the symptoms are a reactivation of those psychotic symptoms shown in the pubertal period. As in the earlier period, there may be an intensification of libidinous needs and a weakening of the superego, so that effective sublimation of impulses and desires become less easy and may cause considerable struggle and conflict. This can sometimes be seen in cases of latent homosexuality, when the intensification of the drive in this direction results in unconscious panic and consequent quarrels with friends of the same sex. As was mentioned in Chapter 2, when the inner homosexual conflict becomes too strong in already maladjusted individuals in this period, paranoid ideas, similar to the pubertal paranoid reactions to homosexual danger, may develop. In general, we often find among involutional psychotics a prepsychotic personality which was introverted, inhibited, uncompromising, rigid, meticulous, highly repressed, narrow, and poorly adjusted sexually. It is also common to find organic factors, such as endocrine imbalance or cerebroarteriosclerosis, associated with the disorder.

Symptoms displayed by the involutional psychotic vary with the individual and his particular type of psychosis; delusions and other paranoid trends tend to predominate in the depressed type. Commonly found are agitation, uneasiness, self-condemnation, depression, anxiety, and fear concerning the body and death. The patient is often troubled with insomnia and lack of appetite; he loses weight, withdraws his interest from outside activities and people, becomes preoccupied with himself, and feels life for him is over and there is nothing worth while left. His psychomotor reactions become retarded, and he shows a desire to punish others as well as himself. Sometimes paranoid trends, which may be either transitory or prolonged, are evident, with delusions of persecution, suspicion, or misinterpretation.

At some time during the course of an involutional psychosis it is common to find a period of agitated depression. This may start as a simple depression with sadness, hopelessness, apathy, and psychomotor retardation and then develop into a more severe state in which restlessness, depressive ideation, wringing of the hands, and rocking back and forth are common. The patient may show marked anxiety and narcissism, and he may express ideas of martyrdom, sin, and unworthiness. He may whine, nag, and be punishing toward others and himself. He may also be fearful and show hypochondriacal delusions, hallucinations, and paranoid symptoms. Suicide and suicidal ideas are common and must be guarded against, especially during the period when the depression seems to be lifting.

In mild or moderate involutional psychoses where endocrine factors are important, the use of hormonal therapy, especially in combination with other therapies, proves helpful. In more severe cases, however, when there is a basic personality defect with perhaps paranoid or schizophrenic trends, endocrine therapy is relatively ineffective. Shock treatment, especially electroshock treatment, is helpful with moderate and severe depressive types. According to Davidoff (7), electroshock treatment of involutional females is most effective in those under fifty with dependent or depressive personalities whose illness is of less than three years' duration. Those near sixty years of age with markedly aggressive, schizoid personalities, severe paranoid trends, and arteriosclerotic involvement, who have been ill more than five years, respond poorly. However, these trends are not so noticeable with men, and in these groups age, arteriosclerosis, and aggressive personality are not contraindicative of response to electroshock therapy. Many consider that, in general, a combination of hormone and electroshock therapy with attention to diet and vitamin intake is most helpful in the acute stages of the disorder, with psychotherapy and occupational therapy during the recovery period. Hydrotherapy and other medical measures should be used as the need is indicated.

The two following cases illustrate respectively the phenomena of involutional depression and of involutional psychosis of paranoid type:

P.W., female, aged fifty, became very depressed following a series of situational difficulties, deaths, and personal disappointments. There was no history of any previous depressive state until the onset of her current condition, which was of about three months' duration. She was the oldest child in a family of five. After the death of her father, she took over the responsibility for the care of her mother and the younger members of her family. She avoided marriage in order to provide for the education of her younger siblings. When they left home, she continued to care for her mother, who had become an invalid. Several months prior to the onset of her illness, her mother died and a younger brother was killed in an accident; following this she failed in her business to receive a promotion for which she had worked very hard. Menopause was practically completed. Her mental illness was initiated by extreme tension, pains in the stomach, headaches, lack of appetite, and insomnia. She felt very lonely in the world and thought there was nothing left for her; she cried, bewailed her unfortunate lot, and expressed ideas that she was being punished for her sins and unworthiness. Her condition was too severe at this time for psychotherapy, but she was hospitalized and responded well to injections of estrogen and electroshock therapy. Following a series of shock treatments, she was given psychotherapy, to which she was then able to respond well. She was discharged nine months later and has remained well for two years.

M.W., female, aged fifty-two, first showed symptoms of an involutional psychosis two years before psychiatric consultation. Six months prior to this, the body of her son who was killed in the second World War was returned to the United States. She grieved deeply over this and showed signs of simple depression, but this was soon followed by paranoid ideas. She accused another son of trying to kill her, expressed fears of being followed on the street, and said the neighbors were talking about her, spreading scandal, destroying her reputation, and ruining her character. She thought she was being spied upon, and she inspected her food carefully for signs of poisoning. Menopause was completed at forty-nine and no special difficulty was reported, although she took endocrine preparations for several years. Her condition was so severe at the time of psychiatric consultation that hospitalization was necessary. Six months

later, in spite of a series of electroshock treatments, endocrine therapy, and psychotherapy, she still had paranoid ideas which were too
strong to warrant her release from the hospital. It is considered
that the prognosis in this case is poor.

Both of these women showed rigid, compulsive, repressed,
emotionally unstable prepsychotic personalities and were maladjusted sexually. In addition, M.W. had always been egocentric, selfish, and inclined to be suspicious and to suspect the
motives of others. No definite history of mental disorder in
either family could be elicited. The paranoid trends in the latter
case account for the poorer prognosis.

Toxic Delirious Psychoses of the Aging

Toxic delerious reactions are among the more common
mental disorders of later life, particularly after the age of sixty
years. According to a report by Robinson (38), over 20 per
cent of all patients over sixty admitted to the hospital in which
he was studying cases had a toxic delirious state as their sole
abnormal mental reaction, and another 20 per cent had this state
superimposed upon some other type of abnormal mental reaction. Although the etiology of the psychoses varies, in all cases
there is a disturbance of the metabolic processes of the whole
organism as well as of the brain itself. Any condition inducing
a toxic state, such as an illness, operation, injury, drug intake,
or prolonged recumbency can precipitate the psychosis. Commonly, however, there is a breakdown of carbohydrate metabolic
functions with a failure of detoxication. This leads to autogenous toxemia and causes the physical and psychic symptoms
by the action of the circulating toxins upon the brain cells and
their function. In general, treatment aims to restore the carbohydrate metabolic functions and to prevent additional toxemia
through certain chosen therapeutic procedures. Usually daily
infusions of 10 per cent glucose in water are an important part
of therapy. Vitamins do not help, and sedatives may aggravate
the condition.

The symptoms of toxic delirious psychoses vary with the individual patient, and anything from complete collapse to severe hallucinosis may be found. The symptoms usually come on with speed following an illness or other toxic-inducing condition; the patient becomes restless, irritable, and unable to sleep and has anorexia. Symptoms are evident in the psychic, physical, and neurological areas.

Psychotic symptoms include diurnal drowsiness, nocturnal restlessness, behavior disorders, hallucinations, clouding of consciousness, and deficient orientation and grasp with occasional dreamlike experiences, although both hallucinations and dreamlike states are more common among the younger than the older patients with toxic conditions. The patient may become noisy and confused, show disorientation of time, place, and person, and be overactive, frightened, and uncooperative.

Physical symptoms include failure to eat and take sufficient fluids, enuresis, fever, loss of weight, exhaustion, and dehydration in the skin and mucous membrane. The red blood cell count tends to be high, sugar and albumin are often found in the urine, and there is frequently a vitamin deficiency.

Neurological signs are tremor, incoordination, ataxia, asthenia, reflex excitability, and perhaps evidence of major vascular disease or accident. Age is a complicating factor in this disorder, and it would seem that the older the patient the more susceptible he is likely to be to this type of psychosis. Nevertheless, it cannot be considered an irreversible psychotic disorder, for a fair number of patients will recover and remain well. The following case is one of toxic-exhaustive delirious psychosis:

O.Q., male, aged sixty-five, was hospitalized for bilateral pneumonia a year previous to this attack. Up until this time he had held a responsible job and shown no abnormal mental symptoms. He had a severe bout with pneumonia, however, with frequent spells of delirium and high fever, although his condition improved enough for him to leave the hospital after several weeks. A few days after his discharge from the hospital he became confused and disoriented and showed memory defects and impaired judgment. He was disoriented for time, place, and person and could not remember day-to-day events. His physical condition was built up with diet, rest, and medication, but his mental condition failed to clear up completely. Some weeks later he had a cardiac attack which resulted in an exacerbation of the mental symptoms he had shown during his first hospitalization. His cardiac condition was brought under control, but in spite of this he continued to show signs of further progressive mental deterioration, so that within a short time he had to be hospitalized. He died one month later of a heart attack.

Psychoses with Cerebral Arteriosclerosis

These are mental disorders which occur in middle-aged and elderly persons and are associated with organic damage resulting from arteriosclerotic involvement of the cerebral blood vessels. The psychosis may have its onset anywhere from the middle forties to the eighties, and the onset may be sudden or gradual. According to Rothschild (40), the neuropathologic picture is one of vascular changes and a variety of focal lesions, in which the cerebral structure is destroyed in varying degrees, while the rest of the tissues are relatively well preserved. There is a destruction of brain areas by virtue of progressive anemia. When thrombi or hemorrhages occur in the blood vessels, convulsions or hemiplegia will result. It is common in those patients with cerebral arteriosclerosis to find associated disturbances in the cardiovascular system and kidneys.

Etiology.—The etiology of arteriosclerosis in general and of arteriosclerotic psychoses is somewhat controversial. The reasons are uncertain why one individual develops arteriosclerosis at an early age and another develops it late in life or not at all, or why one person with severe arteriosclerosis does not develop a psychosis and another with relatively little arteriosclerosis becomes mentally ill. As Robinson (38) has pointed out, 90 per cent of men and 85 per cent of women over sixty show some cerebral arteriosclerosis, but similar percentages in this group are normal, not psychotic. Also, normal individuals over sixty, with no clinical evidence of psychotic or other mental disorder, may show brain pathology, whereas some psychotics in this age group may show little or no brain pathology. Hereditary factors seem to play some part in the picture, since there seems to be in patients with arteriosclerotic psychoses a strong familial tendency to arteriosclerosis in general and not infrequently to emotional instability. However, it is clear that this is only part of the picture and that toxic factors, personality, and situational factors may also be important. This can readily be understood when we consider that a relatively small amount of brain damage may produce severe psychotic manifestations in maladjusted persons. More men than women are affected with this disorder.

Symptoms.—The onset of this psychotic disorder is usually preceded by a gradual reduction of physical and mental capacities, a loss of efficiency, and an impairment of memory. The symptoms include confusion, clouding of consciousness, loss of contact with the surroundings, incoherence, and pronounced restlessness. Hallucinations are sometimes present. There may also be a lowering of moral standards, irritability, aggressiveness, petulance, emotional lability, and explosive outbursts of weeping or laughing. Weakness, fatigue, depressive feelings, fear of waning powers, and suicidal tendencies may be present. The patient may show transitory jealousies or persecutory ideas, spotty memory, and impaired judgment. He may indulge in fabrications in order to fill in the gaps left by his erratic and uncertain memory. Often he has a certain amount of insight but is unable to use it constructively.

About one half of the patients with arteriosclerotic psychoses die; the remainder gradually subside with varying degrees of intellectual impairment. Deaths usually result from pneumonia, cerebral vascular accidents, or arteriosclerotic heart disease. Much of the treatment of this psychosis is medical, but when the psychosis subsides a little, occupational therapy and psychotherapy may help. Bed rest is important during the acute stage only, since, as discussed earlier, prolonged bed rest may induce a toxic delirious reaction which may further complicate the picture and worsen the prognosis. The following case illustrates a psychosis with cerebral arteriosclerosis:

G.A., female, aged seventy-three, suffered a mild stroke two years prior to psychiatric consultation. She was hospitalized at that period for a short time but responded well to treatment and was soon discharged as "improved." She remained apparently well for two months, when she began to exhibit bizarre behavior. She complained of ill treatment and the "traitorous" people around her. She had both visual and auditory hallucinations and heard people accuse her of being unclean and immodest. She had frequent periods of banging on the floor with her hands and face. She got into trouble with her neighbors because of her hallucinations and aggressive behavior. She showed marked impairment of memory and judgment. She was hospitalized immediately upon psychiatric consultation. When examined at the hospital, she showed residual physical signs of the stroke she had had two years previously. Although her acute symptoms disappeared after a while and she seemed to "settle down with her psychosis," she continued to show mental deterioration and some odd behavior, so that permanent institutionalization will probably be necessary for her.

Senile Psychoses (Senile Dementia)

Senile dementia is a chronic mental disorder which occurs in old persons and presents a variety of clinical pictures, although all have in common progressively increasing signs of mental deficit in association with characteristic senile changes in the brain. The etiology of the disorder lies principally in neuropathological changes in the brain, although these changes do not constitute the entire picture, since similar changes are to be found in greater degree in Alzheimer's disease and in lesser degree in some normal old persons. The reasons for the pathological aging of the brain itself are not entirely known but the condition is probably due to a combination of constitutional factors and the insults of the environment. In some cases, it is clear that the damage to the brain tissues is sufficient to account for the abnormal symptoms shown, but in other instances it would seem that the brain damage itself is not sufficient to account for the psychosis. In those who develop senile psychoses without extreme pathology in the brain, it would appear either that the brain damage reduces the capacity of the individual to adjust, or that other factors, such as personality deviation or environmental stress, impair the individual's ability to withstand cerebral damage (40).

Physical Damage to the Brain.—Characteristic changes in the brain of the senile psychotic (25, 40) include, among other things, loss of brain weight, shrinking, and grossly observable atrophy. There is abiotrophy (premature degeneration) of the ganglion cells of the cerebral cortex—a condition of the cells which has been termed "death from old age." There will also be found a widening of the sulci (grooves) and fissures, dilation of the ventricles (cavities), areas of the cortex (outer layer) without cells, a shrunken appearance of the basal ganglia (masses of nerve tissue), and so-called "senile plaques." Senile plaques are small areas or masses of tissue degeneration which occur in the intercellular substance and show up clearly with silver stain. They vary in form, size, and number and often appear as a thready or granular mass with a solid center surrounded by a clear, halo-like area. Frequently glial elements (supporting tissue), especially microglia, and degenerated fragments of nerve fibers and nerve cells can be observed.

Indications of Mental Aberration.—The mental symptoms of the senile psychotic vary with the individual. In general they might be considered as an exaggeration and distortion of normal senescent deterioration—almost like a caricature of the normal personality. Loss of memory is outstanding, and interest, attention, and comprehension are impaired. The patient finds it increasingly difficult to comprehend what is said both in his presence and to him, and he cannot think clearly. Stories are frequently confused, as a result of his impaired comprehension and memory, and gaps may be filled with bizarre fabrications. His orientation is often disturbed. The emotional state of senile psychotics varies with the patient. Usually we find apathy and a lack of interest, but we may sometimes find depression or emotional upset, temper tantrums, and irritability; occasionally hallucinations and delusions are present. Patients frequently are restless, have trouble sleeping, and may wander off and get lost. Some show renewed sex interest and may commit sex offenses, especially against young children. General physical changes include weakness, metabolic changes, tremors, speech disturbances, and sometimes paralyses. Often the picture in senile dementia may be complicated by arteriosclerosis, brain tumor, other physical disorder, or a recurrence of an earlier psychosis. Vitamins, especially niacin and ascorbic acid, are of general help in the treatment of senile psychoses.

Types of Cases.—The main types of senile dementia which are most commonly seen are the cases of simple deterioration, the depressed (and usually agitated) type, and the paranoid type. Some psychiatrists add a delirious and confused type and a presbyophrenic type (characterized by tendencies to be superficially alert, active, rambling, and confused, showing impairment of memory, fabrications, and a jovial or amiable mood) but others would include these two additional types under the aforementioned three main types.

1. The cases of simple deterioration show primarily symptoms which seem to be largely an exaggeration of normal senescent deterioration, the most outstanding symptoms being extreme impairment of memory, defective comprehension, and fabrications. These patients are apathetic and lacking in interest in their surroundings. They frequently wander off and may be found in a confused and disoriented state. An illustrative case follows:

J.H., female, aged eighty-five, was found wandering around the street in a dazed fashion. She was completely disoriented as to time and place and could not tell who she was or where she lived. She insisted that she was going to visit her mother, that she went to see her every Wednesday. She seemed apathetic and dazed but became very angry and irritable when taken to the police station. Her identity and address were discovered from an identification plate in her purse, and she was taken to her home. Her daughter and son-in-law, with whom she lived, said that for the past three years she had become increasingly forgetful and had to be reminded to eat and to follow the simplest routines of life. She showed no interest in anything, although she occasionally had some temper outbursts with little provocation. She was childish, frequently called her daughter "Mother," and had to be watched lest she turn on the gas of the stove without lighting it. Sometimes she accused those around her of stealing things she had mislaid. During the preceding three or four months her deterioration had seemed to be progressing more rapidly. As her family did not wish to institutionalize her, J.H. remained at home under careful supervision until her death six months later.

2. The depressed type of senile psychotic shows deterioration plus sadness, irritability, restlessness, tension, and overactivity. Suicidal ideas are often prominent, as in the following case:

G.S., male, aged seventy-five, had stomach complaints for many years and after hemorrhaging for nine months, was operated on for peptic ulcers. He made a good recovery but continued to voice his complaints. His son and daughter-in-law, with whom he lived, were most unsympathetic and considered him a nuisance. They excluded him from the family group even at mealtime, on the pretext that he was not well enough to join them. His loss of memory, his poor judgment, and his reminiscences and fabrications became increasingly evident. About a year after his operation, he began complaining of severe headaches, inability to sleep, and a poor appetite. He lost weight, became easily annoyed, showed outbursts of temper, had fits of nervous shaking and tension, was very depressed, and had strong feelings of suicide. He became extremely restless and overactive. Finally, his symptoms became so severe that it was necessary to hospitalize him. He showed some slight improvement after being in the hospital for a while but never became well enough to return home. He died of a gastric hemorrhage a year after his admission to the hospital.

3. The paranoid cases also show deterioration, but in addition they are suspicious, overcritical, and given to delusions, especially of persecution. They may have hallucinations, and they may become very difficult to handle. In these types of senile dementia, as well as in all types of psychoses, there seems to be something more than the organic factor to account for the illness, although just what this is we do not know. An illustrative case follows:

T.C., female, aged seventy-two, although not a well-adjusted person, was able to maintain herself fairly well until about two months prior to her hospitalization. For two or three years before her acute symptoms developed, she had shown signs of memory defect and a tendency to be overcritical and suspicious, and these symptoms gradually increased. Finally, she became excitable, irritable, and very difficult. She criticized everyone around her, accused her family of trying to harm her, and spent most of her day in reacting to auditory hallucinations. Her hallucinations were abusive in character and fitted well with her delusions of persecution. She was hospitalized and treated for several months, and her symptoms abated sufficiently for her to return home. Two years later she was still maintaining herself at home, although she continued to be suspicious and overcritical of her family and friends. However, her family had managed, with help, to develop greater tolerance and understanding of her so that there was less pressure from the environment, and this undoubtedly was an important factor in her ability to continue to maintain herself in her home environment.

It will be noted that both of the last two cases showed a slow and gradual onset of mental illness and that both had shown signs of maladjustment prior to the development of the psychosis. Both had unfavorable environmental factors to contend with and showed some improvement upon removal from this environment. When the patient in the latter case showed sufficient improvement to return home, she was able to maintain herself there because her family had displayed enough interest and insight to ameliorate those situational factors which were disturbing to her. Although the brain damage in both may have been severe enough to prevent complete recovery, both did show definite improvement under treatment. This is significant because it tends to indicate that the course of senile psychoses may not always be entirely irreversible. The brain damage, of course, cannot be repaired, but the contributing physical, personality, and situational factors may be improved with a resulting improvement in the general condition and an alleviation of the symptoms of the psychosis.

The Presenile Psychoses

The presenile dementias or premature senile psychoses are those mental disorders which resemble the senile psychoses but which occur at ages earlier than the usual age of onset of senility (4, 25, 31, 32, 34). The etiology of these disorders is unknown, but in all of them familial factors seem to be important. There is considerable evidence for the influence of genetic elements in the premature aging of the brain, and it may be that presenile psychosis is an expression of limited viability inherent in the tissues which renders them more susceptible to the destructive effects of certain exogenous factors.

There are different types of presenile psychoses, some of which are encountered more frequently than others. The symptoms vary, but all have in common a poor prognosis, with more or less early deterioration and death. There is no known cure for the presenile dementias.

Alzheimer's disease is encountered more often than the other presenile psychoses, although it is still a relatively infrequent disorder. It is more prevalent among women than men. It is a premature pathological senility which is possibly due to or associated with constitutional or genetic factors plus exogenous factors probably of toxic or infectious nature. It is similar to senile dementia, save that it occurs earlier in life, has a more rapid and fatal course, and shows greater brain pathology. There is rapid progressive mental deterioration characterized by memory loss, senseless speech, disorientation, worry, increased emotional lability, and impairment of abstract thinking, reasoning, and comprehension. There are also many neurological symptoms, such as tremors, convulsions, aphasia, dizziness, unsteadiness, etc. Brain damage is senile in character but often more extensive. There is marked atrophy of the brain, especially in the cerebral cortex in the prefrontal and temporal areas, senile plaques, and neurofibrillary changes. These degenerative changes are found in all types of cells, but are most conspicuous in the large pyramidal cells. Although emotional changes will depend to a large extent upon the prepsychotic personality, it is rather frequent to find this type of patient depressed, apprehensive with compulsive crying and laughing, and prone to futile hyperactivity; degeneration of morality is not uncommon. The prognosis of this disorder is poor, and the patient usually dies within four years. There is no known cure.

Pick's disease is the second most frequently found presenile psychosis. It is the result of fairly well circumscribed atrophy in one section of the brain, usually the frontal lobe (although it may be in the parietal lobe or in other parts), with progressive dementia. Some have thought that it may be due to a disturbance in the metabolism of the brain tissue. The etiology of the disorder is unknown, although hereditary factors are considered to be important. It usually occurs in the presenile period but has been known to occur late in the senile period. Brain damage shows atrophy in both the gray and white matter, with degeneration in the pathways and overlying cortex; there may be both cortical and subcortical destruction. If the pyramidal tract is involved, hemiplegia (paralysis of one side of the body) will result. There is a slow mental deterioration, with a loss of abstract ability but, at first, relatively well-preserved memory and concrete ability. Emotions gradually become flattened and blunted. In contrast with Alzheimer's disease, euphoria is found more frequently than depression. The course is more gradual than in Alzheimer's disease, but the patient eventually sinks to a vegetative level. There is no treatment for the disorder, and it is usually fatal in two to fifteen years.

Jakob's disease and *Kraepelin's disease* are two other presenile dementias which are not too rarely encountered. Both are of unknown etiology but are considered to have strong hereditary factors involved. Both show brain damage, neurological findings, and gross emotional changes, and both have a rapid course, with progressive mental deterioration and a fatal prognosis. Jakob's disease may be fatal in six months; the patient seldom lives longer than two or three years, and Kraepelin's disease is usually fatal in a year or less. There is no known treatment for either disorder.

Therapy of Psychoses in Later Life

Therapy of psychoses occurring in the senile period used to be considered a waste of time, the argument being that since aging is an irreversible process the prognosis was necessarily poor. Now we know that this is not always the case, for abnormal aging may be reversible to a limited degree. Besides, although brain damage is admittedly irreversible, there are other personality and situational factors involved in the psychoses of later maturity, and these are amenable to therapy. With the exception of the presenile dementias, in which the course is rapid and the prognosis fatal within a relatively short time, most of the psychoses of later maturity are susceptible to at least symptomatic improvement (2, 3, 13, 14, 15, 17, 24, 27, 30, 39, 41, 45).

The kind and extent of therapy will depend, of course, upon the type of psychosis and upon the special needs of the individual patient. However, especially in older patients, one of the most important things is to remove any sources of infection and to rehabilitate, to the extent that this is possible, any diseased or disabled organs of the body. Diet and vitamins, especially niacin and ascorbic acid, are helpful, as well as exercise and a healthy regimen of life. Good personal hygiene is always a helpful adjunct to therapy.

Benzedrine compounds are sometimes indicated to stimulate certain patients, and sedatives to quiet others and to insure adequate sleep.

Hormone treatment, especially sex hormones and pluri-hormone injections, are helpful in certain cases, particularly of the menopausal or involutional type.

Histamine injections have resulted in improvement in a worth-while percentage of schizophrenics, manic-depressives, and involutionals.

Insulin, metrazol, and electroshock therapies have also been tried with all types of psychotics. Of these, electroshock therapy has proved the most successful, particularly with involutional conditions and with depressives of all types. Many believe electroshock treatment to be indicated for older psychotics in spite of their physiological age, but most agree that the general physical condition must be watched. It is more effective with depressives than with any other types of psychoses, and the younger the patient the more hopeful the outlook. Some report success with electroshock therapy in schizophrenic, paranoid, and delusional states, but the recovery rates are not as high as with depressives and involutionals of all types. Also, those having psychoses with arteriosclerosis respond better to therapy than do those with senile dementia.

Prefrontal lobotomy, lobectomy, and topectomy have proved effective in some cases.

Psychotherapy is important, particularly during the recovery period. Many report a marked rise in the recovery rate of those patients who receive psychotherapy following electroshock treatment. Support, reassurance, suggestion, and planning of routine are important parts of psychotherapy with older psychotics. Group psychotherapy has also been tried with positive results on senile hospitalized patients.

Occupational and recreational therapies and group social activities are aids in the rehabilitation of the older psychotic patient.

Manipulation of the environment is also a very important part of the treatment program of older psychotics. If the patient is to remain in his own home, patience, understanding, and acceptance are of paramount importance. Environmental pressures of all sorts must be relieved, and the patient must be made as happy as possible. In an easy, happy, accepting environment, recovery is more likely and, when it does occur, has a better chance of remaining permanent.

Summary

A psychosis is a major mental disorder which alters the feeling, thinking, and behavior of an individual.

The incidence of mental disorder in the general population is high, one person out of every twelve spending some time in a mental hospital and greater numbers needing help. The average age of first admission to mental hospitals in New York State is 48.5 years, and the rate of incidence increases with advancing years. The latter may be due to factors connected with the aging process.

The etiology of mental disorder in later maturity is not always known, but it is thought that constitutional factors, physiological illness, defect, or decline, personality makeup and habits of reacting, and environmental stress play important parts in the development of psychoses in this period.

Changes in the intellectual functioning of aged psychotics is evident in the impairment of abstract thinking, language, memory, and motor functions. Thought disturbances are common.

Changes in the emotions, personality, and behavior of older psychotics are similar to the changes found in psychotics of other ages, although in general the older psychotic tends toward either paranoid or depressive types of reaction.

Functional psychoses found in later maturity are often a recurrence of similar episodes experienced earlier in life. Sometimes the symptoms may be superimposed on an organic or degenerative psychosis.

Manic-depressive psychoses, when found in later maturity, are usually recurring phases of a long-standing mental disorder. In the manic phase the patient becomes excitable, overactive, uninhibited, and sometimes disoriented and uncontrollable. He shows labile emotions and flight of ideas and sometimes has delusions, which are usually of grandiose nature. In the depressed phase he becomes dejected, underactive, lacking in self-confidence, hopeless, and self-accusatory and is prone to suicide. Some cases become anxious, restless, and agitated.

Schizophrenia or dementia praecox usually develops in the withdrawn, tense, egocentric personality. Patients with this disorder show inappropriate affect, disregard the realities of life and live in a world of their own, blame others for their difficulties, and do bizarre things. Delusions, hallucinations, and ideas of reference are common. When found in later maturity, this mental disorder is usually of long standing.

The four main types of schizophrenia are the simple, the hebephrenic, the catatonic, and the paranoid. Any of these types might be found in later maturity, but the simple and the paranoid are more likely to go undetected than either the hebephrenic or the catatonic until that time.

Because of new drugs and therapies for syphilis, general paralysis (paresis) is gradually becoming a relatively rare mental disorder, but it still does occur in older persons. Physical symptoms include headaches, tremors, dizzy spells, disturbances of gait and speech, unequal pupils which do not react to light, and sometimes convulsions. Psychic symptoms include euphoria, grandiose delusions, and poor judgment, although some may be despondent and suicidal. The psychic symptoms displayed will be in accord with the prepsychotic personality.

Alcoholic psychoses may take the form of delirium tremens or Korsakow's psychosis, and the disorder may be complicated by the age factor. Delirium tremens is characterized by restlessness, excitability, sleeplessness, fear, disorientation, and frightening hallucinations. Korsakow's psychosis is characterized by severe memory defect, disorientation, mental confusion, and a tendency to confabulate. Good medical and nursing care are important in both disorders.

Involutional psychoses are mental disorders of middle and late maturity, occur more frequently in women than in men, and are often associated with the menopause. They are usually either of depressed or paranoid type, depending upon the prepsychotic personality. Emotional maladjustment in these patients has usually been evident also in earlier periods of life.

Depressed involutionals may suffer from simple depression, hopelessness, psychomotor retardation, withdrawal, and self-condemnation, or they may be agitated, with restlessness, wringing of the hands, and marked anxiety in addition to their dejection and self-accusations. All depressed psychotics should be guarded against suicide.

Toxic delirious psychoses are among the more common abnormal mental reactions after the age of sixty. The etiology varies, but in all cases there is a disturbance of the metabolic processes of the organism, especially of the brain. The result is autogenous toxemia, which causes the physical and psychic symptoms. Treatment aims to restore the carbohydrate metabolic functions and to prevent additional toxemia. Physical, neurological, and psychic symptoms are present, and age may be a complicating factor. However, with proper treatment a fair number of patients will recover.

Psychoses with arteriosclerosis occur in middle-aged and elderly persons as a result of organic brain damage caused by arteriosclerotic involvement of the cerebral blood vessels. It is characterized by impairment of mental capacity, clouding of consciousness and thought, emotional disturbances, fatigue, poor judgment, and especially poor memory. Transitory delusions, hallucinations, and suicidal ideas may be present. Something more than the organic brain damage seems to be responsible for the psychosis, and some patients show a certain amount of improvement under treatment.

Senile dementia may take several forms, but those most usually found are the simple, the depressed, and the paranoid. The simple type seems to be largely an exaggeration of normal senescent deterioration, with extreme impairment of memory, defective comprehension, fabrications, and apathy. The depressed type is also sad, irritable, and often agitated and has suicidal ideas. The paranoid type, in addition to deterioration, is suspicious, overcritical, and given to delusions, especially of persecution.

The presenile dementias are those psychoses which resemble the senile psychoses but which occur earlier in life. Genetic factors are important in the etiology of all these psychoses. The symptoms vary with the disorder but all have a poor prognosis, with early deterioration and death. Alzheimer's disease and Pick's disease are the most commonly seen types, although Kraepelin's disease, Jakob's disease, and other types may also occur. There is no known cure for the presenile dementias at the present time.

Therapy of the psychoses in later maturity follows the same pattern as therapy in earlier years. Diet, vitamins, sedatives, stimulating drugs, hormone therapy, and histamine injections have proved helpful in some cases. Insulin, metrazol, and electroshock treatments have also been tried, and of these electroshock has proved the most valuable, especially with depressed cases of all types. Prefrontal lobotomy, lobectomy, and topectomy have also been tried with some success. Psychotherapy, occupational therapy, and manipulation of the environment are also important in the treatment of the older psychotic.

REFERENCES

1. ALLEN, E. B., and CLOW, H. E. Paranoid reactions in the aging. *Geriatrics,* 1950, **5,** 66-73.
2. APPEL, K. E. Psychiatric therapy. In HUNT, J. McV. (ed.), *Personality and the behavior disorders.* New York: The Ronald Press Co., 1944.

3. BARKER, L. F. Psychotherapy in the practice of geriatrics. In *Mental health in later maturity*. Publ. Hlth. Rep., Wash., 1942, No. 168.

4. BEBÍN, J., and PAREDES, V. Demencia presenil hereditaria por atrofia cortical (¿enfermedad de Pick?). *Rev. Neuro-Psiquiat.,* Lima, 1947, **10,** 177-88.

5. CAMERON, N. The functional psychoses. In HUNT, J. McV. (ed.), *Personality and the behavior disorders*. New York: The Ronald Press Co., 1944.

6. CLOW, H. E. The outlook for patients admitted to a mental hospital after the age of sixty-five. *N.Y. St. J. Med.,* 1948, **48,** 2357-63.

7. DAVIDOFF, E. The involutional psychoses. In KAPLAN, O. (ed.), *Mental disorders in later life*. Stanford, Calif.: Stanford University Press, 1945.

8. DAVIDSON, G. M. Psychosomatic aspects of the Korsakow's syndrome. *Psychiat. Quart.,* 1948, **22,** 1-17.

9. DEUTSCH, H. *Psychology of women*. Vol. II. *Motherhood*. New York: Grune & Stratton, Inc., 1945.

10. EYSENCK, M. D. A study of certain qualitative aspects of problem-solving behavior in senile dementia patients. *J. ment. Sci.,* 1945, **91,** 337-45.

11. ——. An exploratory study of mental organization in senility. *J. Neurol. Psychiat.,* 1945, **8,** 15-21.

12. FAIRWEATHER, I. S. Mental disorders in old age. *Med. Pr.,* 1948, **219,** 389-93.

13. GALLINEK, A. Electric convulsive therapy in geriatrics. *N.Y. St. J. Med.,* 1947, **47,** 1233-41.

14. ——. The nature of affective and paranoid disorders during the senium in the light of electric convulsive therapy. *J. nerv. ment. Dis.,* 1948, **108,** 291-303.

15. GRANICK, S. Studies of psychopathology in later maturity—a review. *J. Geron.,* 1950, **5,** 361-69.

16. GREENBLATT, M. Age and electroencephalographic abnormality in neuropsychiatric patients: a study of 1,593 cases. *Amer. J. Psychiat.,* 1944, **101,** 82-90.

17. GREENHILL, M. H. A psychosomatic evaluation of the psychiatric and endocrinological factors in menopause. *Fifth med. J.,* Birmingham, 1946, **39,** 786-94.

18. HADFIELD, J. A. *Psychology and mental health*. London: George Allen & Unwin, Ltd., 1950.

19. HAMILTON, D. M., and WARD, G. M. The hospital treatment of involutional psychoses. *Amer. J. Psychiat.,* 1948, **104,** 801-4.

20. HAMILTON, G. V. Changes in personality. In COWDRY, E. V. (ed.), *Problems of ageing*. Baltimore: The Williams and Wilkins Co., 1939.

21. HANFMANN, E. Older mental patients after long hospitalization. In KAPLAN, O. (ed.), *Mental disorders in later life*. Stanford, Calif.: Stanford University Press, 1945.

22. HAYNES, E., and JACOB, J. S. L. The treatment of involutional psychosis in the male. *Wis. med. J.,* 1945, **44,** 209-12.

23. HENDERSON, D. K., and GILLESPIE, R. D. *A textbook of psychiatry* (5th ed.). New York: Oxford University Press, 1941.

24. HUSTON, P. E., and LOCHER, L. M. Involutional psychosis: course when untreated and when treated with electric shock. *Arch. Neurol. Psychiat.,* Chicago, 1948, **59,** 385-94.

25. Jervis, G. A. The presenile dementias. In Kaplan, O. (ed.), *Mental disorders in later life.* Stanford, Calif.: Stanford University Press, 1945.
26. Lindberg, R. J. On the question of psychologically conditioned features in the Korsakow's syndrome. *Acta. Psychiat.,* Kbh., 1946, **21,** 497-542.
27. Lovell, H. W. Electric shock therapy in the aging. *Geriatrics,* 1948, **3,** 385-93.
28. Malamud, W. Mental disorders of the aged, arteriosclerotic and senile psychoses. In *Mental health in later maturity,* Publ. Hlth. Rep., Wash., 1942, No. 168.
29. Malzberg, B. Mental diseases among the aged in New York State. *Ment. Hyg.,* N.Y., 1949, **33,** 599-614.
30. McGraw, R. B. Recoverable or temporary mental disturbances in the elderly. *J. Geron.,* 1949, **4,** 234-38.
31. Nathanson, M., and Wortis, S. B. Severe rigidity in performance and thought in a case of presenile degenerative disease. *J. nerv. ment. Dis.,* 1948, **108,** 399-408.
32. Newton, R. D. The identity of Alzheimer's disease and senile dementia and their relationship to senility. *J. ment. Sci.,* 1948, **94,** 225-29.
33. Overholser, W. Mental disease. In Stieglitz, E. J. (ed.), *Geriatric medicine.* Philadelphia: W. B. Saunders Co., 1949.
34. Palatin, P., Hock, P. H., Horwitz, W. A., and Porzin, L. Pre-senile psychosis: report on two cases with brain biopsy studies. *Amer. J. Psychiat.,* 1948, **105,** 97-101.
35. Palmer, H. D. Involutional psychoses: melancholia. In *Mental health in later maturity.* Publ. Hlth. Rep., Wash., 1942, No. 168.
36. ——. Mental disorders of old age. *Geriatrics,* 1946, 1, 60-80.
37. Pollack, J. M. A statistical review of mental disorders in later life. In Kaplan, O. (ed.), *Mental disorders in later life.* Stanford, Calif.: Stanford University Press, 1945.
38. Robinson, G. W. The toxic delirious reactions of old age. In Kaplan, O. (ed.), *Mental disorders in later life.* Stanford, Calif.: Stanford University Press, 1945.
39. Rockwell, F. V. Psychotherapy in the older individual. In Kaplan, O. (ed.), *Mental disorders in later life.* Stanford, Calif.: Stanford University Press, 1945.
40. Rothschild, D. Senile psychoses and psychoses with arteriosclerosis. In Kaplan, O. (ed.), *Mental disorders in later life.* Stanford, Calif.: Stanford University Press, 1945.
41. Sackler, A. M., Sackler, M. D., Sackler, R. R., and Ophuijsen, J. H. W. van. Nonconvulsive biochemotherapy with histamine: a preliminary report on the treatment of hospitalized schizophrenic, manic-depressive, and involutional psychotics. *J. nerv. ment. Dis.,* 1949, **110,** 149-60.
42. Schilder, P. Old age and aging: psychiatric aspects. Discussion by E. Kahn. *Amer. J. Orthopsychiat.,* 1940, 10, 63-72.
43. Shock, N. W. Physiological factors in behavior. In Hunt, J. McV. (ed.), *Personality and the behavior disorders.* New York: The Ronald Press Co., 1944.
44. ——. Physiological aspects of mental disorder in later life. In Kaplan, O. (ed.), *Mental disorders in later life.* Stanford, Calif.: Stanford University Press, 1945.

45. SILVER, A. Group psychotherapy with senile psychotic patients. *Geriatrics,* 1950, **5,** 147-50.
46. STERN, K., and PRADOS, M. Personality studies in menopausal women. *Amer. J. Psychiat.,* 1946, **103,** 358-68.
47. STRECKER, E. A. *Fundamentals of psychiatry.* Philadelphia: J. B. Lippincott Co., 1945.
48. WOOLLEY, L. F. Personality factors in the psychoses of general paresis. *Urol. cutan. Rev.,* 1945, **49,** 3-6.

PART III
PROFESSIONAL WORK WITH THE AGING

INTRODUCTION TO PART III

So far in this book, we have dealt with the normal and abnormal life changes of aging individuals. In this section we shall discuss ways and means of manipulating these changes so as to ameliorate, in so far as this is possible, the condition of the aged. This manipulation involves the combined efforts of aging individuals themselves and of skilled specialists in this field. First we shall investigate ways and means of retarding personal decline and developing neglected potentials, and then we shall discuss the various professional specialties, within the community and in institutions, in the field of gerontology.

Chapter 9

RETARDING DECLINE AND DEVELOPING
NEGLECTED POTENTIALS

The problems of retarding decline and developing neglected potentials are closely allied, for retarding decline involves developing neglected potentials, and developing potentials will help to retard decline. In regard to both problems, it is participation in life which is the important thing.

While we must recognize that decline in all areas cannot be postponed indefinitely, that true rejuvenation does not occur, and that decline and death at some time are inevitable for everyone, we know also that decline is often accelerated and death is premature, and that much can be done to retard decline and even at times to reverse a too rapid deterioration process. Much of this can be done by medical science, but the major responsibility both for the retardation of decline and the development of neglected potentials must rest with the aging individual himself. Others can aid and encourage him, but in the final analysis it is the aging person himself who must decide whether it is worth his while to make the effort to maintain himself as long as possible at the peak of his efficiency and to develop any latent talents he may possess. As English has said (9), "The future of the older person lies to a large extent in his own hands. He must develop himself so that he remains useful through his physical efforts, or his personality qualities, or both, to the people of all ages around him."

Much work has been done to prolong the life span, and the ever increasing numbers of aged persons in our population testify to the success of this work. Relatively little, however, has been done to make these increased years worth living. The years themselves are not so important as how these years are lived. Are they happy or miserable years? Is the person who is living these extra years a useful citizen or is he a drone in his family and society? Is he spending the years in good health, or is he an invalid? Does he make others happy by his presence, or will they be relieved when he dies? These questions are important both to society and to the aging individual himself, for certainly a deteriorated, irritable, aging invalid is no joy to himself, to his family, or to society. On the other hand, the years of later maturity should be happy, useful, healthy years, mutually satisfying to the senescent and to his associates. They can be, too, if measures are taken to retard decline in various areas and to develop any potentials the aging individual may have for enriched living. Many practical suggestions for achieving these ends are included in the references at the end of this chapter.

In considering the retardation of decline, we must consider the individual as a whole, for rightfully there can be no real separation of the various areas of decline. It is for the sake of convenience and clarity only that we treat separately the retardation of physical, intellectual, emotional, and social decline.

Retarding Physical Decline

The retardation of physical decline is only one aspect of the retardation of the decline of the whole person, although undoubtedly it is a basic and important aspect.

General Appearance.—The general appearance is the first thing to consider in the retardation of physical decline. If one looks well, it is difficult not to feel well. If a man looks into his mirror and sees an alert, alive, fresh image staring back at him, he is inclined to feel pretty good about it. If he then goes down the street and meets several friends who remark on how well he looks, he can't avoid beginning to feel even better. Conversely, persons have been known to become actually ill after having various acquaintances comment on how ill they looked and ask what was wrong.

Posture. There are various things one can do both to maintain and to improve general appearance. One of the most important of these is the maintenance of good posture. As people grow older, they show a tendency to slump, and they seem to grow shorter. They thrust the head forward, bow the shoulders, and relax the abdomen, with the result that the chest appears to be caved in and the abdomen thrust out. As the viscera, when not supported, collect fat, the abdomen becomes more and more prominent, and there is an ever increasing lack of muscular tone. Much of this can be avoided if one will not permit lack of muscular tone, and will take the trouble to develop and maintain good posture. One of the ways to achieve this is to practice stretching and "standing tall." This takes the pressure off the nerves and holds the viscera in better position. Although, as just mentioned, the viscera tend to collect fat, they will not do so if the supporting muscles are not lax. When the viscera are held in better position and there is less pressure on the nerves, one not only looks better but actually feels better, for correct posture is not one of strain, but rather one of optimal body efficiency.

Gait. Closely allied to good posture is a good gait. Many persons, as they grow older, seem to feel they must shuffle and poke along, and this is one of the characteristic marks of the aged person. A slumping body and a shuffling gait are the earmarks of deterioration and suggest to the world that the aging person has given up hope and has nothing left that is worth while in life. In other words, the mental attitude has much to do with both posture and gait, and good posture and gait can be maintained only if one has zest in living. Indeed, daily changes of mood can be noted in another person merely by observing his changes of gait and posture. One should practice a sprightly gait and develop interest in the things about him as he walks along, taking frequent deep breaths to draw fresh air into his lungs. These things automatically make one feel better, improve the mood, and tend to turn the attention outward away from the self. If one sits and stands with good posture and walks with a lively gait it is difficult to complain of how ill he feels, for no one else will believe him and he will soon begin to doubt himself.

Personal Appearance. The matter of good grooming is also most important, and no person should permit himself to grow careless in this respect. This involves frequent bathing, fresh clothing, and good care of the hair, nails, teeth, etc. It was previously mentioned that many old persons do not take enough baths because of their fear of falling on getting into or out of the bathtub, but certainly this is something which can be rectified. Handrails and nonskid mats, for example, can be put into practically any home without too much difficulty or expense, and these alone will eliminate much of this fear. Other aging persons, however, do not bathe frequently enough because they have lost interest in life and can't be bothered to make the effort. These persons often have lost interest too in shampooing their hair or getting it cut when it needs it, in trimming and cleaning their nails and in taking proper care of their teeth. If they wear dentures, they often do not clean them properly, so that they may give forth an unpleasant odor. They wear clothes which are soiled and long since outmoded. These liabilities can all be eliminated with a little effort on the part of the aging person, but of course he himself must be convinced that this effort is worth while. Convinced that it is worth while, he must then bathe, shampoo, manicure, and care for his teeth with clocklike regularity and not succumb to temptations to let things slide now and then. He must then develop and maintain the habit of keeping his clothes clean and well pressed at all times. He must also keep up to date and dress in the fashion of today, not of twenty years ago. This is especially important for women, as the styles of women's clothes change more drastically than those of men, including not only the styles of dresses and suits but also of hats, shoes, and accessories. One's wardrobe need not be expensive or excessive, but it must be up to date. Women, too, must pay especial attention to hair grooming and styling and to the care of the skin. With respect to the latter, the use of estrogenic creams is often helpful when administered under the direction of a physician. An inexpensive sun lamp, which can be purchased for a small amount these days, will also improve the skin tone and general appearance by giving a healthy tan.

Weight and Diet. The matter of weight is another important aspect in the control of one's general appearance. Save in extreme old age, where the tendency is to be too thin and undernourished, the aging person should try not to get too fat. It is better to be a little on the thin side than to increase too much in bulk, particularly abdominal bulk. This means, of course, an adequately controlled and balanced diet. This is generally a low caloric diet, which is low in fats or cholesterol and high in proteins and has adequate vitamins. Hauser (12), a nutritionist, claims that one can increase both his life span and his years of youth and health by an adequate diet which includes brewers' yeast, powdered skim milk, yogurt, wheat germ, and blackstrap molasses. He insists that everyone over forty should supplement his diet with optimum daily requirements of vitamins and minerals, both of which should be included in the food intake and not taken in the form of pills. This, however, is not entirely a new thought as Mechnikov, in the early part of this century, offered similar suggestions regarding diet.

Crampton (5) also, in a report on diet and nutrition in relation to aging, points out that much of man's rate of aging depends upon his diet and nutrition, and that 75 per cent of men over sixty suffer a lack of one or more important food elements. Calcium, iron, and protein are the foremost nutritional defects, whereas carbohydrates and possibly cholesterol are important among the dietary excesses. Calcium, 99 per cent of the bodily content of which is found in the teeth and bones, is one of the most important food elements and one in which the diet is most deficient. It is important to the effective functioning of the heart, nerve, and brain cells, assists in the clotting of the blood, is essential in iron metabolism, and is expended during emotional states. It must be properly balanced with phosphorus intake, the ratio usually being 1 to 1½ or 2, for proper utilization by the body. The most acceptable form of calcium intake is through the diet, preferably milk (although other foods such as dandelion greens, kale, and turnip greens are also good), but it may be advisable with older persons to supplement the natural intake with calcium lactate, one grain daily for each year of age, or with dicalcium phosphate. This, however, should be done only on the advice of a physician.

In addition to having the necessary elements in the diet, the body must be able to digest, absorb, and effectively utilize these elements under normal conditions and conditions of strain. Iron, for example, brings oxygen to the tissues from the lungs through the hemoglobin in the red cells of the blood. The diet may be adequate for iron intake, but iron poverty may result from deficiency of hydrochloric acid in the stomach, poor assimilation, or loss from hemorrhage. It may also result from a lack of trace elements, such as copper, cobalt, manganese, etc., which aid in its absorption. Likewise, protein poverty may result not only from inadequate intake but also from impaired digestion or processing in the liver, or through illness or other organ dysfunction. It is thought now that protein poverty may play a large part in such disorders as anemia, asthenia, edema, cirrhosis of the liver, and ulcers of the stomach.

Good nutrition then, with a view to retardation of the aging process, must include ample quantities of calcium, iron, phosphorus, and protein and effective utilization of these in the body. Adequate vitamin intake is also most important, particularly the vitamin B complex, which is thought by some to be influential in the prevention of cancer. Thiamine and its chloride, vitamin B_1, have produced marked general improvement in many aged persons. Niacin (nicotinic acid), riboflavin (vitamin B2), and iodine have also been seen to produce marked changes when deficiencies occur. The importance of vitamin C, or ascorbic acid, at all ages is well known. Vitamin D likewise is essential for its help in the utilization of calcium. Vitamin A plays an important part in the maintenance of energy, good vision (particularly night vision), and smooth skin. Adequate vitamin A intake will tend to prevent itchiness and the development of certain respiratory conditions. Thiamine, nicotinic acid, and riboflavin are concerned with the metabolism of carbohydrates and are known to be important in the prevention of certain nervous and mental conditions. Some states of mental confusion have shown improvement following the administration of these and other vitamins.

Overweight should be avoided, for it seems that overweight after the age of twenty-five shortens the life. Caloric requirements decrease with increase of years, and the number of deaths increases with increase in the percentage of overweight. The lean, in both humans and animals, remain young, healthy, active, and virile longer than those who are inclined to be fat. Therefore it is advisable to keep the carbohydrate intake low.

Some persons beginning the period of later maturity overeat because of their unconscious feeling that this is the only thing left to them in life. These people often are discouraged and depressed and have little satisfaction in life. Their overeating is on a neurotic basis. The more they eat, the fatter they get, and the fatter they get, the worse they look and the more unhappy they become. The core of the problem here is to determine the cause of the overeating and then try to eliminate this by helping the person to understand himself and to substitute other satisfactions and interests in life, thus reducing the need for overeating. Sometimes, on a physician's order, the use of aminopropanes may help, as these tend to inhibit the appetite, to make the patient more ambitious and energetic, and to give him a sense of well-being. If he shows an unfavorable reaction to one form of the medication, he can be switched to another form without difficulty. The most important things, though, are the mental outlook and the interests one has in life.

Exercise and Rest. In proper proportions exercise and rest are also essential to good health and an attractive appearance. Without exercise it is difficult to maintain muscular tone, and without rest one cannot have zest in living or recuperate from the strain of everyday life. With insufficient rest, fine lines of tension and strain appear in the face and one tends to become tired and irritable. Exercise in the form of not too strenuous recreation is usually better than "setting-up" exercises, as recreational exercise is more meaningful and interesting, and few persons will continue to do setting-up exercises with any regularity. Older persons, though, require more time to recover after exercise, and this must be taken into consideration in planning both exercise and rest periods.

Another important aspect of rest is the matter of relaxation, for the rest of many persons does them little good because they cannot relax. Relaxation is something which will do much to maintain good health and appearance, but it is something which must be learned and practiced. It does little good to lie down to rest if one's body is too tense and his muscles too rigid to permit relaxation. With concentration and practice, however, one can learn to relax muscle by muscle until a relatively short period of rest becomes more beneficial than a longer period under conditions of tension. The practice of relaxation will also help many who suffer from insomnia and are always too tense to get to sleep. Today, both courses and books are available which will teach one the art of relaxation, and the value of this to many persons is marked (10, 13).

However, in regard to the matter of sleep, it must be remembered that many older persons do not need as much sleep as they did when younger, so that wakefulness of itself need not necessarily cause concern. Rather, the older person should endeavor to use his sleeplessness profitably—to read, to plan,

and to think constructively. If he does this, he will be amazed
to find how much he accomplishes in hours which were once a
source of irritation and frustration to him. Many older persons
even find that they grow to enjoy these periods after a while.

Physical Examinations.—Periodic physical examinations
are advisable at all ages, but with the aging they are especially
important. This in no way implies that one should become
hypochondriacal in one's concern over his health, his aches, and
his pains, but rather that proper care of the body is important
and that it can best be accomplished under the guidance of an
expert. With periodic physical examinations, early diagnosis
can be made of beginning difficulties, which are often most effectively checked in the very early stages. Many diseases and
disorders with an essentially poor prognosis can be ameliorated
only if treatment is begun as soon as symptoms become manifest.
Also, in some instances, at least temporary reversal of some
early manifestations of aging may occur. For example, Kaufman reports success in improving joint mobility in 500 male
and female patients (15). Through the proper use of niacina-
mide therapy, given as a supplement to the patient's diet, others
likewise have had success in rehabilitating even some markedly
debilitated aged patients (35).

Hearing and Vision. The sense organs should be checked
regularly, and any noted defect should be treated. Beginning
deafness, which may be not severe enough to require a hearing
aid, can sometimes be compensated for by special effort on the
part of the aging person to pay more careful attention to conversation and what goes on around him. If there is reason to
believe that the deafness may become progressively worse, it
will be helpful for social contacts to learn a little lip-reading. In
recent years such splendid progress has been made in the development of hearing aids that one need no longer hesitate about
wearing one when it is required. Whereas the large, cumbersome ear trumpets of old were so conspicuous as to cause considerable embarrassment to the wearer, the modern hearing aids

are so small and inconspicuous that some individuals have been known to wear one for years without their friends being aware of it. Devices of this sort should certainly be utilized by all those who have need of them.

Vision also should be checked regularly. Although the eye has potentially a long life span, there are visual defects which occur with advancing age, and the most common of these is far-sightedness. Decline of visual function can probably be retarded to a limited degree by the use of eye exercises and relaxations (34), but when glasses are needed, it is advisable, for the sake of comfort and convenience, to procure them without delay. This, however, can only be determined by a complete eye examination.

Teeth. The habit of regular dental examinations should be practiced, and needed repairs of teeth and dentures should be made at once. The condition of the teeth is important to good digestion and general health. Abscesses, for example, are points of focal infection which may cause damage to other areas, and because of this they should always be treated promptly. Care of the teeth also has considerable cosmetic value, and this is important to the aging person. In addition to this, the removal of teeth offers a psychic trauma to the individual, and for this reason it is usually advisable to repair teeth instead of removing them whenever this is possible. Some persons may become so upset emotionally by the loss of teeth that they need help in adjusting both to the loss and to the new dentures.

Digestive System. Examination of the digestive system will point to needed changes in diet, and the oldster must be willing to institute these on the advice of his physician. Some aging digestive systems cannot stand the customary excessive use of alcohol, tobacco, or rich foods, and, in spite of many years of habit, the older person when so advised must be ready to modify his dietary habits to suit the needs of his system. It is also advisable to have regular checks on the amount of hydrochloric acid present in the stomach, as lack of this much-needed aid to digestion is basic to many of the digestive disturbances of later life.

Heart and Blood Vessels. An important part of the physical examination of the aging person will include a careful investigation into the condition of the heart and blood vessels. Particular attention will be paid to the blood pressure and any indications of heart disease or arteriosclerosis. The examining physician will, of course, prescribe as needed. The lungs and other organs will also be examined and note made of any beginning signs of cancer, prostate trouble in men, and other diseases and disorders common to aging persons. An EKG (electrocardiogram) is always advisable.

Endocrine Glands. The examination of the endocrine system is of especial importance in the physical checkup of the older person, for, as we have already seen, the use of endocrines, especially of estrogens and androgens, can do much to retard the aging process. While we must recognize that as yet there is nothing known which will prolong youth or retard aging indefinitely, the endocrines, within limits, are of considerable help in this area. They should, however, be taken only under the supervision of a physician.

Psychosomatic Complaints. The physical examination offers a good time to note the presence of psychosomatic complaints. Psychosomatic complaints may have a psychic or somatic origin or components of both. The organic features, of course, will be treated first, but when these have been either ruled out or eliminated, the aging person who would retard his decline and live more effectively must be ready to accept the fact that his complaints are psychogenic in nature and require treatment other than medicines. The examining physician who has a tactful, understanding approach can do much to help his patient to accept this fact and the required treatment. However, with respect to psychosomatic diseases, it must be noted that the number of these in the aged has not been found to be disproportionately larger than those found at other periods of life.

Physical Limitations. Finally, the older person who would retard his physical decline must recognize his physical limitations but not overemphasize them. He must recognize the fact that he cannot run as fast or as long and that he cannot exercise or work as strenuously as once he could, but he must not let these things lead him to the belief that he can do nothing but sit in a rocker all day long. Perhaps he cannot run fast or engage in strenuous exercise, but he still can walk with a sprightly gait, and he still can exercise enough to get plenty of real fun out of life. He does what he feels like doing, but he does not overtax himself, and he takes all the time he needs to recuperate after strenuous play or work. He will take reasonable precautions to protect himself from harm, but he will continue to live a full and active life.

Retarding Intellectual Decline

In considering the retardation of mental decline, we must first remember the high and low points of mental decline—that is, those abilities which are most resistant and those which are least resistant to deterioration with advancing age. We must recall that verbal abilities are relatively well retained and that the aging person tends to keep fairly well preserved the vocabulary, abstract reasoning, judgment, and creative imagination he has always had. On the other hand, speed is decreased, and new learning is slowed; there is less flexibility, and perceptions are slower. The aging person then must concentrate on the continued development of his good abilities and try in every way possible to compensate for his declining abilities.

Education.—One way of retarding mental decline is to continue one's education as long as one lives. This does not necessarily mean going to school for the rest of one's days, but it does involve learning something new each year, concentrating on those things where abstract reasoning, judgment, and past experience will help. It is easy to get out of practice in learning, and when the habit is once broken it is hard to rebuild. Learning something new each year will keep one in practice, so that learning becomes less arduous than when one has not tried to learn anything new for a long time. Success in learning new things is also an ego-builder. It brings feelings of emotional satisfaction and personal accomplishment which make the aging person happier and give him a better outlook on life.

An important aspect of learning new things is keeping abreast of new developments in one's own field, appraising these developments carefully and being ready to accept that which is good. Sometimes the aging person's rejection of new things is tied up with the threat he feels of the younger workers in the field, but unfortunately the rejection works against him instead of giving him the greater security he is seeking. If he will face this problem realistically, the older worker will see that it is decidedly to his advantage to know all about the new developments in his field, to separate the chaff from the wheat, and to be ready and willing to make effective use of the wheat.

Those in later maturity who would like to maintain their youthful mind and spirit must also keep an interest in current affairs and have some awareness of new developments in different fields. This prevents stagnation of ideas and makes the older person more interesting to himself and to others. A stimulating conversationalist who has broad knowledge on different subjects is more likely to be in demand than in discard, regardless of his age. On the other hand, those who have interest only in themselves and in their troubles, aches, and pains are bores whom nobody wants around. Actually, no one is interested in hearing the constant, repetitious, detailed recital of another's somatic complaints. Friends or acquaintances may listen for a while to be polite, but they soon begin to dread these menaces. The older person who shows an interest in others—not a morbid, gossiping curiosity but a healthy, wholesome interest in other individuals, their ideas, views, and knowledge—will find his company sought and his own knowledge increased. He will maintain his mental alertness and keep an interest in life which will give him less time to become unhappy, depressed, and irritable, thus helping to retard decline.

Practice.—The decline of new learning and memory can be retarded to a limited degree by practice. Many older persons cannot learn new things or remember very well because they have not tried to do anything of the sort for so long. When they finally do try, the results at first are often discouraging because they are so out of practice, but when they persist they usually find that it gradually becomes easier for them. This indicates that the decline in this area may be reversible to a limited degree. A way of practice is to read a few sentences either aloud or to one's self, remove the selection, and then try to repeat the thought of the passage. This does not mean a verbatim repetition of the sentences but giving the general idea or essential thoughts in the passage. As one becomes proficient in doing this with short selections, the length of the passages should gradually be increased.

The older person can also compensate for his memory loss to some extent by more practice and other helpful devices. He must recognize his memory loss, but he must not use it as an excuse to get out of doing things he does not want to do, and he must not make use of denial or fabrication to cover up his deficiencies. Habits of jotting down things to be remembered or new things to be learned and reviewing these at leisure, depending upon one's self instead of others to remember the things one should remember, and keeping alert to surroundings and new activities will do much to ease the problem of memory loss.

Thinking.—The period of later maturity should be a time for one to think, and the older person should take time to do this regularly and constructively, endeavoring to use his judgment and past experience to develop new ideas. The following little quotation illustrates cleverly the change of stress from the physical to the intellectual as one grows older:

King David and King Solomon
Led merry, merry lives,
With many, many lady friends,
And many, many wives;
But when old age crept over them—
With many, many qualms,
King Solomon wrote the Proverbs
And King David wrote the Psalms.*

Retarding Emotional Decline

The first step in retarding emotional decline is for the person in later maturity to recognize himself as he is and to accept the reality of the aging process. The acceptance of the self is necessary at all stages of life, but it is especially important in the later years. We are all growing older all the time and, whether we like it or not, we shall all be old some day if we live long enough. As aging is inevitable, we must admit that we are growing older and look for the plus values rather than overemphasize the disadvantages. The person who has reached the period of later maturity must recognize the different values of the different stages of life and try to develop those values which are appropriate to his age group. Old age must be viewed as merely another period in the total growth cycle—a period which has its own worth, joys, and satisfactions as well as its minus values—and one which can be another adventure if the person himself is willing to exert the effort to make it so.

The importance of forward attitudes cannot be overemphasized. The aging person who would remain emotionally healthy, happy, and flexible must recognize the importance of the here, the now, and the future and not dwell on the past and on former achievements. He must recognize the values of his present life, for it is the present that others around him will appreciate, not the past, and he must look to a future in this life, not only in the next. To this many old persons will reply that

* Written by Dr. James Bell Naylor and reprinted by permission of Lucile Naylor.

there is nothing to look forward to, that since there is nothing
in the present or the future for them, the past is all they have
left. The answer to this is that each person can, if he is willing
to make the effort, develop a constructive, satisfying life for
himself in the present and plan for a good future, but that it will
take effort.

Usefulness.—If he will retard emotional decline the older
person must also be useful in some capacity. If possible, he
should keep at a paying job as long as he is physically and
mentally able to do so. If retirement from his regular job has
been forced upon him, it may be possible for him to have a small
business of his own. It need not be extensive, but it should be
enough to bring him an income and keep him happy, interested,
and useful. If neither paid employment nor a business of his
own is possible, he should plan to make himself useful in
another capacity, perhaps by baby-sitting, reading to the blind,
making visits to shutins, etc. In any case, he should engage in
some kind of work—some kind of work which will contribute
to his feelings of adequacy and of being wanted and needed in
the world. Work will also preserve his independence and self-
respect and give him an interest in life. In the measure that he
himself feels adequate, independent, and useful, others will
likewise so regard him.

Outward Interests.—It is most important for the aging
person to keep his interests turned outward, away from himself.
As one grows older, there is a tendency for the interests to
narrow and turn inward toward one's self, toward one's illnesses
and unhappinesses. If, as one grows older, he can make a habit
of concentrating on persons and things outside himself, there
will be little time left for magnifying aches and pains and
troubles. As one has interest in others and helps others, he
will find peace and harmony within himself and have no need
to stress his misfortunes. It is an easily observable fact that
the more one concentrates upon himself, the less satisfying he
finds life and the more unhappy he becomes.

Flexibility and Tolerance.—Those who are in the period of later maturity must also make conscious efforts to avoid increasing rigidity and inflexibility. There is a normal tendency as one grows older to become progressively more rigid and inflexible, both intellectually and emotionally, but much of this can be avoided by conscious efforts to keep flexible in ideas and attitudes and to be ready to accept changes and innovations.

Tolerance is likewise important to the retardation of emotional decline. The intolerance of many elderly persons is well known, but those who would remain emotionally healthy and happy must make a definite effort to avoid this and to develop tolerance in all areas. They must develop tolerance for the views of others—religious, social, scientific, political, and others, for the present times, and for the younger generation. It is customary for older persons to deplore the habits, views, and activities of the present day and the evils of the younger generation. If they face the situations honestly and realistically, though, they must recognize that there is more progress than regression in the times and the people of each generation. There may be many things they do not like, but they must learn to accept these and to look for the good rather than the evil in them.

When people evaluate the aging individual as being "too old," he must be ready, as Lawton (17) has suggested, to counter with, "Too old for what?" He himself must be convinced that he is not too old to be physically, mentally, emotionally, and socially alert, to enjoy life, and to do anything within reason that he feels like doing. He must be willing and ready to try new things, recognizing that not all the new is bad, but that some may be good. Many old customs and ways of living and thinking are good and worth retaining, but others should be discarded. On the other hand, many new things are faddish and unworthy, but more of the new ideas and changes which come about are good and should be embraced. The wise older person who is not bound by his resistance to change should, by virtue of his experience in life, be able after trying the new to evaluate its worth—but he must be willing to try it before he can evaluate it.

Earning Recognition and Affection.—Finally, the aging person must earn recognition and affection through his present deeds, for it is this which brings emotional independence and security. He must not bask in the reflected glory of his past achievements or demand gratitude and affection from his offspring for the early care he took of them, for these claims will seem hollow and shallow. Rather, he must have a life of his own—a useful life which is intellectually, emotionally, and socially apart from the lives of his offspring—for this will bring with it feelings of inner competence and security that are more satisfying than the crumbs of begrudging affection he might beg from irritated offspring.

We might sum this up briefly by saying that it is the emotional attitudes and interests of the aging person which will either accelerate or retard emotional decline. Healthy emotional attitudes and interests can be developed and maintained by care and effort on the part of the individual, and this care and effort are worth while, for they will result in the increased happiness of the individual.

Retarding Social Decline

Social decline, of course, is closely allied to intellectual, physical, and emotional decline, particularly emotional decline, and cannot rightfully be separated from decline in these areas. The retardation of social decline, therefore, cannot easily be considered apart from the retardation of decline in other areas. It is, rather, a matter of treating the retardation of decline from another aspect—the social.

Employment and Retirement.—The first consideration in the retardation of social decline is the matter of the job and retirement, which has been dealt with in Chapters 3 and 5.

Many aging persons could remain employed if they were willing to step down a bit, and for the sake of their own social competence and sustained interest in the external world, it would be advisable for them to consider this. When they are no longer able to keep up with their regular job, a slower or simpler factory operation, for example, might be better suited to their declining abilities. Although this would bring reduced remuneration, the oldster would still be working and useful and thus be able to retain his self-respect and feelings of inner security and social competence. In other instances, he might be able to work part time in a less taxing or different kind of job and during hours when he could avoid the usual commuters' rush. The advertisements and the propaganda of the insurance companies concerning the joys of retirement and leisure look fine on paper, but in practice these are actually frustrative and deteriorative to the happiness and well-being of the older person.

Of course, there are many instances where the retirement rules of a firm cannot or will not be altered, so that it is impossible for an individual to continue employment there after a certain age; then, naturally, he is too old to secure employment elsewhere. In situations such as this, many individuals might create their own jobs. Lawton (19) has written a little pamphlet containing suggestions for ways in which older women might create jobs of their own, and many of these suggestions are equally applicable to men. These suggestions include shops of various sorts, particularly specialty shops, such as an artificial flower shop, a baby shop, a second-hand magazine shop, a candy shop, specializing in home-made candies, a pastry shop, a shop for larger women or men, a drapery shop, a knit shop, a garden shop, etc. Baby-sitting is practiced by both older men and women. A boarding house or an entertainment house which might be hired for homelike entertainments might well be run by an older person. A mending service for clothes or books, a laundry service for special and fine pieces only, a business research service, a day nursery, a reading service, a menu service, a

placement agency for older workers, a personal shopping service, a center for the training of domestic workers, practical
nursing, particularly in the home care of convalescent invalids,
and a colony or recreational center for older persons are a few
other suggestions for jobs which those older might create for
themselves. For those who are interested in outdoor activities, garden specialties can often be made profitable—specialties
such as a particular kind of flower, fruit, berry, or vegetable.
These specialties, of course, could also be grown under glass in
the winter and made even more profitable.

Making and Maintaining Friendships.—The next most important consideration in the retardation of social decline is the
development of friendships, particularly friendships in the same
age group. Friendships with persons of all ages and both sexes
are necessary, but usually friendships with contemporaries prove
the most satisfying. This is not always easy as one grows
older and friends of long standing die, but these departed friends
should be replaced by others. New friends should be made each
year, and the aging person must feel free both to give and to
receive affection rather than fear it. In his friendships he must
be able to give of himself, but he must not be possessive and
selfish and try to prevent his friend from being friends with
others as well.

New Experiences.—The aging person who would keep his
social competence will seek new experiences—new persons to
meet, new places to go, and new things to see. He will not keep
to himself and vegetate as he meditates on his ills, misfortunes,
and past achievements. Instead, he will maintain an active
interest in everything which is going on about him and welcome
new experiences of all kinds. He will be curious about new
developments in different fields and about the different ideas
of the new persons he meets. He will want to learn new things
and will welcome opportunities which will satisfy this interest.

Social Usefulness.—The development of social usefulness is
a too-often neglected but potentially productive area of social

life in older persons. The period of later maturity is an especially good time to take a more active interest in civic affairs
that the pressure of work might have prevented earlier. When
the pressure of supporting and raising a family has eased, there
is more time to devote to community affairs, and the wide
experience of the older person should make him especially
valuable in this respect. Just what role he will play, of course,
will depend upon his personal inclinations. Some individuals
enjoy a role of active leadership in which they hold office or in
another way run things, whereas others prefer a background
role in which they serve the leaders or act in an advisory
capacity of some sort.

Schedule of Time and Plan of Life.—Martin (25-32 inclusive), in her work on rehabilitation of the aged, has stressed
the need of making a schedule of time and a plan of life, always
keeping a forward view in mind. Many unhappy older persons
aimlessly waste their time from day to day and all day because
they feel they have nothing to live for, no aim in life, and no
goals.

To get away from this, Martin had her older clients fill out
charts of their daily activities and then plan them more productively so that they would include suitable times for useful work,
rest, eating, and recreation. They then made out a plan of life
which included a clear statement and evaluation of near or
immediate goals and of far goals and worked first toward the
attainment of the near goals and then toward the attainment of
the far goals. The life plan also included a sensible plan of
work and play, in which ample time was allowed for each.
Work and play are necessary in all periods of life, and the period
of later maturity is no exception to this rule. The budgeting of
time and money was another part of the life plan, and actually
this gave the aging person more freedom, since he was then
able to use both his time and his money more effectively. These
suggestions for the rehabilitation of the aged might also be
used effectively by the aging individual himself, who does not

necessarily feel the need of rehabilitation but does feel the need of trying to maintain his social competency.

The development of hobbies will also do much to retard the social decline of the aging individual, since hobbies can provide an activity which will keep one's interest alive and active. Even those hobbies which are followed largely in solitude can serve as a stimulus to social intercourse by offering a subject of interesting conversation or by bringing together persons of similar interests. The particular hobby one chooses will naturally depend upon his special interests and aptitudes, but, regardless of its nature, a hobby is a decided asset in the retardation of social decline.

Clubs and recreational centers for older persons are excellent outlets and can do much to retard social decline if the older person will attend. They not only provide social intercourse with contemporaries but give opportunities for learning new things, developing new hobbies, exchanging new ideas, and feeling accepted in the group. Then too, many unacceptable social faults of the aging person can best be corrected in a group of contemporaries. A group of contemporaries also serves as a stimulus for keeping up to date, looking one's best, and acting one's most charming self.

Developing Neglected Potentials

As one grows older, he must recognize the diminishing of the physical side of life and try to develop the pleasures of the mind and spirit. He must accept the fact that each period of life brings its own satisfactions and try to develop the potentials of his own period. In the period of later maturity one must strive to cultivate his inner resources, to develop greater human understanding, reasoning, judgment, and imagination, and to build up proficiency in creative activities (7, 11, 16, 18, 19, 21, 22, 36, 37, 38, 44). Instead of deploring his diminished activity in his vocational field, he should consider that this lessened requirement of work leaves him time. The fact that his offspring have grown up and are on their own, so that he now has fewer responsibilities, will give him greater opportunity to develop those inner, perhaps creative potentials which, prior to this, have had to be subservient to the necessity of earning a living.

Travel.—In considering how to develop neglected potentials or to occupy one's time during retirement or increased leisure, one must consider his major interest first and follow that, as this often broadens out later into other things. For example, one may always have had a desire to travel and may begin his retirement or increased leisure years by traveling to all the places he has wanted to visit. For a while he may enjoy this, but after a time, if he has no interest other than just going from place to place, interest in travel as such begins to wane. Also, traveling is so expensive that relatively very few can afford to keep it up for very long. However, when traveling develops an interest in a special field, it begins to assume more meaning and becomes more purposeful and challenging to the individual. When the traveler develops an interest in ethnology, anthropology, geography, geology, art, architecture, or archaeology, for example, he sees things on his trips which are related to his special interests, and he may go on and on and begin to search through books and documents in his quest for further knowledge. His first casual interest then may develop into something intellectually challenging and satisfying and offer the opportunity of developing hitherto unrecognized intellectual potentialities. Likewise, collections of various sorts make travel more meaningful and offer opportunities for the development of intellectual potentialities and artistic appreciation and knowledge. Given sufficient interest, ability, and time, one might even develop into an expert critic on certain types of art specialties, native crafts, and the like.

Music.—Music is a creative activity which most persons enjoy but in which relatively few participate, and yet it offers an excellent medium for the development of neglected potentials.

Interest in music may vary from collecting recordings, going to concerts and operas, and listening to the radio to the redevelopment of earlier musical skills and learning to play a new musical instrument. Passive interest in music can be most enjoyable, but whenever there is any slightest interest in participating, this interest should be encouraged and developed. Many of the simpler musical instruments can be learned easily enough to be played fairly well by the older person and can give much enjoyment and satisfaction to the one who accomplishes this. Even the piano, which is generally conceded to be a difficult instrument to play, can be learned with relative ease by some of the more modern methods. True, one will not become a concert pianist if he does not start playing the piano until an advanced age, but he can learn in a short time, by means of the newer chord techniques, how to play popular and light classical selections—enough for his own amusement and for the enjoyment of his associates. Those who have greater talent and better background may even be interested in trying to compose simple selections of their own. Because there are few things which can bring greater satisfaction and emotional release than the production of music, active participation in some form of music should be encouraged to a far greater extent than it is. Unfortunately, too many persons have the idea that only an expert should play a musical instrument, whereas, in reality, home concerts and evenings of music can bring much enjoyment and a great feeling of family solidarity.

Arts and Crafts.—Art work, particularly in the form of painting, drawing, and sculpturing, is another creative activity which can be followed well into old age. Many older persons starting work of this kind for the first time may even discover that they have hidden talent which needs only activity to bring it out. "Grandma" Moses, with her charming primitives, is an example of this sort—a woman who never tried to paint until well along in the period of later maturity and yet in a few years has made a name for herself. Relatively few, of course, can do this, but a great number can derive considerable enjoyment from sketching or painting familiar things or well-loved scenes. Even finger painting is an interesting medium for some. The final production need not be a masterpiece but if it brings enjoyment and satisfaction, it is good and serves its purpose. The manual activity itself in drawing, painting, and modeling is restful to many tense persons, and the color too offers considerable emotional release. Cartooning for amusement is also an excellent artistic medium for developing neglected potentials if one has a sense of humor. Granted the sense of humor to start with, cartooning will help to keep it alive and can be the source of much fun among family and friends.

Crafts of various sorts likewise offer excellent possibilities for the development of hidden talent and interests. There are many different types of crafts, and the individual may choose any which appeals to him. Woodwork, ranging from whittling to making intricate ship models, is most popular among older men, particularly retired seamen, and some create really beautiful pieces. Metalwork, in the form of jewelry, table and kitchen utensils, trays, bowls, and the like, is also popular and offers a good medium for the expression of artistic talent and manual skill. Ceramics offers another wide field for creative activity because of the diversified nature of the things produced in this medium. All these types of crafts—wood, metal, and ceramics—can be developed either for personal enjoyment or with a view to creating a commercial market for the products.

Sewing, knitting, and crocheting have always been popular crafts among women, and these can be made more meaningful when there is a definite purpose connected with them. When there are children and grandchildren to make things for, this is no problem. When there are no relatives, many elderly women could make themselves both happy and useful by turning their skills to the making of clothes and other needed things for orphanages and charitable organizations. A nice example of this is the beautiful rug which was made by the Dowager Queen Mary of England and recently brought to the United States for sale, the proceeds of which were destined for charitable organizations. Others may use their talents in the creation of new designs, in opening a shop of their own, or in teaching their art to others. Weaving of all kinds is especially popular.

Leatherwork and bookbinding, especially the binding of fine books, are creative activities enjoyed by both men and women, and these are crafts which may easily prove of remunerative value as well as personally satisfying. Leatherwork is wide in scope, varying from the making of simple belts, key cases, and wallets to fine tooling of bags and purses. Finely tooled bindings of prized books offer an especially good field for the use of creative imagination and skill.

Others may prefer paperwork—papier-mâché, artificial flowers, paper decorations, and similar things. Craft work of this sort is especially popular for parties, and in this way it may prove profitable as well as satisfying to the creative urge. Craft work of any sort offers a good medium for the development of neglected potentials.

Writing.—Writing is another excellent creative outlet which might be developed by many who have always had an urge to write but could never seem to find the time to start. This is especially good for those who have been engaged in intellectual work and have a natural gift of expression but never have worked at developing this gift. It is never too late for anyone to try writing, and many, from their wide experience in life and in their own particular fields, may have much to offer. Some excellent writing has been done by persons well advanced in age.

Household Specialties.—Many individuals, though, have neither interest nor talent in music, art, craft work, or writing, and yet they too need creative outlets. They also may have undeveloped potentials, but they may lie along different lines. For example, many housewives who are excellent cooks may develop their own household specialties. They may develop their own special recipes for pie, cake, or some prized dish and use these at special parties of family or friends. Or perhaps they may develop individual recipes for sale or for competition in contests. Others, more ambitious, may work on a book of special recipes and either publish it or promote its use among family, friends, and neighbors.

Gardening.—Gardening offers another wide field for the development of neglected potentials along agricultural or horticultural lines. Some may be content to grow the usual vegetables or flowers and take pride in good crops of each, either retaining them for the use of one's own family or giving them away to friends and relatives or selling them in the neighborhood. Others may gain greater enjoyment and profit by developing some specialty—a special kind of berry, fruit, vegetable, or flower. This may lead to studies along the lines of one's interests and to experiments, either outdoors or under glass, with the chosen specialty. Many worth-while things might be developed in this manner, and considerable satisfaction as well as possible income might accrue to the experimentally inclined individual.

Adult Education.—Adult education courses in anything that suits one's fancy might be the beginning of a new interest and result in developing latent and unsuspected talent. When one has reached the period of later maturity, he should not plan his courses with the same functional purpose as when he was in his youth and had to plan on a lifetime career. Rather, he should choose anything which happens to appeal to him, whether or not it seems to have any reason or utilitarian end in view. This should be the time when he feels he may study anything he likes, whether in his own or in an entirely new field, and may attempt any new art he pleases. For example, the older person may wish to take courses in any of the above-mentioned activities, or in a foreign language, history, archaeology, mathematics, or any other subject, and if he wishes to do so, he should do it. He may also become interested in entirely different fields such as dancing, either folk or social dancing, or in puppets and puppet shows. Work with puppets may include making the puppets, working with them, writing the plays, or directing the shows—certainly a wide field for creative activity.

The Art of Conversation.—Finally the art of conversation is one of the most neglected yet one of the most important potentials to develop. This involves the ability to get along with others and to be able to participate in the give-and-take of a spirited discussion without monopolizing the floor or becoming angry when opinions of others differ from one's own. A good conversationalist is always in demand, but a soliloquist is always shunned. Some who are gregarious by nature but find verbalization difficult may offset their handicap by becoming good listeners. This should make them popular, since few persons, especially older persons, are good listeners. (The learning of magic is another good entertainment device which may be enjoyed by many older persons who are not good conversationalists and yet have a touch of showmanship in them.) In all this getting along with others, though, it is thinking of the other person that is important—the ability to turn one's attention away from one's self toward others.

Summary

The retardation of decline and the development of neglected potentials are closely allied, for the development of neglected potentials will help to retard decline. Both involve participation in life and keeping up to date physically, intellectually, emotionally, and socially.

The retardation of physical decline involves keeping up one's general appearance to the best of one's ability, keeping well groomed and up to date in dress, maintaining good posture, gait, and personal hygiene, and taking proper exercise and rest.

Diet is important and, save in extreme old age where malnutrition is common, is better if of low caloric content, low in fats and cholesterol, and high in proteins, calcium, phosphorus, and iron, with adequate vitamins. Generally speaking, it is better to be a little on the thin side in the period of middle and later maturity.

Periodic physical examinations are important for early diagnosis of beginning difficulties and their amelioration whenever possible.

Periodic examinations should be made particularly of sensory processes, teeth or dentures, heart, blood pressure, digestive system, and endocrine system.

The use of endocrines will do much to retard physical decline within limits, although it must be recognized that nothing is yet known which will postpone the aging process indefinitely.

The aging individual must recognize his personal limitations but not overemphasize them. He must take time out to analyze himself and his relationships in order to develop insight and a healthy self-interest.

The retardation of mental decline involves recognition of the high and low points of decline, concentrating on the development of the well-preserved abilities and trying to compensate for those which are declining fastest.

To prevent intellectual stagnation, it is important to continue one's education throughout life, learning something new each year, keeping abreast of current affairs, and being aware of the new developments in one's own field.

The decline of learning ability can be offset or compensated for to a limited degree by practicing new learning and utilizing various devices to help one to remember important things.

The retardation of intellectual decline also involves taking time out to think and using one's judgment and experience to develop new ideas.

The retardation of emotional decline demands a forward attitude and the avoidance of rigidity, stagnation, and inflexibility.

In the period of later maturity, one must admit that he is growing older, but he must feel that he is not too old to try anything new he wants to try.

If one would retard emotional decline, he must keep useful and interested, keep his interests turned outward away from himself, develop tolerance for others, and earn recognition and affection through his present deeds, not his past achievements.

He must look to the present and future, be ready to try anything, and refuse to be relegated to the "scrap heap."

The retardation of social decline, which is closely allied to the retardation of emotional decline, involves keeping on working as long as possible either at a paid job or at a personal hobby or interest—anything which will keep one feeling alive, interested, and useful.

It is also important for the maintenance of social competence to keep friends, to make new friends, and to be emotionally independent of one's offspring. The older person must not fear affection, for he needs close relationships with persons other than his offspring.

Keeping up to date socially, seeking new experiences, being socially useful, and planning one's work, play, and budget will help to retard social decline.

Clubs and recreational centers for older persons are good social outlets.

In growing older, one must recognize the diminishing pleasures of the body and develop the neglected potentials of the mind and imagination.

The period of later maturity is a good time to try to create something along intellectual or artistic lines. The production need not be a masterpiece, but if it brings satisfaction and enjoyment, it has definite worth.

Music, painting, drawing, craft work of various sorts, writing, household specialties, horticulture, agriculture, magic, and puppets are good mediums for the development of neglected potentials.

The development of the art of conversation, getting along with others, and a genuine interest in others instead of one's self are important.

Older persons should take adult education courses in anything which suits their fancy, and this may sometimes result in the development of latent and unsuspected talent.

In short, to retard decline one must develop neglected potentials and *participate* in life as long as he lives.

REFERENCES

1. ADAMS, C. W. The age at which scientists do their best work. *Isis,* 1945-46, **36**, 166-69.
2. BJORKSTEN, J. The limitation of creative years. *Sci. Mon.,* N.Y., 1946, **62**, 94.
3. BOGOMOLETS, A. A. *The prolongation of life.* New York: Duell, Sloan & Pearce, Inc., 1946.
4. CAVAN, R. S., BURGESS, E. W., HAVIGHURST, R. J., and GOLDHAMMER, H. *Personal adjustment in old age.* Chicago: Science Research Associates, 1949.
5. CRAMPTON, C. W. Dietary aids and dangers for the aging. *Public Health Nurs.,* June, 1949, 320-26.
6. DARIC, J. *Vieillissement de la population et prolongation de la vie.* Paris: Presses Universitaires de France, 1948.
7. DE GRUCHY, C. *Creative old age.* San Francisco: Old Age Counselling Center, 1946.
8. DONAHUE, W., and TIBBITTS, C. *Planning the older years.* Ann Arbor, Mich.: University of Michigan Press, 1950.
9. ENGLISH, O. S. A brighter future for older persons. *Geriatrics,* 1949, **4**, 217-24.
10. FINK, D. H. *Release from nervous tension.* New York: Simon & Schuster, Inc., 1943.
11. GILES, R. *How to retire—and enjoy it.* New York: Whittlesey House, 1949.
12. HAUSER, G. *Look younger, live longer.* New York: Farrar, Strauss & Young, Inc., 1950.
13. JACOBSON, E. *How to relax.* New York: Whittlesey House, 1948.
14. JOHNSON, W. M. *The years after fifty.* New York: Whittlesey House, 1947.
15. KAUFMAN, W. Therapeutic reversal of common clinical manifestation of the normal aging process, decreased joint mobility. Paper delivered before the 2d International Gerontological Congress. Abstract in *J. Geron.,* 1951, **6**, 111.
16. LAWTON, G. *New goals for old age.* New York: Columbia University Press, 1943.
17. ——. Mental decline and its retardation. *Sci. Mon.,* N.Y., 1944, **58**, 313-17.
18. ——. *Aging successfully.* New York: Columbia University Press, 1946.
19. ——. *Women go to work at any age.* Chicago: Altrusa International, 1947.
20. ——, and STEWART, M. S. *When you grow older.* Public Affairs Pamphlets, 1947, No. 131.
21. LEHMAN, H. C. "Intellectual" vs. "physical" performance. *Sci. Mon.,* N.Y., 1945, **61**, 127-37.
22. ——. Some examples of creative achievement during later maturity and old age. *J. soc. Psychol.,* 1949, **30**, 49-79.

23. Lewis, N. D. C. Mental hygiene in later maturity. In Kaplan, O. (ed.), *Mental disorders in later life*. Stanford, Calif.: Stanford University Press, 1945.

24. Lieb, C. W. *Outwitting your years*. New York: Prentice-Hall, Inc., 1949.

25. Martin, L. J. *Sweeping the cobwebs*. New York: The Macmillan Co., 1930.

26. ——. *Salvaging old age*. New York: The Macmillan Co., 1933.

27. ——. *A handbook for old age counselors*. San Francisco: Geertz Publishing Co., 1944.

28. Martin, L. J., and De Gruchy, C. *Salvaging old age in industry*. Publications of the Old Age Center, San Francisco, n.d., No. 1.

29. ——. *Salvaging old age in social work*. Publications of the Old Age Center, San Francisco, n.d., No. 2.

30. ——. *Salvaging old age in family relations*. Publications of the Old Age Center, San Francisco, n.d., No. 3.

31. ——. *Salvaging old age in institutions*. Publications of the Old Age Center, San Francisco, n.d., No. 4.

32. ——. *Salvaging the unemployed*. Publications of the Old Age Center, San Francisco, n.d., No. 5.

33. Mechnikov, E. The prolongation of life. Translated by P. C. Mitchell. New York: G. P. Putnam's Sons, 1908.

34. Peppard, H. M. *Sight without glasses*. Garden City, N.Y.: Blue Ribbon Books, 1940.

35. Perlman, R. M. Rehabilitation of markedly debilitated aged and aging subjects. Paper delivered before the 2d International Gerontological Congress. Abstract in *J. Geron.*, 1951, **6**, 134.

36. Powys, J. C. *The art of growing old*. London: Jonathan Cape, 1944.

37. Ray, M. B. *How to conquer your handicaps*. Indianapolis: Bobbs-Merrill Co., 1948.

38. Revese, G. L'âge et le talent. In Albert Michotte (ed.), *Miscellanea psychologica*. Paris: Librairie Philosophique, 1947.

39. Siedel, H. How to grow old gracefully. In Soden, W. H. (ed.), *Rehabilitation of the handicapped: a survey of means and methods*. New York: The Ronald Press Co., 1949.

40. Stieglitz, E. T. *The second forty years*. Philadelphia: J. B. Lippincott Co., 1946.

41. Tibbitts, C. (ed.). *Living through the older years*. Ann Arbor, Mich.: University of Michigan Press, 1949.

42. Vischer, A. L. *Old age: its compensations and rewards*. New York: The Macmillan Co., 1948.

43. Weyberg, L. E. Mental health and nutrition in old age. In Kaplan, O. (ed.), *Mental disorders in later life*. Stanford, Calif.: Stanford University Press, 1945.

44. Wolfe, W. B. *A woman's best years*. London: George Routledge & Sons, Ltd., and Kegan Paul, Tench, Trubner & Co., Ltd., 1947.

Chapter 10

PROFESSIONAL WORK WITH THE AGING IN THE COMMUNITY

With the steadily increasing numbers of older persons in our population and our present early retirement policies, we find increasing numbers of chronically ill, unhappy, economically dependent old persons in our midst. The majority of them are living and will continue to live in the community, so that the problem becomes constantly a more pressing one for society. The problem of the aging concerns not only the aging themselves but also those with whom they must live, work, and socialize—in other words, society in general. The field of work with the aging is a broad one and one which is attracting more and more persons from the various professions.

Professional work with the aging, as with any other group, requires cooperation of services. There may be many specializations of interest, and this is desirable, but for total effectiveness there must be an integration of the various specialties. We cannot consider the health of the older person, for example, without also looking into his living conditions, his employment, his recreational outlets, and his emotional adjustment. If we want to do counseling and guidance work with him, we must examine and treat all facets of his life. Because of the interdependence of all aspects of the personality and of life, the gerontological specialist must collaborate with allied workers so that together they can achieve the best possible results.

Health Care of the Aging

The Physician.—Of course, the physician is the person who has the most to do with the health care of the aging individual

(4, 32). Unfortunately, however, too many older (as well as younger) persons do not consult a physician until a real illness presents the urgent necessity for consultation. Others, who have the tendency to call the doctor for many seemingly minor complaints, are often dismissed with sugar pill placebos as being neurotic or as suffering from the inevitable but unimportant complaints of old age. Many of these individuals may be neurotic, but they may also have some organic basis for their somatic complaints, and these should not be overlooked. In addition, no physical complaint should be considered either unimportant or inevitable. Regardless of its organic basis or lack of such a basis, every physical complaint is significant and should be investigated. Illness is not the inevitable accompaniment of advancing age; it is an abnormal condition which should be prevented if possible and, when it is present, eliminated as quickly as possible.

The family physician is the logical person to whom to entrust the health care of the aging individual, and in smaller communities he is often particularly well suited to this job. In large cities, where everything is crowded and rushed, it is seldom that a physician can really get to know his aging patient *as a person* or get a true picture of his family life, whereas in smaller communities the physician may have known his patient and his patient's family for years. Even if the physician does not know the patient personally, he usually knows enough about him by reputation to understand his needs and the stresses to which he is subject, and this of course enables the physician to treat his patient more effectively.

We already know that more people are living to advanced ages than ever before and that the number is steadily increasing. In order to make these years worth living, in order to make them happy and productive, we must stave off the aging process as long as possible and use whatever means are available to prevent abnormal life changes or decline. For this purpose many physicians advocate a very complete medical examination in the middle years, with periodic health examinations for the rest of life after that. Most agree that this should be a very complete study of the whole person, including his past and present life. Preventive measures include a good physical and mental hygiene and a healthful regimen of life.

Crampton (7), in discussing the essentials of the geriatric examination, considers that there are two classes of ages: the ages of record, which include chronological, statistical, and hereditary ages; and the biological ages, which include anatomical, physiological, psychological, and pathological ages. He advocates the investigation of each. His examination would be done in three parts, each taking about an hour. The first interview would consist of a complete life history, including hereditary factors, told by the patient or filled out partly on a form prior to the interview and discussed during the thorough examination of all body parts, organs, and systems. Clues to aging are sought, and tests, X rays, and so on, are ordered as need is indicated. On the second interview, the data would be thoroughly analyzed and interpreted in terms of the whole body and the total life. Anti-aging action, in terms of indicated corrections and treatments and a constructive, remedial life program, is initiated. After several weeks of trying out this program, the patient returns for his third interview. At this time the results are checked, retests are made, and the full health program for six months or a year is given. De-aging procedures include the removal or amelioration of pathological conditions, the rehabilitation of malfunctioning physical processes, and the improvement of bad life management. Crampton stresses the importance of the geriatric examination as an introduction to lifelong geriatric service, which should be preventive, remedial, and constructive.

Thewlis and Gale (37) also stress the importance of preventive geriatrics, which includes a study of the patient's susceptibilities to disease and an endeavor to prevent diseases which are likely to occur. Preventive measures include good physical and mental hygiene, correction of focal infections, adequate nutrition, and avoidance of obesity.

The normal decline of organ functioning, added to the insults of the environment over a long period of time, may result in one or more ailments in the aging person. Wherever possible, the causes of these ailments should be removed, whether it be by removal of focal infection or other pathological condition or by rehabilitation of a malfunctioning physical process. When this is impossible, palliatives may be given and the body as a whole built up so that it can function fairly well in spite of the specific organ disability.

Nutrition.—Those concerned with the health care of the aging should pay particular attention to nutrition, for many elderly persons show the effects of malnutrition. Obesity should be avoided, so that usually a diet of low caloric content is advisable, although, of course, this would not hold true for every older person. Generally, a diet which is low in fats and cholesterol and high in proteins, calcium, phosphorus, and iron is desirable. Adequate vitamin intake is essential, especially components of the vitamin B complex and vitamin C, although vitamins A, D, and E are also important. Because of either lack of absorption or lack of utilization, it seems that the aging person may need more vitamins than the average, healthy young adult, and it may be necessary to supplement the diet of the older person with vitamin pills. Thiamine, niacin, riboflavin, ascorbic acid, and nicotinic acid appear to be important among the anti-aging agents. Stieglitz (35) recommends the following minimum daily dietary requirements, which may be supplemented by additional calories in accordance with taste and desire:

> One pint of milk (may be used raw or in cooking)
> One liberal serving of orange, grapefruit, or tomato juice
> One serving of a green vegetable
> One serving of some other vegetable
> One or more eggs
> One serving of meat or fish
> Two or three pats of butter or fortified margarine

Proper nutrition of the aging person, however, can be achieved only through the cooperation of the aging person himself and of those with whom he lives. Therefore the importance of nutrition in the retardation of the aging process should be stressed both to the patient and to his family.

In establishing a healthful regimen of life for the older individual, the factors of posture, relaxation, exercise, work, and recreation, as well as diet, must be taken into consideration. The physician who has the patient's confidence and is undertaking his treatment and anti-aging planning is probably the best one to prescribe action in these areas, although he may need the help of other services. Often he may have to be direct, matter-of-fact, and detailed in his planning, but at the same time he must always show consideration for the patient's feelings, tastes, desires, and ideas. Wherever possible, it is desirable to plan *with* the patient rather than *for* him and contrive to make him believe that many of the ideas and plans are his own. This may take a little more time, but it will insure better cooperation in the end.

The Environment.—As has been suggested many times previously, optimal health cannot be maintained unless living conditions and family relations are satisfactory. Mental and physical health are so closely allied that the older person who is unhappy and feels himself unwanted and excluded from the group will often develop physical symptoms and show evidence of decline beyond that which is normal for his age level. There-fore, in the anti-aging campaign these things must be given careful consideration. The environment must be adequate from the point of view of the patient, his tastes, and his desires. Where the environment is not suitable and the aging person is unhappy and ailing, manipulation of the environmental circumstances may be the first step toward amelioration of his condition. As Ginzberg (14) has pointed out, we try to help younger persons to adapt to the environment, but with older patients we often have to try to adapt the environment to them. It is because of this that Ginzberg thinks that when conflict exists between the older patient and his relatives, it is better at first to support the attitudes of the old person in order to establish better rapport with him. While many may not agree with this view entirely, most will see the frequent need of working with the relatives of older patients in order to establish optimal living conditions and effective functioning of de-aging plans.

Nursing Care.—Many older persons whose general deterioration has advanced to such a point that the possibilities of rehabilitation are very limited will require nursing care (2, 13) which they cannot receive in a hospital or nursing home. Others will need this care during acute or chronic illnesses. Besides being expensive, most hospitals and nursing homes have so many applications for admission that they have long waiting lists. Home nursing care, especially over a prolonged period of time, is also very expensive and beyond the reach of moderate incomes, so that many chronic patients are cared for by practical nurses. Whether a registered or practical nurse, it is assumed that the person caring for the older patient has the knowledge of and is skilled in the usual nursing procedures. Beyond this, a genuine liking for and understanding of the old is essential. Many patients, not being acutely ill, will need a minimum of actual nursing care, but this care will be required over a prolonged period of time, either because of the chronic nature of the illness or because it takes the older patient so much longer to recover from the illnesses he has. Therefore, the nurse who must spend long hours in the company of an elderly person who is ill enough to require only a moderate amount of nursing care but much attention, can function effectively solely if he or she has a real interest in old people in general and in this patient in particular. The opinion has been voiced by some that the middle-aged nurse can usually function the most effectively in the field of geriatrics.

Many old persons are unhappy because they feel rejected and useless, and for this reason they may be difficult patients. They may have strong, unconscious revenge motives or early selfish trends may have become accentuated, so that they are demanding and show a lack of consideration for those around them. The nurse must be ready to deal with these situations as well as with the usual nursing routines. Recognizing the psychosomatic unity inherent in the human organism, the geriatric nurse will try to work toward the happiness of the patient and combat any tendency on his part to vegetate, to retire from living, and to look forward to death. The nurse will make every effort to keep alive the patient's interest in living and in taking part in life to the fullest extent that he is able.

One of the first things to consider is the older patient's habits and attitudes. By the time old age is reached, these are usually firmly fixed and not easily subject to change, and to try forcibly to change them may result in retarding the recovery of the patient. Only when the patient feels that his nurse has a real liking for him and a genuine respect for his feelings and ideas will he be amenable to suggestions for desirable changes in his habits and attitudes. Suggestions for needed dietary changes and routines of rest, fresh air, exercise, occupations, and recreation may be accepted by the older patient only if approached by his nurse in a tactful, diplomatic manner. The nurse must also know when to allay fears—fears of pain, uselessness, dependency, and death—and how to make the patient feel that his early recovery, or at least an amelioration of his condition, is expected. It is not an easy job to encourage return to activity and at the same time see that a patient does not attempt more than he can do or remain too long dependent, and yet with the older patient this is very important.

The nurse who is skilled in working with older persons will use every device possible to encourage interest and participation in life. Helping the patient to keep well groomed and complimenting him on his appearance is one simple and effective means of keeping alive this interest. Seeking his advice or opinion on some problem in his own line of former activity or interest is another useful tool. Conversing with him on current events and asking him about his ideas concerning the future will give him a feeling of being still of some importance in life. Often discussing special recipes and differing methods of child-raising will prove very stimulating to the elderly housewife who can no longer continue with these routines.

As it is important to the older person's physical and mental health to feel useful and to have some constructive activity to occupy his time, it will often devolve upon the nurse to find something along these lines which is suitable for this particular patient. Taking into consideration the individual's health, abilities, and interests, it may require considerable ingenuity on the part of the nurse not only to find the suitable activities but also to induce the older patient to attempt them. Many aging persons are not only resistive to change but are also hesitant about attempting new things because of their fear of failure and their belief that "you can't teach an old dog new tricks." These resistances must be overcome and the patient given confidence in his ability to learn new things and to accomplish what he wishes (within limits, of course).

Finally, and this may be one of the most unpleasant tasks in the field, the nurse must often serve as a buffer between the elderly patient and his relatives. When there is conflict, there is probably much justification on both sides, and while objectivity and impartiality are desirable, it is frequently necessary for the nurse to side with the old person, in the beginning at least. If the nurse can have sympathy for and understanding of the aged patient and can help his family to give him a greater degree of acceptance, there is a greater possibility that this same patient can be helped later to modify his behavior and attitudes in such a way as to contribute more to happy and effective family living.

Housing Problems of the Aging

Living With Younger Relatives.—Housing problems have long been acute in this country, and with aging persons the situation is especially difficult (36). In times when rural living was the rule, houses and families were large, and there was much work to be done, even the very aged could usually find a niche for themselves and keep busy and useful. They could mind the baby, shell the peas, and perform numerous other useful, nonarduous tasks, or they could retire to the privacy of their own rooms when they wanted to escape from the rest of the family for a while. They had some opportunity to remain active participants in family and community life and yet retain their own privacy and not get in the way of the younger generations. With modern apartment and small-house living accommodations this is more difficult. There often is no room for the older person, and he remains in the household on sufferance, solely because there is nothing else to do with him. He may have to share his room with another member of the family and have no privacy or place to entertain his own friends. With the cramped quarters, smaller families, packaged and canned foods, and efficient household appliances, there is little for him to do, and no way for him to keep busy and useful if he has retired or is unemployed. This lack of interest and activities engenders restlessness and discontent. The old person may then become fault-finding, complaining, suspicious, cantankerous, overly inquisitive, and generally difficult. Rejecting family members may be overprotective or openly hostile, with the result that family relationships may become almost unendurable for all concerned. When the old person is unemployed and dependent, of course, the situation is usually more acute.

Some have solved the problem of family living by having the aging parent or parents live in a small house, cottage, or apartment nearby—a place near enough to give assistance if it is needed and yet separate, so that each family unit can maintain its own independence. Others have provided special units or apartments within the framework of the household, in these cases the old person usually taking his meals with the family but having space of his own where he may entertain his own friends as he chooses. These plans seem to work out satisfactorily when there is a moderately good family relationship in the beginning, but when the relationships are poor and conflict is marked, it is often better for the oldsters to be completely away from their offspring and other relatives.

Those who are interested in housing might do well to consider these points in designing new houses and apartment units, for certainly something constructive must be done for the increasing number of our aging population. Even when older persons and their adult offspring do not find it possible to live happily together under the same roof, a similar plan might be carried out on a residence, foster, or boarding home basis. Boarding home plans of various sorts have been tried out successfully with older persons by different social agencies in this country and abroad, and were facilities within the homes more adequate, no doubt the plans could be extended considerably.

The Foster Home.—Foster home care has also been tried out with some success. The boarding home plan is used for those who need to have some feeling of home life and personal relationships, yet want to be independent, and thus offers a field of endeavor to those who are interested in and want to work with older persons. It differs from the cold impersonality of a boarding house, where one can come and go for years and not get acquainted with anyone in the house, in that it presumably provides some warmth and semblance of family life. The plan has proved successful in both houses and apartments. Sometimes, a semiprivate apartment in a home has been provided, or an apartment with other old people, and these too have been satisfactory.

In the final analysis, the way in which he will live must be decided upon by the old person himself. Others may suggest different plans and point out the advantages and disadvantages of each, but if he is to adjust satisfactorily, the old person himself must make the final decision regarding his way of life. If foster home care is decided upon, preliminary study should be made both of the old person and of the home into which he is to go in order that the relationship may prove mutually satisfying.

It is important, for example, to match religions, since many rigid old persons (and also many rigid young persons), who cannot accept a viewpoint differing from their own, find it very disturbing and a source of friction to live in a home where there are religious differences. Personalities should be studied in order to avoid personality clashes in so far as this is possible, and in this connection it is most important that those who take an old person into their home have a genuine interest in old people and an acceptance of them as they are. Care should also be taken to see that the old person will have wholesome food, conveniences, and some privacy in his new home. Inaccessible baths, stairs which are too steep, and unmended rugs which are easily tripped over should be avoided wherever possible, and it should be assured that the old person will have no intrusion on his privacy when he feels the need to be alone. For care of this sort in New York City, charitable organizations currently may provide as much as $70.00 a month, plus $9.50 for incidentals. This obviously can secure more adequate care than the meager amount provided for by state old age assistance and most incomes under social security insurance payments.

Cooperative Apartment Living.—Cooperative apartment units may be planned for city and suburban housing for elderly people. Such plans may be carried out either by social agencies or by those who are interested in the aged. In cooperative apartment living there is usually a large apartment, preferably on the ground floor, with comfortable bed-sitting rooms, several bathrooms, a large general living-room, and a cooperative kitchen. Each elderly person may entertain as he pleases, either in his own room or in the general living-room. Meals may all be communal or communal once a day, with the remaining two meals prepared by the tenants themselves. Although there must be someone in charge of the apartment and the preparation of meals, each tenant has some responsibility for the care of his room and the common rooms of the apartment, and for assistance in the preparation of meals. Guests can arrange for inviting their friends to dinner when they choose. In apartment living of this sort, however, it is most important that individuals of not too dissimilar background and interests be included. It is unsuitable for those who require a great amount of physical care.

Cooperative apartment units are run along lines similar to those discussed above, but instead of separate rooms in the same apartment, there are small, separate, complete apartments with bedroom, bath, and living-room, possibly with kitchenette. Some may be even smaller, with a bed-sitting room, bath, and kitchenette. It is desirable to have these apartments on one floor with a central recreation room and dining-room where the guests can be served dinner, and perhaps breakfast, if they choose. Apartment communities similar to this are found in some Danish cities.

Cooperative living plans of the type just described may be carried out very simply or more elaborately, depending upon the incomes of the group. They are slightly different from foster homes and boarding houses, but any one of these offers a source of income and interesting work with aging persons. Those in the middle-age range are probably best suited to this sort of enterprise.

Colonies for Older Persons.—In less urban areas colonies for older persons, both married and single, have been tried out with some success. For example, Roosevelt Park, near Millville, New Jersey, a locally supported colony, offers accommodations of this sort to a limited number of aging persons who receive old age assistance or have incomes too small to enable them to live independently. There are two- and three-room cottages in the colony which rent for minimum amounts to single persons and slightly more to married couples, and a recreation hall where members may gather for entertainment or sociability. The members provide their own food and clothing, do their own cooking and cleaning, and often have small flower or vegetable gardens. The colony is readily accessible by bus to Millville, where recreational outlets and stores are available.

The members of this colony probably have the most independent living of any group of their economic level.

Moosehaven, located within the village of Orange Park, near Jacksonville, Florida, is another old age colony, although run along somewhat different lines. This is run by the Loyal Order of Moose for those members of sixty or over who have no means of support, the only provisions being that they must have paid their annual dues and be members in good standing. The members take care of their own rooms and buildings and each takes his turn, according to his interests and abilities, at other tasks about the home. It is beautifully situated and easily accessible to Jacksonville, and there is a large and varied program of recreational activities. In this home every attempt is made to meet the physical, intellectual, emotional, and social needs of the aging person. There is a large staff of professional workers at Moosehaven, and much research is being done on the problem of aging.

Colony plans similar to these might well be developed for other than purely philanthropic reasons, dealing with other than dependent income groups. The small cottage plan for single persons or married couples, with facilities for cooking, small gardens, and so on, and a central recreation hall, seems to be generally the most practical and desirable. Again, work of this sort is probably best suited to interested middle-aged persons who are seeking a moderate income.

Employment

We have already noted the steady increase in total life expectancy. Other things being equal, this should be noted with pride, but unfortunately other things are not equal. Employment, social acceptance, usefulness, happiness, and other things which make life worth living have not kept pace with the years which have been added to the life span. It has been and still is (with the exception of the war years) the tendency of both industry and the professions to fix and enforce early retirement ages, regardless of the fitness or desires of the individual worker. These ages are considerably below the life expectancy, so that the average worker can expect to spend a number of years outside the labor force (26). For example, in those firms which fix sixty years as the retirement age, this leaves an average difference of more than seven years between retirement and death. Social security and retirement funds are seldom sufficient to enable the average worker to live these remaining years independently and comfortably, so that additional work or supplementary aid is essential. As Clague (6) has pointed out, the discrepancy between the average working life span and the total life expectancy increased from less than three years in 1900 to five and a half years in 1940. If this trend continues, the average male worker in 1975 can expect to spend almost ten years outside the labor force. Also, of men sixty-five years old and over, the percentage in the labor force dropped from 70.1 in 1890 to 45.6 in 1949 (see Table 3). The increasing dependency occasioned by this discrepancy may before long create an economic burden too great to bear.

TABLE 3

PERCENTAGE OF MEN, 65 YEARS AND OVER, IN LABOR FORCE *

Year	Per Cent	Year	Per Cent
1890	70.1	1940	43.4
1900	65.0	1945	49.9
1920	57.2	1949	45.6
1930	55.5		

Source: Adapted from the United States Bureau of the Census; prepared by the Bureau of Labor Statistics, United States Department of Labor, Washington, D.C.
    * Reprinted by permission from E. Clague, "The Social and economic problems of employment of older workers," in W. Donahue and C. Tibbitts, eds., *Planning the older years.* Ann Arbor, Mich.: University of Michigan Press, 1950, page 194.

What then can industry and employers in general do about the situation? Or could it perhaps be the job of society as a whole? We might first ask whether the economic dependency of later years is justified either from the standpoint of the worker or from that of the employer. Is this what the worker wants, and is he happier to retire and "enjoy a well-earned rest"? This, of course, cannot be given a sweeping affirmative or negative reply, since the feeling about it will vary with the individual. Nevertheless, it would seem that the majority of workers do not want to retire, and when they do retire, they are not particularly happy about it. For example, a survey by the federal Bureau of Old Age Survivors Insurance found that only about 5 per cent of those receiving old age insurance benefits in 1941-42 had retired while in good health and wishing to retire. More than half of those retired were laid off by employers, and most of the rest retired because of ill health (34). This lack of happiness is probably caused in large part by the fact that many have no interest or activity to keep them occupied and that dependency often brings with it loss of prestige, rejection, and feelings of uselessness. There is evidence also that unemployment may bring about a sudden and rapid deterioration of mental efficiency (12).

From the standpoint of the employer, we must be realistic. A man is in business to make money, and if he employs people to work for him, he must employ those who can produce enough to justify the wages he is paying them. If the older worker is so inefficient that his employment results in decreased production and loss of money, the employer cannot afford to hire him or to retain him in his employ. This, however, does not seem to be the case (33). It is true that the older worker is generally slower and less adaptable, but it is also true that he has fewer industrial accidents and spoils less material. There is, in addition, less turnover among older workers. Disregarding for the moment enforced retirement ages, we find that many employers claim they are reluctant to employ older workers because they are unlovely in appearance and personality, are too slow in their performance and in learning new things, lack initiative, and are resistive to change in ideas and in methods. They claim they are too personal and incline to be either over- or underemotional and that they are intolerant, cantankerous, bossy, and hard to get along with. Many, perhaps because of their own insecurity, are troublemakers.

Other employers, fortunately, take the reverse view and prefer to hire older workers because they consider them more stable and devoted to their job. They find older workers more willing to use safety devices and to obey rules and regulations; they consider them to have more patience and control in emergencies and to have greater judgment, wisdom, and strategy. They point with pride to their fewer accidents and spoilage of materials. Also, although many workers show a decrease in efficiency with advancing years, others retain their efficiency of functioning to advanced ages. Also, as the very brightest tend to retain their efficiency longer than those who are less bright, the automatic discard of all who reach a certain age, regardless of what they can still produce, results in considerable waste of good material. A more sensible plan would seem to be one in which the individual's efficiency or capacity to produce would be determined, along with his desire to work or to retire, before deciding to discard him from gainful employment. A decreasing salary scale commensurate with his decreasing capacities would be fair to all concerned. Experience during the second World War, in which many persons in the sixties, seventies, and even older went back to work and produced creditably, shows that older workers can produce and do a good job when given the opportunity and incentive.

That this problem of the prolongation of the active working life of man is universal and not confined to the United States is brought out clearly by a very thorough study of this problem in France (8). Daric, the author, believes not only that it is a waste of good material to discard the older worker (regardless of his ability) but also that it is an economic necessity to do something about the prolongation of his active working life. He believes the state should play a part in these efforts.

In this country, many industries and some states are making an effort to salvage, or at least to retain in employment, the older worker, and there are wide opportunities in this area for those who are professionally interested. The Eastman Kodak Company and the Ford Motor Company, to mention two well-known industrial organizations, currently employ a fairly high percentage of older workers and find them satisfactory. New York State has formed a legislative committee to study the problem of aging, and this committee is active in research and in formulating plans for the improvement of the lot and opportunities of the older worker (3, 26). Some unions too are beginning to take an interest in the problem and to seek a practical solution to the continued employment of the older worker. For example, the New York local of the ITU (New York Typographical Union No. 6) permits a retired member to work at his trade two days a week and still draw his retirement pay, and also, with decreased efficiency on the job, to continue work at a reduced salary rather than be fired or retired. Many other companies and other unions are also seeking a practical solution to the problem of the older worker, but much educational work still needs to be done in order to make the movement widespread.

One of the widely held objections of employers to the hiring of older workers is the belief that both workmen's compensation rates and insurance rates go up when the elderly are employed. Fortunately, this is a mistaken belief, but again, employers need to be educated to their error. These things have been brought out clearly by the work of the New York Joint Legislative Committee on Problems of the Aging.

Much research, campaign, and educational work on the employment of the older worker needs to be done. Research is particularly needed in regard to job analyses and appraisal and training of individual skills. There is also a need for enterprising and far-sighted employers who will experiment with plans for using the elderly that will be mutually beneficial. The need for this is evident both in industry and in the professions, for in both areas the waste of good manpower is deplorable. Hastings College, the law department of the University of California, which employs only retired scholars and university professors sixty-five years of age or over, is an interesting and successful venture into the utilization of splendid material which might otherwise be discarded. A campaign for extension of the employment of older persons and the values of these older workers is badly needed.

Recreational Work

Recreational and leisure-time activities are most important to the happiness and welfare of older persons. Many individuals in the middle and later years are lonely and find that time hangs heavy on their hands, and this is particularly true of those who are unemployed. They may have little money and few friends, so that they tend more and more to withdraw from social contacts. Many have worked so hard for so many years without taking time out to play that they have forgotten how to enjoy themselves. These are the unhappy old people who seem to be just marking time as they wait for death. They are often irritable, cranky, fault-finding, and complaining, all of which is understandable, since they have nothing to do and no interest in life. Facilities for recreation and opportunities for associating with others and making new friends will often do much to change these attitudes and develop malcontents into happy, well-adjusted old people (31). Groups may comprise only men or only women, but the most successful ones involve both sexes. The stimulation offered by members of the opposite sex is decidedly beneficial.

For those who are interested in recreational work and in occupational therapy, work with the aging offers wide opportunities. Recreational centers and clubs, church groups, and educational programs for older persons are springing up in many communities, and good directors, workers, and leaders in these fields are greatly needed. Workers are needed who understand the normal personality and personality deviations and who are genuinely interested in older persons. Without these as a basis, no amount of assets in other areas will be effective and the "clubs" will probably fall apart.

Older persons, of course, are interested in many different types of recreational and leisure-time activities, and the worker should be prepared to offer something in each of the different general areas in order to provide sufficient variety in the program and to meet effectively the needs of the members. For example, the worker might follow Menninger's (25) classification of types of recreational activity in accordance with the psychological needs they meet: (1) entertainment which caters to passive desires and provides opportunities for passive participation; (2) competitive games which provide a social outlet for otherwise unexpressed feelings of aggression; and (3) the opportunity to create or produce something which provides expression of the erotic, constructive, or creative drive and arrangement of outlets in each of these areas. The worker, though, must be one who can give warmth, who has sufficient initiative, originality, and drive to promote and carry through constructive plans, and who can inspire and stimulate others to develop and use latent abilities and initiative.

The programs of recreational centers and clubs vary considerably, but it seems that practically every type of activity has been attempted. Probably the most effective program is one which includes a variety of activities from each of the areas mentioned above. General entertainment programs include teas, dances, and dinners; bus, boat, and train trips; picnics and summer camps; sightseeing, concerts, lectures, movies, the theater, and holiday celebrations. Competitive games for the aging are usually of the less strenuous type and include card games of various kinds, golf, shuffleboard, croquet, etc. Other, more hardy souls may prefer more active sports like swimming, ball-playing, roller-skating, ice-skating, etc. Creative work might include music, arts and crafts of all types, gardening, and cooking; the making of useful articles, toys, and clothing for charitable organizations; dramatics, creative writing, publishing a magazine or paper, and the like. An especially good field for the development of latent creative talent can be found in dramatics, for here not only the actors can play a part but also those interested in writing, art work (for the programs and scenery), construction, food (refreshments), and perhaps music.

The worker who can arrange for entertainments, exhibitions, auctions, and hobby shows by the group members and contrive to have each member of the group contribute in some way will do much toward developing a cohesive, constructive group, whose members are interested in cooperative living. Much happiness and good social living in general can develop from a good recreational group.

Educational activities with courses in various fields, lectures, and discussion groups also provide opportunities for satisfying the intellectual and constructive needs of some persons. They may result in getting the older person more actively interested in community affairs and projects government and social problems, with considerable benefit both to himself and to the community.

Given a good leader and congenial members, the group can flourish on the companionship and activities which tend to create feelings of adequacy, accomplishment, usefulness, and belonging, and an increased capacity to deal with problems. Many organizations report that after a while the members of the group become more alert and interested, develop friendships, and tend to complain less, to devote less time to a discussion of physical ailments, and to become less quarrelsome and irritable. The recreational worker, however, must have sufficient skill and insight not only to direct, encourage, and stimulate the members of the group but also to refer for case work and psychiatric or psychological consultation those individuals who are emotionally disturbed and need more help than the group can provide.

Over and above this work with the group as a whole and this alertness to the emotional disturbances of the individual, the clever recreational worker will also be on the lookout for special talents and interests and try to encourage, along with participation in various activities, concentration on and development of a specific hobby.

Social Work With the Aging in the Community

Social work with the aging in the community is a specialized branch of social work for which there is a dearth of adequately trained personnel. The social worker who enters this particular branch of the profession must have a genuine liking for older persons, endless patience, and complete and detailed information on community resources for the aging. The worker must know which doctors and medical clinics will best serve the individual patient, where he can receive psychological guidance or psychiatric treatment, what living arrangements are possible, what and where the employment possibilities are (or at least where to send the client for this need), and what recreational facilities are available in the community and best suited to this individual. The worker in this field must also have a special understanding of older persons and of their needs. Some knowledge of both medical and psychiatric social work are important for the geriatric social worker (29), and a good knowledge of mental hygiene is especially important, because the emotional needs and problems of the older person are inextricably bound up in his general adjustment and even in his physical complaints.

Case work with the aged (5, 17) must be based upon the conviction of the individual's worth and his right to a fitting place in society. Work should be carried on in cooperation with a medical doctor and with regard to community planning. The bases of case work with the aged are the same as those with other age groups, save that probably with the aged more directive work is necessary, although this must never be obvious and the client must not be made aware of it. The worker with the aged must be both accepting and directive at the same time and always let the client feel that he is making his own decisions. There is not sufficient time to be completely nondirective, but the client must be made to feel that he is free and independent. He should be permitted to decide, for example, on the doctor to whom he will go and on the kind of place he will go to live. The worker may help him to accept a mode of living by helping him to work through his feelings about his family or about living in a boarding home, an old age home, a hospital, or an old age colony, but the old person himself must make the final decision.

As a client has the ability to manage his own affairs, he must be helped to use this ability in adjusting to age handicaps. The worker must accept the old client as he is and, at least at first, assume that the client is right, and not his relative, when there is an argument. Listening to the oldster is one of the most important (although often one of the most wearying) jobs of the case worker, for it is only by listening to him that a relationship can be developed with him, and only by means of a good relationship can a worker help the oldster to accept needed care, placement, recreational outlets, occupational therapy, and so on. In listening to an old person, though, the case worker must try to differentiate between complaints based on organic illness and those based on neurotic illness for, as Dunbar (11) says, "the attention given to a case should probably be in inverse proportion to the degree of neurotic symptomatology manifested." Illness is often a form of aggression, and of this the worker must be aware. Medical treatment is essential for organic illness, but psychotherapy, rather than medicine, is more effective with neurotic illness.

Much of the case work with the aged will be supportive in nature and planned to rebuild or sustain ego strength to the point where they can resume normal ego functioning. Aggressions, particularly those in old age homes or clubs, are often a reactivation of early life problems, such as sibling rivalry and hostility, and must be dealt with by trying to direct the energy into constructive channels. The worker must remember, though, that the old are usually slow to accept new ideas and have lived longer to harden and develop resistances, so that work with them will be slow and require much tact. The pace of an old person is so much slower that he cannot be rushed into things, so that the worker will have to be gradual and tactful about trying to get him into social and recreational outlets. Much imagination and skill are necessary in working with the old. The worker must first be aware of his own feelings toward his parents, so that they will not unduly affect his relationship with his clients. Then he must accept the premise that the old *can* change and be optimistic and genuinely interested in the aged.

Counseling and Guidance of Older Persons

When counseling and guidance are mentioned, youth usually comes to mind. Most of us take it for granted that young persons need counseling and guidance, but that, when maturity is attained, this type of service is no longer needed. Nothing could be further from the truth. With our population ever growing older, more and more persons in the later years of life are unhappy, maladjusted, and in need of help in vocational planning and in effecting a better adjustment to life.

One of the first persons to recognize this need and to try to do something about it was Lillien J. Martin, who opened the first Old Age Counseling Center in 1929 in San Francisco (22, 23, 24). Dr. Martin, following her retirement from university teaching because of age, opened a child guidance center in this city, but in her work with children and their families, she noted the frequent difficulties presented by grandparents and other aged persons in the home. Instead of discounting their presence or trying to get rid of them, she decided to try to salvage them— and thus the old age counseling movement was started. Dr. Martin believed that almost any old person could be salvaged if he were willing to put forth enough effort.

Dr. Martin's method of rehabilitation (22) was essentially a directive one and included a series of planned visits during which a detailed and careful appraisal of the client's assets and liabilities was made, plans for daily living were evolved, and goals were set forth. The problems of employment and social living were tackled, and the old person was given definite and concrete tasks to accomplish for his own improvement. While not everyone may agree entirely with the details of Dr. Martin's method of rehabilitation of the aged, she was the pioneer in this field and for many years, until her death at the age of more than ninety, she did a fine job of rehabilitation. For this reason and because the Martin method is still in use in some areas, a more detailed explanation of this method is presented.

The first visit, in the Martin method, consists of a preliminary study of the personality of the client. This includes a careful observation of the general appearance, since this is considered to be of utmost importance for acceptance in a social or work group, and an investigation into the physical condition and health habits. If there is any question as to the state of his health, the patient is referred for a physical examination. His life history is also secured during the first interview and his pattern of reaction to life situations is noted. As the client tells his story, he is also encouraged to mention any side thoughts which enter his mind and to relate any recurring dreams he can remember. Following the life history, an abbreviated mental test, lasting about twenty minutes, is given in order to determine the individual's functioning and the extent to which mental rehabilitation can be expected. This test is used qualitatively rather than quantitatively, with rating of average, average plus, and average minus instead of conventional scores. The test series consists of (1) the recall of a paragraph (taken from the ten-year level on the Stanford-Binet test of intelligence); (2) recall of designs (from the same test); (3) repetition of digits forward and backward and of simple sentences; (4) the ball and field (or purse and field) test on the Stanford-Binet; (5) a test of imagination in which the subject tells what he sees in one of the simple black-and-white pictures of the same test series; (6) the Fernald Ethics Test, in which a series of ten cards giving examples of various sorts of misdeeds is presented for the subject to arrange in order of seriousness; (7) a test of suggestibility in which the client is presented with a highly colored picture on the back of which are twenty questions about the picture, ten of which ask if the subject has seen objects which are not there or are incorrectly described; (8) a test of rapidity of response, in which the subject is asked to write his name and address or two dictated sentences in ink, and to complete the patience test from the Stanford-Binet; and (9) tests for muscular strength and coordination, in which the client is asked to tie a bowknot, to lift a four-pound stack of books with arms extended, and to execute other pertinent movements. Sometimes a tenth test of higher reasoning is used with those who assume personal superiority because of past educational achievements.

The counselor then analyzes with the client the results of the observation, life history, and mental tests and encourages him to realize the importance of banishing physical and mental resistance and adopting a "will-to-do" attitude. Psychotherapeutic methods used include discussion, suggestion and autosuggestion, and the use of slogans. The client is then given two charts, on one of which not more than three setting-up exercises for rehabilitation are indicated and on the other space for recording his daily program. The interview ends with much encouragement and support from the counselor.

The second visit a week later consists of analyzing charts 1 and 2, which have been filled out by the client for the past week. If he is gainfully employed, the questions of whether he is really earning his salary and on what his advancement depends must be considered. A new daily program for a well-balanced day is then worked out.

The third visit consists of working on the money budget, the client filling in a chart on this, discussing it with the counselor, and working out a new one for permanent use if this is indicated. The influence of poverty, the use of wealth, the importance of a well-balanced budget, investments, and the possibilities of increasing the income if this is insufficient are some of the topics discussed in this area.

The fourth visit is for the purpose of establishing the client's effective functioning as an individual and a citizen. Near and far goals are discussed, and the patient is helped to establish these if he has not set any for himself. This ends the first part of the counseling plan, which was to help the patient to gain "a realistic understanding of himself as he was, is, and hopes to become." According to Martin, the first four visits deal with the client from a purely subjective point of view, helping him to analyze his own activity and to improve himself as an individual.

The second part of the rehabilitation plan aims to direct the thinking of the client toward those outside of and around him. It consists essentially of a "re-education of the client in objective thinking for active participation in community and industrial life." Dr. Martin took the view that the old person's being shut out of group life is due largely to himself and his defective early training, which taught him to think first of himself rather than be considerate of the rights of others.

The fifth visit then is concerned with participation in community life, and the client is helped to realize that this is not only something which will increase his own pleasure by restoring him to usefulness and power but also something which he as a citizen owes the community in return for its services to him. Welfare work is stressed, both because of its helpfulness to the group and because it provides an opportunity to form relationships with others and broaden interests. Political activity and resumption of active membership in organizations are also recommended, although the particular kind of social participation best suited to the individual client is decided upon only after careful evaluation of the material secured in his first four visits. The patient is encouraged to discard the old, to accept the new, and to develop a forward-looking attitude toward life so that he will be an asset in a group. It is stressed that participation must be *earned* and that the self-centered individual has no place in a group. Errors of thinking based on the ideas of a past generation are corrected by reason and persuasion, not by force, for authoritarian methods only increase resistance and cause worry and unhappiness.

Placement in industrial work is also considered in this visit, the job to be sought being decided upon in accordance with the mental capacity, the physical fitness, the emotional preference, the education, the social adjustment, and the industrial opportunities. The client is directed toward suitable placement agencies or other sources of information regarding employment opportunities, or, if need be, he may be directed to special schools or classes where he can receive the required training for the job he seeks. The client, however, must always seek his own job, since it is felt that this experience is important to his rehabilitation.

The ideal of the Martin plan is "to make old age the richest, happiest period in a lifetime." This means discarding apathy and old, worn-out ideas, attitudes, and ways of living, accepting the new and developing an active, forward-looking life. Four or five visits are claimed to be "sufficient and beneficial in 87 per cent of all successful cases," although many require fewer visits.

There can be no quarrel with the ideals and little with much of the procedure of the Martin plan of rehabilitation. Some counselors may question the possibility of accomplishing as much as is claimed by the Martin plan in four or five visits and hold for the greater efficacy of a more nondirective technique which takes a longer time. These same critics may question the use of charts and slogans, such as, "Growing old is living in the past," "Each immoral act makes reformation more difficult," "Temper is a weapon held by the blade," etc. Certainly, there are many persons to whom charts and slogans would definitely not appeal, but the fact that they do appeal to and help many is attested by the number of successful Martin rehabilitations.

The mental test procedures of the Martin method might also be criticized. In defense of the procedure, we might say that the tests used do provide the counselor with considerable useful information in a short time. Many psychologists are prone to overtest, and, in working with the old, this might prove a definite handicap to rehabilitation because of the resistance it engenders. The old take a longer time to do tests than younger persons and many are self-conscious about their failing abilities and resent what they feel is making a display of their inadequacies. They often tire quickly, and when they do, their feelings of inferiority become intensified. Thus, they may tolerate short periods of testing but show increasing resistance as the time is prolonged. Nevertheless, one cannot but wonder whether the Babcock Test for the Measurement of the Efficiency of Mental Functioning (either in full or shortened form) or the Wechsler-Bellevue Adult Intelligence Scale and one of the projective techniques, particularly the Rorschach, might not prove more valuable than the series suggested by Martin. Some of the Thematic Apperception Test cards might be of special value in pointing out the core of adjustment difficulties. These tests need not all be given or given all at once. They can be given in small sections in successive interviews and discontinued if resistance is encountered.

The Martin method rejects the use of hypnosis and psychoanalysis, and yet many counselors find these important aids to rehabilitation, particularly of emotionally disturbed older persons. While it is certainly desirable for activity to be self-initiated whenever possible, hypnosis can sometimes serve as a much needed ego-builder and starter to activity. This is particularly true of those older persons who are timid, troubled with feelings of inferiority, and fearful of rejection. The use of psychoanalysis with older individuals was rejected for a long time, but recently more and more therapists are beginning to realize its desirability and helpfulness in many cases. However, because of the time and expense involved, many believe that some of the briefer forms of psychoanalysis are more efficacious with older persons. While psychoanalysis is certainly not indiated for every older person who seeks counseling and guidance, it is needed for the successful rehabilitation of some.

In the rehabilitation of aging persons (aging here being considered more a matter of ideas, attitudes, and emotions than of actual years), the use of group therapy as a valuable technique should not be overlooked, even though relatively little has been done with it in this area. Either complete interview sessions or combined activity-interview sessions can be used, but probably the latter are the more valuable. A group of six or eight older persons, either of one or of both sexes, meets for weekly sessions with a trained therapist. Materials for creative work are provided, as well as provisions for refreshments following the session. With some stimulation from the therapist, group members discuss freely those problems which most concern them. Their freedom to discuss their problems and voice their resentments and troubles serves as a much-needed catharsis. The relationships they form with the therapist and with other members of the group help to strengthen their egos and develop insight into their own problems and the part they themselves play in their own difficulties and in their rejection by society. Their creative activities also serve as ego-strengtheners and offer possibilities for sublimation. Group members can do much to help and offer support to one another, and the group itself is a good place for beginning reality testing. Psychodrama is also one of the newer techniques which should prove valuable with older persons.

In regard to the counselor who seeks to work with the older group, it is fairly obvious that this should be a person who genuinely likes persons of this age group and believes optimistically in the possibilities of their rehabilitation. If he becomes irritated by the slowness, the peculiarities, and the often endless and complaining monologues of the old, he should choose a different age group with which to work. The counselor for older persons must have much patience, courtesy, respect, sympathy, imagination, and ingenuity. He must be able to visualize a real future for his clients and help them to share this with him. At the same time, he must be able to face their problems with them realistically and without flattery and deception. He must particularly be aware of community resources: he must know where his patient can get the best physical care and the most suitable housing; he must know the social resources and recreational possibilities; and he must be able to counsel constructively on vocational possibilities. Working with older persons in this capacity is a relatively new field; therefore the counselor must continue his own education along with that of his patient.

Summary

Professional work with the aging in the community requires the cooperation and integration of services from the various specialties.

Health care of the aging is generally taken care of by the family physician, and many recommend a complete geriatric examination in the middle years, with periodic examinations thereafter. Examination would embrace an investigation into all facets of the patient's life. Remedial and preventive measures would be instituted and these would include good physical and mental hygiene, correction of focal infections, adequate nutrition, and avoidance of obesity.

When home nursing care is required for the aging person, it is often for a chronic rather than an acute disorder and may require a minimum of actual nursing care over a prolonged period of time. There is a good field for the practical nurse in this area. The person who enters this field should be one who likes, respects, and understands older persons and can stimulate them to participate in life and devolp an optimistic, forward-looking attitude. Often the middle-aged person who is endowed with much patience is best suited to this type of work.

Professional work with the aging is greatly needed in the area of housing. Housing plans for older people include small, independent houses or apartments near the family unit, boarding houses, foster homes, cooperative apartments, cooperative apartment units, and old age colonies. Accessibility, income, privacy, and conveniences must be considered in housing plans.

The welfare of older people and the increasing economic burden on society caused by retirement and unemployment of older persons makes employment desirable. It has been shown that the older worker can be useful in industry and the professions and has certain advantages over younger workers, but more far-sighted employers are needed who will experiment with plans for using the elderly which will be mutually beneficial. Campaign and educational work is also needed in this area as well as research, particularly in regard to job analyses and appraisal and training of individual skills.

Trained recreational workers and leaders who are interested in older persons are needed. This area includes work in recreational centers, clubs, church groups, and educational programs.

Social work with the aging in the community covers a wide field, but it is a specialized branch of work for which there seems to be a dearth of adequately trained personnel. The worker in this area must have a genuine liking for older persons, endless patience, and complete and detailed information on community resources for the aging. Much of the case work will be supportive in nature and planned to rebuild or sustain ego strength to the point where the aging individual can resume normal ego functioning.

Counseling and guidance comprise the final major field of professional work with the aging in the community. The Martin plan of rehabilitation, which was the pioneer method of working with the aging, is still used with some modifications, and in a large percentage of cases it is claimed that the plan is helpful in four or five visits. It is a rather directive method which requires effort on the part of the patient to change in all areas of his life. Discussion, suggestion, autosuggestion, slogans, and charts are used, and the patient is helped to achieve active participation in life and develop new ideas and a forward-looking attitude. Although hypnosis and psychoanalysis are rejected by the Martin method, some counselors find these techniques helpful, especially the briefer psychoanalytic techniques. Group therapy and psychodrama are also valuable techniques.

The counselor who works with the aging should be one who genuinely likes older persons and has patience, courtesy, respect, sympathy, imagination, and ingenuity, who believes optimistically in the possibilities of rehabilitation of the aging, and who has a good knowledge of community resources.

REFERENCES

1. *Age will be served*. Brooklyn, N.Y.: Brooklyn Council for Social Planning, 1948.
2. *Aging*. "Family Health Series," Guide for Public Health Nurses No. 8. New York: Community Service Society, 1948.
3. *Birthdays don't count*. Albany, N.Y.: New York State Legislative Committee on Problems of Aging, 1947.
4. BLUESTONE, E. M. Medical care of the aged. *J. Geron*, 1949, **4**, 205-9.
5. *Case work with the aged*. New York: Family Welfare Association of America, 1938.
6. CLAGUE, E. The working life span of the American worker. *J. Geron.*, 1949, **4**, 285-90.
7. CRAMPTON, C. W. The essentials of the geriatric examination at fifty. *Geriatrics*, 1950, **5**, 1-14.
8. DARIC, J. *Vieillissement de la population et prolongation de la vie active*. Paris: Institut National d'Etudes Demographiques, 1948.
9. DONAHUE, W., and TIBBITTS, C. (eds.). *Planning the older years*. Ann Arbor, Mich.: University of Michigan Press, 1950.
10. ——. *Growing in the older years*. Ann Arbor, Mich.: University of Michigan Press, 1951.
11. DUNBAR, F. *Mind and body: psychosomatic medicine*. New York: Random House, Inc., 1947.
12. GILBERT, J. G. Senescent efficiency and employability. *J. appl. Psychol.*, 1936, **20**, 266-72.
13. GILBERT, J. G., and WEITZ, R. D. *Psychology for the profession of nursing*. New York: The Ronald Press Co., 1949. Chap. x.
14. GINZBERG, R. Psychology in everyday geriatrics. *Geriatrics*, 1950, **5**, 364-65.
15. GRIFFIN, J. J. The sheltering of the aged. *J. Geron.*, 1950, **5**, 30-43.
16. KUHLEN, R. G. Psychological trends and problems in later maturity. In PENNINGTON, L. A., and BERG, I. A. (eds.), *Introduction to clinical psychology*. New York: The Ronald Press Co., 1948.
17. LAVERTY, R. Supportive therapy in geriatric casework. *J. Geron.*, 1949, **4**, 152-56.
18. LAWTON, G. (ed.). *New goals for old age*. New York: Columbia University Press, 1943.
19. ——. Mental decline and its retardations. *Sci. Mon.*, N.Y., Apr., 1944, pp. 313-17.
20. ——. *Aging successfully*. New York: Columbia University Press, 1946.

21. LAWTON, G., and STEWART, S. *When you grow older.* Public Affairs Pamphlet No. 131. New York: Public Affairs Committee, 1947.
22. MARTIN, L. J. *A handbook for old age counselors.* San Francisco: Geertz Printing Co., 1944.
23. MARTIN, L. J., and DE GRUCHY, C. *Salvaging old age.* New York: The Macmillan Co., 1930.
24. ——. *Sweeping the cobwebs.* New York: The Macmillan Co., 1933.
25. MENNINGER, W. C. Recreation and mental health. *Recreational Mag.,* 1948, **42**, 340-46.
26. *Never too old.* Albany, N.Y.: New York State Legislative Committee on Problems of Aging, 1948.
27. POLLAK, O. *Social adjustment in old age.* Soc. Sci. Res. Council Bull., 1948, No. 59.
28. *Proceedings of the Conference on Social Treatment of the Older Person.* New York: New York School of Social Work, 1947.
29. RANDALL, O. A. The essential partnership of medicine and social work. *Geriatrics,* 1950, **5**, 46-60.
30. ROWNTREE, V. S. *Old people.* Published for the Trustees of the Nuffield Foundation by Geoffrey Cumberlege. London: Oxford University Press, 1947.
31. SCHULZE, O. Recreation for the aged. *J. Geron.,* 1949, **4**, 310-13.
32. SHELDON, J. H. *The social medicine of old age.* Published for the Trustees of the Nuffield Foundation by Geoffrey Cumberlege. London: Oxford University Press, 1948.
33. SHOCK, N. W. Older people and their potentialities for gainful employment. *J. Geron.,* 1947, **2**, 93-102.
34. STEAD, W. H. Trends of employment in relation to the problems of aging. *J. Geron.,* 1949, **4**, 290-97.
35. STIEGLITZ, E. J. *The second forty years.* Philadelphia: J. B. Lippincott Co., 1946.
36. *Survey of the needs and facilities for the care of the Jewish aged in New York City.* New York: Central Bureau for the Jewish Aged, 1946.
37. THEWLIS, M., and GALE, E. T. Ambulatory care of the aged. *Geriatrics,* 1950, **5**, 331-37.

Chapter 11

PROFESSIONAL WORK WITH THE AGING IN INSTITUTIONS

The Need for Institutional Care

Although the majority of older persons remain in the community, and it is desirable that they should do so, there will always be some individuals in this age group who will, for one reason or another, require institutional care. Physical or mental illness, of course, is the principal reason for most older persons entering an institution, but there may also be other reasons. Those who have no income of their own and no one to provide for them, those who are unable not only to support themselves but to look after themselves adequately in other ways, and those who have no family or friends and are lonely often seek admission to an institution.

The type of institution an older person enters will depend upon his reasons for seeking this type of care as well as upon the available facilities. Generally, those who are physically ill seek admission to a general hospital, a hospital for chronic disorders, or a nursing home. Those who are mentally ill are usually sent to a mental hospital or to a special type of nursing home, and those who need institutionalization for other reasons seek admission to old age homes. Unfortunately, however, facilities for the care of the aging are so limited and inadequate that many older persons, who may be somewhat deteriorated but are not psychotic, are sent to mental institutions because they cannot look after themselves in the community and there is no other place where they can receive the care they require. This is a deplorable procedure, but it is one that has been condemned so much and so often that, in most states where it is practiced, efforts are being made to arrange more suitable provisions for those persons.

Types of Institutional Care

If we wish to get away from the idea of an institution for the aged as merely a place for custodial care, and certainly there can be little question as to the desirability of this departure, it would be advisable to look into the types of institutions which are available, the services offered, the possibilities of improvement, and the opportunities for professional work in these institutions.

General Hospital Care.—General hospital care, of course, is designed for those individuals who are ill. However, as Thewlis and Gale (23) point out, most of the illnesses in the aged are ambulatory, and only about 1 per cent require hospital care. They consider that the types of patients who are best treated, either temporarily or permanently, in a hospital or institution are those who need help in getting out of bed, those who cannot feed themselves, those who are incontinent, those who live alone and can't prepare their own meals, those who are seriously ill, and those who need surgical treatment. Because of the generally better therapeutic program and facilities, these patients can usually be cared for more adequately in a general hospital (2, 23). Even those patients whose illnesses are chronic could no doubt be cared for better in a special ward in a general hospital. Unfortunately, however, many professional workers and those in charge of a general hospital do not like to take older patients, particularly those who might become permanent residents of the institution. They feel that the older patient with his chronic illness takes away a bed from a younger person who may have an acute illness and need it more. Many also have a pessimistic outlook in regard to the illnesses of older persons, viewing them as the inevitable accompaniments of old age and something about which little or nothing can be done.

Obviously, some re-education in this area is needed. Steinberg (17) advocates the close cooperation of the general hospital with other agencies for the care of the aged and cites the beneficial liaison between the Mount Sinai Hospital in New York City and the Home for Aged and Infirm Hebrews. Here the infirmary of the Home is considered as an extension of the Hospital and patients in need of hospital care are accepted as transfers, to be retransferred at the completion of the hospital care.

In addition to the development of a chronic disease wing for aged patients, Kogel (9) suggests the provision of a suite of sound-proofed rooms and ancillary facilities for the temporary care of elderly psychotics whose disturbed episodes might be transitory. Both Kogel and Steinberg also have suggestions to make for the improvement of rehabilitation programs for the aged in the general hospitals. Pleasant rooms, attendants who like the old, and facilities for physical, occupational, and recreational therapy and for psychiatric treatment should be available.

Mental Hospitals.—Mental hospitals house large numbers of mentally ill aged persons and, as mentioned previously, many aged who are not mentally ill. While most people consider it detrimental to the welfare of a normal old person to be placed with the mentally ill, others argue that it is better for them to receive the care they need in a hospital of this sort than to be neglected and not to receive any care at all. Perhaps if they could be segregated from the rest of the institution and put in little units of their own, this might be so. If not, there can be little doubt as to the emotional disturbance a placement of this sort will cause many older persons. Also, even with those patients who are mentally ill, it is probably better to be segregated with others like themselves than to be in a mixed group of younger psychotics—better both for them and for the younger psychotics. The needed facilities discussed above in connection with general hospitals should also be available for oldsters in mental hospitals.

The medical and nursing care and the facilities for rehabilitation in both the general and the mental hospitals vary with the hospital, but undoubtedly many hospitals are doing an excellent job of care, rehabilitation, and research in the field of geriatrics. It is only unfortunate that many more hospitals are not available for this much-needed work.

Nursing and Convalescent Homes.—Nursing homes and convalescent homes are usually used for those aged persons in need of nursing care or of nursing and medical care. They stand midway between hospitals and old age institutions. The facilities and services in these homes vary considerably—all the way from a made-over half of a double house with a practical nurse or maid to help out to a spacious hospital-like setup with registered nurses in charge and doctors in attendance. Often they are private affairs and rather expensive. Unfortunately, there are too few adequate nursing homes with fees suited to the moderate income.

Homes for the Aged.—Old age homes show considerable variation in the physical setup of the home and in the care and services offered the aged who enter them (1, 4, 8, 20, 22). Some of these are privately owned and operated and some are supported through public funds. Many are denominational— Catholic, Protestant, or Jewish—and supported by religious organizations. Often these homes will admit only those of the same religious faith, and many exclude Negroes, although the Negroes themselves have relatively few facilities for institutional care of the aged. Some of the privately operated homes currently require an admission fee of $500.00 or more plus the signing over of all property and assets to the home; others will admit those able to pay a minimum of $80.00 per month, which sum they could get from old age assistance for an approved home. Some will admit married couples and permit them to remain together; others admit both men and women but separate the married couples so that they can house the men in one dormitory and the women in another. Probably because the average life span of women is longer than that of men, there is usually a preponderance of females in old age homes. Generally they either have no family or have poor family relationships; they feel their professional, business, or industrial careers are ended, and they are seeking peace and economic security in entering an old age home (13, 14). Sometimes they find what they are seeking and effect a good adjustment to the group activities, hobbies, religious life, health care, and friendships offered in the institution. In other instances, however, where the facilities are not so good, the institutions seem to be merely places for the vegetation of the aged rather than places for their care and happiness. In these the inmates tend to become constricted and withdrawn; they grow irritable, cantankerous, and fault-finding and give evidence of both intellectual and social impairment.

Old age homes are a necessity, not only economically but also because a home or institution of this sort best fits the needs of some old persons. With forethought and sound planning, these homes can be refuges of happiness and security to the aged, but the planning must include a recognition of the physical, intellectual, emotional, and social needs of the old person (16, 21). First of all, the location of the home should be taken into consideration. A quiet place with a good view and enough ground for gardens and walks is desirable. It is most unpleasant to contemplate spending the twilight years of one's life in a cramped, dingy house overlooking a railroad, stockyard, or factory with no trees, flowers, or grass to add a spot of beauty to it. Pleasant surroundings are conducive to acceptance of the home, which might otherwise be met with resistance and interpreted as a symbol of the rejection of society. In selecting the location, care should also be taken to see that there are no hazardous approaches—no tortuous steps, steep hills, or obstructions which might result in a fall or other injury to the aging person. Although in a quiet place, the location should nevertheless be accessible to transportation. It is inadvisable to build an old age home away out in the country where transportation facilities are so inadequate that the aging person never has an opportunity to leave the home, and friends and relatives are loath to visit. A better location is near the center of a city or town in order that medical resources may be readily available, that friends and relatives may drop in for frequent visits, and that the oldster may get to church easily or drop into town for the movies, the theater, or other recreational outlets whenever he so desires.

The buildings of the home should next be taken into consideration. It is better that these be not too large, for it is difficult to get the needed homelike atmosphere when buildings look like an institution and are so large that the people in them cannot readily get acquainted. They must be provided with adequate fire protection and safety devices, for older persons do not get around as well as younger persons and are harder to evacuate in case of fire. Sufficient lighting is important, especially in the halls, since many old persons have poor vision and motor coordination and are prone to trip and fall over things or to get lost. For these reasons, care should also be taken to see that the halls are not too slippery and are provided with handrails. Ramps rather than stairs should be used whenever possible, as these are easier both for those old people who can walk and for those who must use a wheel chair. Elevators are a necessity in a well-run old age home, and it is advisable that these be automatic and large enough to accommodate wheel chairs and stretchers or beds. With ramps and elevators the majority of the "guests" in the home can go wherever they wish without the need of an attendant, and even if an old person is confined to a wheel chair, this gives him some small measure of the independence which is so necessary to him. Adequate ventilation throughout is especially important in old age homes.

In regard to other effects in the building, a solarium, one or more large recreation or game rooms which can be used as assembly halls when needed, and smaller living rooms where individuals can entertain with greater privacy are desirable. These should be furnished pleasantly, with cheerful coloring both in regard to wall coloring and furniture, comfortable chairs and sofas, reading lamps, tables, books, plants, and flowers. The plan of pleasant furnishings and wall coloring should also be carried into the bedrooms, and the oldsters should be permitted to have plants and flowers in their rooms if they wish.

There should be some single and some double bedrooms in every old age home. Some old persons prefer to be in a room alone and cannot readily adjust to the presence of another person, so that when they are forced to do so, friction ensues. Others react in the opposite manner and are unhappy and depressed if they must remain alone. However, dormitory living seldom proves a happy arrangement for the old. If the old age home accepts both men and women, married couples should always be permitted to remain together unless they specifically desire to be separated. If possible, the bedrooms should be sound-proofed, as many old people have trouble sleeping and are easily disturbed by noises around them, and there should be some way in which they can signal for help in the event that they become ill when they are alone. There should also be provisions for service help when it is needed. Women too like to have a place where they can wash and iron a few little personal things they do not like to send to the laundry, and, if possible, this should be provided for them.

Special attention should be paid to the bathrooms to see that the floors are not too slippery and that the tubs are easy to get into and out of. It is a good plan to have a rubber mat on the floor of the tub and perhaps a seat in it so that the old person has less danger of slipping and falling. It is also advisable to have a handrail on the wall by the tub so the old person can enter and leave the tub more easily.

The food in an old age home should be nourishing but not fattening. As we have already noted, aging persons tend to become bulkier and heavier for a while and then, in extreme old age, to become thin and to show signs of undernourishment. For this reason, the diet should be watched carefully. The atmosphere of the dining-room should be as cheerful and home-like as possible, and oldsters should be placed at mealtime with congenial companions. Sometimes this can better be effected at large tables, but usually small tables seem to be enjoyed more. Often too it is desirable to shift dining companions every week or so, but most consider that the individual members of the home should have some choice regarding those with whom they will eat. Attractive dishes, eating utensils, and table linen (or even plastic if need be), flowers on the table, and food appetizingly served are inducements to healthy eating and happier people. Although it is desirable for all those in the home to eat together if possible, provisions must be made for room service for those who are unable to come to the dining-room. Provisions should also be made for those who wish to help in the kitchen or to cook a little. For some women this is particularly important, and it makes them feel happier and more useful.

Recreation in an old age home should be varied and rich. The most popular forms of recreation are musical instruments, particularly the piano, the radio, television, and the library. The most unfortunate thing about the library in many old age homes is that it often has only old, discarded, and often unsuitable books in it. Good and modern books in good condition are essential to the happiness of every old age home, as many aging persons spend a large part of their time reading and want to have interesting books in decent condition. Games and entertainment are also popular, and popular entertainments include both those planned by the old folks themselves and those brought in from outside. Recreational and occupational therapy are good, and a skilful therapist can often draw an old person into satisfying activities he would never have dreamed of attempting on his own initiative. Under proper leadership, group discussions can prove both stimulating and satisfying to members of an old age home. Lawton (11) tried this with interesting results in a group the average age of which was seventy-five years.

Some provision should be made for work for those who wish and are able to work. The work may be light and relatively inconsequential, but if it makes the aging person feel happy and useful, it is good. The plan of permitting the members of the home to work and paying them accordingly has proved successful in Sailors' Snug Harbor, Staten Island, New York.

Those who live in old age homes should be given as much freedom as possible. They should have some spending money and be permitted to come and go as they please within reason. They should be permitted to attend the religious service of their choice, go to the movies and theater outside the home, visit friends, have their friends visit them, and feel that they are not tied down to cumbersome, juvenile rules. The more freedom and independence the aging person has, the more satisfied he is.

Types of Professional Workers in Institutions

The health and happiness of aging persons in institutions will necessarily depend in large part upon those who run the institution and in particular upon the director and professional staff, since these will be the ones who determine the policies. While the location, physical setup, and other aspects of housing just discussed are most important, they can amount to little in actual practice if the institutions are inadequately staffed. Adequate staffing refers not so much to the numbers, although obviously a sufficient number of persons to carry on the various duties is essential, but to the attitudes and skills of those in charge. Nonprofessional workers, if chosen carefully, will generally follow the lead of the professional workers in this respect, so that the choice of professional workers is of paramount importance.

To begin with, only those professional workers to whom institutional work appeals and who have a real interest in the aging and an optimistic, forward-looking attitude toward their problems should consider a position in an institution or hospital for the aging. If any person views work in an institution as confining and narrowing or finds aging depressing and irritating, he should choose another kind of work, for his efforts in this field will surely make him unhappy and his unhappiness will reflect itself in the discontent and disharmony of those with whom he works.

The Director.—The director of an institution for the aging is the key person in the institutional setup. Besides having good administrative skills in handling people, managing finances, and dealing with innumerable details, the director must be a person who fully understands the problems of aging, likes and is sympathetic toward old people, and is modern and flexible in his outlook. He must be able to attract and select professional workers of similar interests and attitudes and stimulate the institutional personnel to optimal efficiency in their various specialties. He should encourage research as a means of furthering understanding and knowledge of the aging process and of ways of retarding it, as well as of making the later years of life worth living.

Doctors and Nurses.—Medical and nursing services in an institution for the aged vary with the institution and the type of older persons accepted, but obviously good services in this area are essential to the welfare of the inmates of all institutions. At the risk of being redundant, it should be stressed again that the doctors and nurses, as well as all others, who enter the field of geriatrics should like old people and have a genuine feeling for the importance of their problems.

By the time of entering an institution for the aged, it is usually too late to do much in the way of preventive medicine, although some of course is possible. Rather, the stress must be on palliative measures, on the control or cure of existing disease, and on the improvement of general health. Because of the impaired homeostasis of the aged, the symptoms of disease tend to be less conspicuous, repair is slower so that it takes the patient longer to recover, and, because of the weakened compensatory activities of other physiologic processes, the effect of an impairment of function is more serious (18, 19). These things must be taken into consideration in the examination and treatment of older patients.

In most institutions for the aged a preadmission physical examination, more or less thorough, is required. On admission, a more complete physical examination should be made and evaluated in terms of the patient's history, particularly of his past illness, accidents, and health habits, and pertinent health information concerning forebears, collaterals, and offspring. In addition to the usual thorough physical examination, during which the examining physician must be especially alert for subtle hints of disorders, Stieglitz (19) recommends laboratory and supplemental studies which include examination of the blood, urine, basal metabolic rate, electrocardiogram, stress tests, and X-ray studies. He emphasizes the importance of patience, thoroughness, and attention to details, plus the fact that, since health is a relative matter, there is always room for improvement. Zeman (24, 25) has said that "disease in the aged is characterized by multiplicity, chronicity, and duplicity," and for this reason he would consider the physical examination in terms of the whole individual and his functional capacity. Since this and other modern innovations are practiced in the Home for Aged and Infirm Hebrews in New York City, it might be well at this point to mention something of the work in this institution. The determination of the functional capacity of each resident is based on a thorough physical examination, the classifications being as follows:

Class A. Individuals capable of unlimited and unsupervised activity, to be trusted to go about the city in safety.

Class B. Individuals capable of moderate activity, to be trusted in the neighborhood of the Home, who may require escort of younger persons for extended or tiring trips.

Class C. Individuals whose capabilities are limited and whose activities need both supervision and assistance; require escort on street; practically house-bound.

Class D. Individuals who are confined to bed or its immediate vicinity.

Class E. Individuals who are totally blind, or whose vision is so impaired that they cannot take care of themselves.*

* Reprinted from *Geriatric Medicine*, edited by E. J. Stieglitz, by permission of W. B. Saunders Company, publishers. Page 125.

From the careful health evaluation (considered in connection with psychological and psychiatric examinations when these are given) plans for the improvement of physical and mental health are made. Work possibilities are also evaluated, and occupational therapy, physical therapy, and recreational activities are offered.

In this Home, in addition to the initial physical examinations, each resident is given an annual physical examination and daily clinics are held for ambulatory patients. There is an infirmary which cares for most acute and chronic cases, although, as mentioned earlier, those requiring major surgery or complicated diagnostic or therapeutic procedures are referred to Mt. Sinai Hospital, which is located nearby. Occasionally also, other hospitals are used.

The nurse who cares for the aged person in a hospital or other institution must have, in addition to the usual nursing skills and a kindly attitude toward the aging, an awareness of the mental hygiene of the aged and what it means to this particular patient to be in a hospital. The necessity of entering any institution generally intensifies already existing feelings of rejection, inadequacy, and uselessness. Add to this the fear many old persons have of hospitals and the feeling that they are merely places to go to when you are ready to die, and the emotional trauma the oldster may be experiencing can the more readily be understood. The fears of the ill oldster who is in a hospital are often even greater than those of the patient who remains in his own home, and with these the nurse must deal. Fortunately, however, the nurse in a hospital does not usually have to serve in the same way as a buffer between the old person and his family as when caring for the patient in his own home, and there will be greater support and reinforcement from other members of the professional staff. In general, though, the principles of dealing with the emotional aspects of the patient's illness are the same whether he is being cared for in a hospital or in his own home. As these have already been discussed in the last chapter, we must only emphasize again the need of the patient to feel that the nurse genuinely likes and respects him and has confidence in his early recovery. In a hospital setup, the nurse can also do much to stimulate the patient to engage in occupational therapy or recreational activities and to develop a receptive attitude toward other members of the professional staff who are ready to help him in other capacities (7).

   The Dietitian.—The dietitian in an institution for the aged plays such an important role in the health care and planning of the residents that a few words must be said of the work of this profession. Zetterstrom (26), in discussing this, points out that the duties and responsibilities are comparable to those of the dietitian in a general hospital. She is responsible for the purchase and inspection of food, supplies, and equipment, menu-planning, and supervision of food products, and she must be aware of the different requirements of those of varying degrees of health. She must cooperate with other members of the staff, particularly with the medical and budget departments, and be alert to the individual patient's lack of appetite or peculiar reaction to food. In menu-planning she must be aware not only of adequate nutritional standards but also of food appeal and its acceptability by persons of various cultural backgrounds. Much of this can be determined by careful inspection of tables and trays to see the amounts and types of foods which are rejected. Although no specific standards for the aged have been set up, it is considered that the desirable caloric content is between 2,000 and 2,200 calories per day, with high protein content and adequate amounts of other elements and vitamins. In general, it has been found that the aged prefer soft, easily masticated foods and tend to reject foods with small seeds and those foods which are hard to chew. As some of the dietary needs of older persons have already been discussed in the preceding chapter, these will not be repeated at this time. However, before leaving the subject, it must be pointed out that food is generally very important in the life of the older person. Its importance for his physical well-being is well recognized, but perhaps it is even more important psychologically. Appetite and digestion are among the first things to be affected by emotional upset or maladjustment. As has been previously mentioned, some aging individuals want to eat all the time because they have no other satisfactions in life, whereas others have little appetite and much digestive disturbance. The emotional trauma of being institutionalized might thus result in a food reaction to the feelings of rejection. The importance of having nourishing meals daintily prepared, attractively served, and consumed with congenial companions cannot be overemphasized.

The Psychiatric Consultant.—Psychiatric service in an institution for the aged (with the exception of the mental hospital) is generally on a consulting basis. In mental hospitals and in some general and chronic hospitals which admit the aged, full-time psychiatrists are on the staff, but most of those institutions which have psychiatric service have this on a part-time or consulting basis. A psychiatric examination prior to or on admission is desirable in order to exclude those psychotic aged who are so ill mentally that they cannot adjust in a group of normal old persons. Some mildly disturbed old persons may be able to adjust better in a normal old age home than in a hospital for the mentally ill, and it will be the job of the psychiatrist to determine this on the admitting psychiatric examination. Psychiatric service should also be available for those residents who become emotionally disturbed during the course of their stay in the institution. Some of these, of course, will have to be removed to a hospital for the mentally ill, where the usual therapeutic measures can be administered, but others may be able to respond to psychotherapy and other therapeutic procedures which may be carried on in the institution.

Although we shall not repeat here the therapeutic procedures already discussed in Chapters 7 and 8, we might point out that a controlled environment such as an institution for the aged offers advantages therapeutically in that the psychiatrist has someone to see that recommended procedures are carried out. For example, removal of infection, rehabilitation of body processes, modification of diet, use of drugs, hormones, and histamine, transfer to a more congenial group, recreational activities, or occupational therapy can be recommended with full confidence that the recommendations will be carried out, which, of course, is quite different from extramural private practice. Also, if psychotherapy is indicated and the psychiatrist has not the time to carry it out himself, he may refer the patient to the psychologist or possibly to the social worker for this help.

The Psychologist.—Psychological service is available in many institutions for the aged, and there is a wide field for expansion of services in this area. The psychologist who works in an institution for the aged should be ready to aid in a program of selective intake, deal with problems of adjustment, assist in educational programs and in programs of recreational and occupational therapy, and aid in placement outside the home when this is indicated (12). As discussed in the preceding chapter, the psychologist must be ready with his diagnostic tools to determine the intellectual and emotional status of the aged individual and evaluate his personality makeup. There is no need for further discussion of these tools at this time, but it should be pointed out that the psychologist's job is to study the potentialities of the oldster, determine his fitness for and possibilities of adjustment in the group to which he is seeking admission, and, in cooperation with other members of the staff, work out a plan of activities best suited to his individual needs.

The psychologist should be ready to initiate, carry out, and cooperate in research on the problems of aging. He should also plan, direct, and assist in carrying out activity plans and other projects designed to aid in the rehabilitation of the residents of the institution. The importance of projects of this sort in the restoration and preservation of personality in the aged has been shown by Donahue in her experiment in a county home in Michigan (5). Donahue took a small, relatively poor institution "filled with chronically ill, defeated, fearful, insecure old people" who engaged in little constructive activity, or indeed in little activity of any sort. Recorded observations revealed "a shocking degree of deprivation and personality deterioration of the residents." Following more than thirty hours of observation, a three-month activities program was initiated for the purpose of stimulating the residents to greater physical and psychological activity in order that they might become happier and effect better personal adjustments. It was also hoped that community interest might be so stimulated as to result in the institution of a permanent program following the close of the experiment. Provisions were made for daily activities Monday through Friday and for the participation of outside groups. The projects included a weekly newspaper, which provided recognition of personal status, increased communications, and stimulation of interest and anticipation; an occupational therapy program, which provided for creative expression, social contribution, group enterprise, financial reward, and recognition; a garden project, which provided equal participation in group activity with outsiders, increased activity, and social contribution; motion pictures, which provided intellectual activity, entertainment, recreation, and a recognition of personal worth; an auction sale, which provided increased communication and decreased passivity; and other activities such as parties, picnics, and games. Although most were slow in starting, the results showed considerable personality growth in most of the cases, and gave evidence of expansion and strengthening of the ego. The residents began to show greater interest in their personal appearance and cleanliness, to engage in more conversation, to initiate activity instead of being completely passive and apathetic as when they were first seen, and to evince a desire to work. In general, the results were most gratifying in their indications of the possibilities of restoring and preserving the personalities of even those aged individuals who seem badly deteriorated in this respect. The experiment showed clearly the importance of having individuals act as participants rather than recipients or spectators. Donahue believes that such a program should be a functioning part of all institutions housing older persons.

In addition to assisting in the planning of projects and activities of this sort for the institution as a whole, the psychologist should also be prepared to serve as a liaison between individual residents and employees. He should interpret the behavior and needs of difficult residents to the employees in such a way that they will be helped to overlook and accept some annoying behavior and be alert to emotional needs indicated by other types of conduct. He should help the difficult and emotionally disturbed resident to accept the reality of his situation and to understand himself and his own reactions better. He should try to direct the resident's attention away from himself, his illnesses, and the way life has treated him and turn it toward others. The psychologist should also try to get the resident to resume activity and direct this activity into constructive channels best suited to his needs and abilities. Individual interviews and close cooperation with the social worker and the recreational and occupational therapists will prove helpful in these plans.

Group therapy and psychodrama are psychotherapeutic tools useful in an institution for the aged, for these provide opportunities for verbalizing problems and feelings in a unique manner. Psychodrama particularly offers good possibilities because of the entertainment value it provides as well as the opportunity for airing grievances, expressing hostilities, and other emotional releases.

Occasionally in an institution for the aged the problem arises of transferring a resident to another institution or of permitting an individual to secure employment outside the home. With these problems the psychologist must also be prepared to deal, working in close collaboration with the physician and the social worker. He must be able to say in what type of institution the one resident might adjust and in what kind of work the other might reasonably be expected to be successful if he returns to the general community.

The Social Worker.—In an institution for the aged, the social worker, according to Zeman (24), has at least three major functions: "giving advice to applicants for admission and to their relatives, the investigation of prospective candidates for admission, and the follow-up of these individuals when admitted to insure that they adapt themselves successfully to the new way of life." He also considers it important for the social worker in carrying out these activities to be aware of the medical status and the functional rating of the individual being helped.

Perhaps in the field of social work, even more than in any other professional area, it is essential that the worker have a genuine interest in, liking for, understanding of, and sympathy with older persons and the problems of aging (3). It is usually the social worker to whom will fall the task of preparing the old person to enter an institution, and often it is only because of the faith and trust the oldster has in his social worker that this can be accomplished without too much difficulty and emotional trauma. Only one who understands and is sympathetic with the feelings of another human being who faces institutionalization, with its implications of complete social rejection, can handle the situation with the proper skill and tact. To interpret the institution and the needs of the old person to the client himself, and to his family if he has any, is a task requiring not only skill but human understanding, warm sympathy, and maturity. Only if the worker himself is fully mature emotionally and has worked through his feelings toward his own parents can this be achieved. Early childhood and adolescent attachments, resentments, hostilities, and aggressions toward one's own parents must be understood and worked through before one can function most effectively with the old.

The social worker in this field must cooperate closely with the medical advisers of the old person (15). This means not only the doctors in the institution but also those who have cared for him prior to his need of institutionalization. Often it is the family doctor who first suggests placement in an institution, and the social worker who tries to effect this placement without first knowing the reasons and the medical diagnosis is working in the dark. Only by having all available information concerning the client's physical, mental, emotional, and personality makeup, as well as his social situation, can his best interests be served. A knowledge of these factors will help determine the type of institution to which he should go, how his needs can best be served in this particular institution, in what work and activities he should engage, and similar matters.

The social worker must also be prepared to deal with the family problems involved in institutional placement—sometimes to lessen the tension, anxiety, and guilt reactions which arise frequently even when placement is inevitable, unavoidable, and undeniably the best thing, and at other times to encourage continued contact when, in spite of open rejection, this contact is needed and craved by the old person who is being institutionalized. Visits back and forth between the old person and his relatives can be encouraged by the social worker, who can also help the relatives to understand the emotional needs and peculiarities of the oldster.

Within the institution itself, the social worker can also do much to facilitate the adjustment of the old person, for it is to the social worker that the newly admitted patient will first cling. As this may be the only person who, he feels at the time, understands and likes him, it will be the worker to whom the oldster will look for help and emotional support. He may feel that only the worker who has previously seen him in his own home can understand his need, for example, of having certain personal possessions remain with him or of having a son or daughter visit him. Often it is only the social worker who can first influence him to participate in entertainments and activities in the institution. The worker can do this only by understanding his need of feeling independent, active, useful, and a member of society and his fear of failure and rejection in his attempts to achieve these.

Laverty, in discussing supportive therapy in geriatric casework (10), shows how aggressive, hostile behavior reactions such as excessive demands, unwarranted complaints and criticisms, overanxiety, petty quarreling and jealousies, regressions, and the like are often not based on reality but rather are reactivated responses to earlier life experiences and can be treated through supportive therapy. The purpose of this therapy is to give these discontented persons some emotional satisfaction and divert their aggressive energy into constructive channels. She points out that in an institutional setting, particularly in a small one, the family group is simulated, with the staff in the role of the parents and the other residents in that of siblings. Thus sibling rivalries and hostilities, especially when a new member enters the group, are reactivated and behavior difficulties of various sorts ensue. Likewise, some may react to stern administrators in a rebellious way if their early life experiences were with stern, harsh parents. As mentioned earlier, some of these individuals have well-developed egos but are suffering from a temporary breakdown because of heavy environmental pressures, whereas others have weak egos and have been anxious and dependent all their lives; nevertheless, both are in need of supportive therapy. Although no attempt is made to bring to the awareness of the old person the connection between his present behavior and his early life experiences, every attempt is made to relieve environmental pressures, to give reassurance, encouragement, kindness, consideration, and affection, and to relieve anxiety by assuming a role of protectiveness.

Occupational Therapists.—The occupational therapy department of an institution for the aged should be one of the most important departments of the whole institution, for it is this department which will contribute perhaps more than any other to the prevention of vegetation and stagnation of the inmates of the institution. Besides holding an O.T.R. certificate, which presupposes professional skill, the occupational therapist must have a special liking for the old. The work of an occupational therapist requires such close and prolonged contact with individuals that the importance of having a special interest in the types of patients worked with can readily be understood. Patience too is extremely important in working with the old, since many are slow to grasp instructions and slow to execute them. Many become discouraged easily and are irritable, demanding, and fault-finding, and with all these personality peculiarities the occupational therapist must cope. The therapist must also remain calm, accepting, and understanding and give the old person the feeling that he is both respected and liked.

Although the importance of work and activity for the aging has been mentioned more than once before, this cannot be overemphasized. Despite the fact that, by the time they have reached the point of being institutionalized, most old persons have also reached the point where they are no longer employable in the community, these same "unemployables" are often able still to do much useful or creative work. Some, of course, can be rehabilitated for employment in the community, and whenever this plan is feasible, it should be carried out. The remainder should be helped and encouraged to find satisfying work and activities within the institution.

Occupational therapy covers a variety of activities, some useful, some creative, and some merely diversional (6). The occupational therapist, in collaboration with other members of the staff, can devise a plan of activities best suited to the individual oldster and see that this plan is carried out. Useful work around the institution includes such activities as cleaning, making beds, and doing other chamber work; cooking, washing dishes, setting the table, preparing vegetables, salads, and desserts, and doing similar work in the kitchen; acting as receptionist and guide for visitors to the institution, helping in the office, assisting the bedridden, working in the hospital or infirmary, or helping around the farm. The time spent in these activities should not be too long or the work too arduous, and only those patients who really want to do the work should be assigned to it. Usually, however, work in an institution can be found which will not be too far afield from that which an individual has done during his life in the community. To re-engage in work of this sort will help to rebuild the self-confidence and feelings of importance and usefulness of the aged person and restore his self-esteem.

Creative activities can often be useful as well as creative and, as such, are good ego-builders. Arts and crafts of various sorts, such as sewing and mending of clothing and linen for the institution, for individuals, and perhaps even for orphanages, fancy hand sewing and embroidery, knitting, crocheting, pottery work, woodwork, shellcraft, jewelry-making, woodcarving, weaving, metalwork, and leatherwork are a few of the more popular types of craft work in many institutions. Drawing, painting, china painting, finger painting, and cartooning are also well liked. Exhibits and fairs for the sale of articles made are especially stimulating and satisfying to the individual workers.

Working on a newspaper is another very useful activity which offers work and creative activity for many individuals in the institution. Some will prefer to set up the type, others to solicit material, others to write articles, others to collect jokes, and still others to contribute the art work or distribute the papers.

Music is a therapeutic tool which has probably not been used to its fullest extent. The interest of aging persons in the radio and television is well recognized, but more active participation among individuals could be developed. Group singing is usually popular and sometimes can serve as a stimulus to individuals to resume an earlier interest in music. Those who have once played a piano or other musical instrument might be encouraged to renew their activities along these lines. Some might be helped in this direction by use of the newer and quicker chord methods of learning to play the piano, as by these methods they can learn rather quickly to play the familiar songs they like so well. Use of a "tune finder" for the harmonica might also encourage efforts on this instrument. Search among the inmates might sometimes reveal enough latent or disused talent to form a small orchestra, making much use of the simple tone instruments and encouraging the participation of all who are interested.

Dramatics and all sorts of entertainment by the residents of the institution help to stimulate active interest and morale, and the clever occupational therapist will do everything possible to encourage some form of participation by each individual. Some, of course, will not like to take a role in the plays or musicals but they may be interested in another aspect of the entertainment, such as building or painting the scenery, making posters advertising it, making or distributing programs, acting as ushers, etc. The use of psychodrama as a therapeutic tool has already been mentioned. Working in collaboration with other members of the professional staff, the occupational therapist can take an active part in arranging these sessions.

Gardening also offers a very good field for both useful and creative activity. Some oldsters will prefer to work with flowers and others with vegetables, but, regardless of the product, those who are interested in this sort of activity will derive much satisfaction from the results of their efforts. Many can be encouraged to specialize, and if there is a greenhouse attached to the institution, these activities can be carried on both winter and summer. Flower shows, to which outsiders are invited, offer additional satisfaction in this area. Picnics, outings of various sorts, parties (particularly birthday parties), and entertainments by outsiders are good diversional activities.

In all these activities, the occupational therapist is forming a relationship with the oldster which is helping him once again to feel useful, respected, liked, and of some worth in the world. The activities themselves serve to keep alive his interest in persons and things outside of himself, to rebuild his ego, and to encourage his continued participation in life.

The Clergy.—Pastoral work is particularly important in an institution for the aged. As mentioned previously, many of the private institutions for the aged are denominational, although public institutions are nondenominational. In any case, the pastoral work will, of course, be carried on by a priest, minister, or rabbi, or by all three. While it is not within the province of this book to treat of religion, it is felt that some mention of it must be made because of the important part it can play in the lives of the aging. Even many who may have neglected their religion while living in the community may, when they have entered an institution, be helped to find comfort and solace through the religion of their choice, as well as to develop a less self-centered outlook on life.

Perhaps one of the most important parts of the work of the clergy, however, will be to prepare the aged for death. Many fear dying tremendously and are greatly disturbed by this fear, in spite of their unconscious belief in their own immortality. If these individuals can be helped to develop a different philosophy of life and death, to view death as a natural part of the life process, and to understand that dying itself is not painful but generally comes quietly and often in the midst of pleasant reveries, they can achieve greater peace and calm within themselves and adjust with more happiness to the life that remains for them.

Cooperation of Professional Workers

The importance of cooperation of services has been mentioned several times throughout this book, and nowhere is this more important than in an institution for the aged. It is important both within the institution itself and in the relationships between the institution, the hospital, and the community. As Grossman (8) has pointed out, an institution for the aged is no longer merely a custodial institution, but rather a therapeutic agency both from the social and the medical viewpoint. It requires a firm professional and community plan in which all agencies must participate for greatest efficiency. Only by close cooperation of all agencies and of the professional personnel can the aged receive the best and most effective care. Also, research into the problems of the aging can best be undertaken only if all concerned with aging individuals cooperate to the fullest extent possible. Personal and professional pride must be submerged in the interest of the total plan for the care and rehabilitation of the aged, each contributing his bit and working cooperatively with the rest.

Summary

Although most older persons remain in the community, there are always some who require institutional care, either because of physical or mental illness or because they cannot adequately look after themselves in the community.

Ill persons may be cared for in hospitals for the mentally ill, in general hospitals, or in hospitals for chronic disorders, but there are insufficient facilities to care adequately for all who need this type of care. Nursing homes and convalescent homes also care for numbers of aged patients, but again there are not enough of these homes and they are often expensive.

Old age homes, which may be public or private, denominational or nondenominational, care for the majority of the remainder who need institutional care. These should be planned as refuges of happiness and security to the aged, not merely as places for custodial care where the inmates vegetate and wait for death.

The location of the home, the buildings and facilities within the buildings, the food, the professional personnel, and the programs of work, recreation, and therapy should be so planned as to consider the physical, intellectual, emotional, and social needs of the individual.

Professional workers in an institution should be only those to whom institutional work appeals and who have a genuine interest in and liking for the aged and an optimistic, forward-looking attitude toward their problems.

Besides a competent director, professional workers in an institution include doctors and nurses, dietitians, psychiatric consultants, psychologists, social workers, occupational and recreational therapists, and clergymen. All members of the professional staff must cooperate fully in order to insure the most effective care and rehabilitation of the aged persons in the institution. Cooperation with hospitals and agencies in the community is also important.

Work with the aged in institutions should aim toward developing and maintaining the best possible physical and intellectual status and helping the old person to achieve emotional security, peace, and happiness. It should encourage active participation in life, the development of the individual oldster's interest in other persons and things outside of himself, and the rebuilding of self-confidence, self-esteem, and the feeling of being useful, wanted, respected, and liked. It should also help to prepare the aged person for death, which is inevitable and not too far away, in such a manner as to eliminate fear and help him to achieve inner serenity and happiness in his remaining years.

REFERENCES

1. *A study of the needs of the Negro aged in New York City.* New York: Federation of Protestant Welfare Agencies, 1946.
2. BLUESTONE, E. M. Medical care of the aged. *J. Geron.,* 1949, **4,** 305-9.
3. *Case work with the aged.* New York: Family Welfare Association of America, 1938.
4. *Current problems in Catholic institutional care of the aged.* Washington, D.C.: National Conference of Catholic Charities, 1948.
5. DONAHUE, W. An experiment in the restoration and preservation of personality in the aged. In DONAHUE, W., and TIBBITTS, C., *Planning the older years.* Ann Arbor, Mich.: University of Michigan Press, 1950.
6. EMERY, M. Occupational therapy. In LAWTON, G. (ed.), *New goals for old age.* New York: Columbia University Press, 1943.
7. GILBERT, J. G., and WEITZ, R. D. *Psychology for the profession of nursing.* New York: The Ronald Press Co., 1949.
8. GROSSMAN, B. L. The institutions for the aged in the total community plan. *Jewish soc. Serv. Quart.,* 1948, **24,** 422-30.
9. KOGEL, M. Hospitals and the elderly. *Geriatrics,* 1950, **5,** 234.
10. LAVERTY, R. Supportive therapy in geriatric casework. *J. Geron.,* 1949, **4,** 152-56.
11. LAWTON, G. A discussion group: average age seventy-five. *J. adult Educ.,* 1939, **18,** 389-95.
12. ——. Opportunities for psychologists in work with the aged. *J. consult. Psychol.,* 1942, **6,** 89-91.
13. PAN, JU-SHU. A study of the influence of institutionalization on the social adjustment of old people. *J. Geron.,* 1948, 3, 276-80.
14. ——. Personal adjustment of old people in church homes for the aged. *Geriatrics,* 1950, **5,** 166-70.

15. RANDALL, O. A. The essential partnership of medicine and social work. *Geriatrics,* 1950, **5**, 46-50.

16. ROWNTREE, B. S. *Old people.* Published for the Trustees of the Nuffield Foundation by Geoffrey Cumberlege. London: Oxford University Press, 1948.

17. STEINBERG, M. R. The general hospital in community planning for the aged. *Geriatrics,* 1950, **5**, 231-35.

18. STIEGLITZ, E. J. Principles of geriatric medicine. In STIEGLITZ, E. J. (ed.), *Geriatric medicine.* Philadelphia: W. B. Saunders Co., 1949.

19. ——. Medical care of normal senescents. In STIEGLITZ, E. J. (ed.), *Geriatric medicine.* Philadelphia: W. B. Saunders Co., 1949.

20. *Study of institutions for the aged.* Washington, D.C.: National Conference of Catholic Charities, 1946.

21. *Suggested standards for homes for the aged.* New York: Welfare Council of New York City, 1948.

22. *Survey of the needs and facilities for the care of the Jewish aged in New York City.* New York: Central Bureau for the Jewish Aged, 1946.

23. THEWLIS, M., and GALE, E. T. Ambulatory care of the aged. *Geriatrics,* 1950, **5**, 331-36.

24. ZEMAN, F. D. Medical care of the normal aged. In STIEGLITZ, E. J. (ed.), *Geriatric medicine.* Philadelphia: W. B. Saunders Co., 1949.

25. ——. Medical organization of an old age home. *J. Geron.,* 1950, **5**, 262-65.

26. ZETTERSTROM, M. H. The dietitian in the modern home for the aged. *J. Geron.,* 1951, **6**, 43-45.

INDEX OF NAMES

INDEX OF SUBJECTS